CALIBRATION IN AIR MONITORING

A symposium

presented at the

Seventy-eighth Annual Meeting
AMERICAN SOCIETY FOR
TESTING AND MATERIALS

ASTM SPECIAL TECHNICAL PUBLICATION 598
J. R. E. Chapman, symposium chairman
D. G. Shaw, symposium co-chairman

List price $32.00
04-598000-17

AMERICAN SOCIETY FOR TESTING AND MATERIALS
1916 Race Street, Philadelphia, Pa. 19103

CALIBRATION IN AIR MONITORING

A symposium
presented at the
University of Colorado at Boulder, Colo.
5–7 Aug. 1975
AMERICAN SOCIETY FOR
TESTING AND MATERIALS

ASTM SPECIAL TECHNICAL PUBLICATION 598
R. L. Chapman, symposium chairman
D. C. Sheesley, symposium cochairman

List price $33.00
04-598000-17

 AMERICAN SOCIETY FOR TESTING AND MATERIALS
1916 Race Street, Philadelphia, Pa. 19103

NOTE

The Society is not responsible, as a body,
for the statements and opinions
advanced in this publication.

Printed in Lutherville-Timonium, Md.
May 1976

Foreword

The Symposium on Calibration in Air Monitoring was presented at the University of Colorado at Boulder, Colo., 5–7 Aug., 1975. The symposium was sponsored by The American Society for Testing and Materials through its Committee D-22 on Methods of Sampling and Analysis of Atmospheres. R. L. Chapman, Beckman Instruments, Inc., presided as symposium chairman. D. C. Sheesley, Ambient Analysis, Inc., presided as symposium cochairman.

Related
ASTM Publications

Instrumentation for Monitoring Air Quality, STP 555 (1974), $15.25 (04-555000-17)

Measurement of Lead in the Atmosphere; Sampling Stacks for Particulates; and Determination of Oxides of Nitrogen in Combustion Products, DS 55-S5, S6, S8 (1975), $18.00 (05-055099-17)

A Note of Appreciation
to Reviewers

This publication is made possible by the authors and, also, the unheralded efforts of the reviewers. This body of technical experts whose dedication, sacrifice of time and effort, and collective wisdom in reviewing the papers must be acknowledged. The quality level of ASTM publications is a direct function of their respected opinions. On behalf of ASTM we acknowledge with appreciation their contribution.

ASTM Committee on Publications

Editorial Staff

Jane B. Wheeler, *Managing Editor*
Helen M. Hoersch, *Associate Editor*
Charlotte E. DeFranco, *Senior Assistant Editor*
Ellen J. McGlinchey, *Assistant Editor*

Contents

ARE REFERENCE METHODS ABSOLUTE?

Introduction

In August of 1973 Committee D-22 on Methods of Sampling and Analysis of Atmospheres of the American Society for Testing and Materials together with the Environmental Protection Agency and the National Center for Atmospheric Research, sponsored a conference in Boulder, Colorado (published as *ASTM STP 555*) which examined instruments for the continuous monitoring of ambient air quality. One conclusion from that conference was the outstanding need for accepted methods for the calibration of such instruments. A similar need exists for instruments used for continuous monitoring of emissions.

A wide variety of calibration techniques are in use, and virtually all of them involve traceability to a standard of known composition or to referee analytical methods of well-established performance. The purpose of the 1975 conference was to determine the state of the art of calibration techniques and to examine critically the means of traceability to known standards. With the help of the National Bureau of Standards, the conference did just this, and the bulk of the papers that were delivered in Boulder in August 1975 are presented in the present volume.

The sponsors of this conference feel that, through the publication of these papers, wider knowledge of the problems and techniques of calibration will ensure and that the practitioners of the art will develop a more critical eye for the methods they use. The book also provides an introduction to the field for new users of the monitoring instruments, providing an insight to the requirements for their calibration and to some of the preferred techniques.

It is hoped that the various techniques may be evaluated, and as a result an attempt made to visualize standard methods of traceability whereby data from various sources may become truly comparable. For example, the value of standard reference materials from a single national source such as the National Bureau of Standards should become more obvious. As the demand grows, the supply will increase and as the supply increases use will spread.

R. L. Chapman

Beckman Instruments, Inc., Fullerton, Calif. 92634; symposium chairman.

Philosophy/Policy of Calibration

R. L. Chapman[1]

Calibration of Stack Gas Instrumentation

REFERENCE: Chapman, R. L., **"Calibration of Stack Gas Instrumentation,"** *Calibration in Air Monitoring*, *ASTM STP 598*, American Society for Testing and Materials, 1976, pp. 5–15.

ABSTRACT: Experience in stack gas instrumentation calibration is presented, based on a study involving the measurement of sulfur dioxide in the stack of a power plant and in the exit gases from a Claus sulfur recovery incinerator. Calibrations were performed by the use of analyzed cylinders of gas. The method of presenting the calibration gas to the analyzers is described, and data are presented to provide comparisons of the resulting instrumental readings with correlated, independant determinations made by the standard reference (manual) method for sulfur dioxide in stack gas.

KEY WORDS: calibration, sulfur dioxide, emission, monitors, standards, chemical analysis, electrochemistry, infrared analysis, flame photometry

Stack gas instrumentation can be categorized as either extractive or *in situ*. Extractive types can be further characterized by the analytical method as spectrometric, electrochemical, flame photometric, etc., while current *in situ* analyzers are all spectrometric. One thing they all have in common is the need to be calibrated periodically. The two common methods of calibration are the introduction of known gas blends, or, in the case of spectrometric instruments, an optical filter may be used to simulate a known gas blend. In either case, the primary calibration is the known gas blend, whether a cylinder gas standard is actually used in the routine calibration or whether an optical filter of known relationship to the gas blend is substituted.

This report presents the analytical data obtained with several extractive type sulfur dioxide (SO_2) monitoring systems on two types of emission sources, while calibrating with cylinder gas standards. The purpose is to evaluate the analytical results and, by inference, to determine the validity of this calibration technique.

[1] Principal application engineer, Process Instruments Division, Beckman Instruments, Inc., Fullerton, Calif. 92634.

Monitoring Systems

"Monitoring system" (or "measurement system") has been defined [1][2] as "the total equipment required for the determination of a pollutant gas concentration in a given source effluent." According to this definition, the system consists of three major subsystems: sampling interface, analyzer, and data presentation.

In any performance test of a monitoring system, the complete system must be involved, and, for field test, the system should be installed at a typical source emission site as it might be for actual monitoring.

Four monitoring systems were employed in this investigation. Two had completely independent sampling interface subsystems, while the other two shared the same probe and sample interface. Each analyzer had its own continuous recorder, and, in addition, all signals were fed into a data logger which controlled a teletypewriter for digital printout at set intervals.

Infrared Analyzer with Reflux Sampling

The first system consisted of a nondispersive infrared analyzer (Beckman Model 865) combined with a reflux filtration probe and permeation dryer sampling interface system. This sampling system has been described previously [2]. The reflux probe and a follow-up filter remove particulates, while the permeation dryer removes water vapor selectively. The sample is maintained above its dewpoint up to the dryer. The system is shown in block diagram, Fig. 1.

Electrochemical and Flame Photometric Analyzers with Diffusion Dilution Sampling

The second and third systems shared a common filter probe equipped for blowback, heated line, heated particulate filter, and heated, temperature controlled Teflon diffusion membrane diluter. Beyond the diluter, the sample passed first through the electrochemical analyzer and then to the flame photometric detector. As shown in Fig. 2, the heated filter and the diffusion diluter are integral parts of the flame photometric analyzer (Meloy Model FSA 190-2A) incorporating the Dyfusatron dilution module. The electrochemical analyzer (Dynasciences Model SS-310), incorporating a membrane, is a fuel cell type sensor.

Since the sample was kept hot up to and including the Dyfusatron module, it contained the full amount of water vapor. The rate of diffusion of the sulfur dioxide is a function of its partial pressure. Therefore, since the total pressure is always 1 atm, the concentration of SO_2 in the stream leaving the diffuser is directly proportional to that in the wet stream, and the measurements are on the wet basis.

[2] The italic numbers in brackets refer to the list of references appended to this paper.

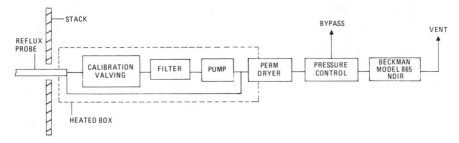

FIG. 1—*Block diagram of infrared system.*

Electrochemical Analyzer with Condensation Sampling

The fourth system consisted of an electrochemical analyzer (Dynasciences Model SS-330) combined with a conventional condensation type sampling system. The Model SS-330 is very similar to the SS-310 except that the sensor is designed for a higher concentration range.

The sample interface system consisted of a filter probe equipped for blowback followed by a depth filter to remove particulates and a refrigerated condenser to remove water vapor. The sample is kept hot up to the refrigerated condenser (Fig. 3). It has been reported that this type system causes no significant loss of SO_2 due to solubility in the condensed water [*3*].

Provisions for Calibration and Probe Blowback

Frequently, calibration is executed by introducing the calibration test gas into the analyzer and by-passing the sampling interface. The Environ-

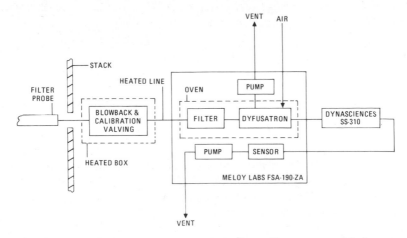

FIG. 2—*Block diagram of electrochemical and flame photometric combined systems.*

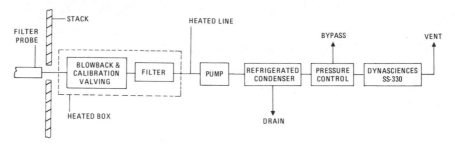

FIG. 3—*Block diagram of electrochemical system.*

mental Protection Agency (EPA) requires that the entire measurement system be included in any test procedure [*1*]. This means introducing the calibration test gas at the sampling interface upstream of the analyzer. Thus, the sampling interface is provided the same opportunity to have an impact on calibration as on the source measurement. Therefore, for these tests, valving was provided in the interface systems to introduce the calibration gases as closely as possible to the sample probe.

Valving for calibration gas introduction consisted of electrically operated solenoid valves arranged in block-and-bleed fashion to eliminate the possibility of contamination. Air operated valves were also incorporated in the diffusion dilution system and the condensation system to isolate the probe and provide probe blowback each time the analyzers were zeroed.

Sites and Installation Notes

All four monitoring systems were installed and operated on the stack of a power plant, and, subsequently, the first three systems were reinstalled and operated on the outlet of a Claus sulfur recovery unit incinerator. The only modifications required for the transfer were to change the range of the infrared analyzer by shortening its sample path length and to change the dilution ratio of the Dyfusatron by substituting a thicker membrane and readjusting its temperature. The nominal SO_2 concentration in the power plant stack was 250 ppm, while that in the incinerator exit was about 5000 ppm. Other sample conditions are indicated in Table 1.

Power Plant

A 125 MW unit was selected which burns about 1500 tons per day of coal containing 0.48 percent sulfur. The flue gas is split and cleaned in twin wet scrubbers, one of which uses limestone slurry. The gases are then reheated and combined in the lower part of a 250-ft stack.

A temporary platform was constructed adjacent to the stack at the 42 ft level, about 14 ft above the top of the confluent ducts. Five breaches were

TABLE 1—*Sample conditions.*

Location	Temperature, °F	Pressure, in. H_2O	Particulate Loading
Power plant	118	±1 to 2	moderate
Claus unit	1000	−1	light

made in the stack 4 ft above the platform and about 2 ft apart; four for instrumentation and one for manual sampling. The three analytical system probes were mounted in the breaches so that their tips were in close proximity near the center of the stack. An 8-ft heated manual sampling probe was mounted on a trolley so that it could be run in close to the instrument probe tips or removed when not in use, and for cleaning.

The complete reflux sample interface system was mounted on the stack at the butt end of its probe. Heated boxes containing the blowback and calibration valving for the condensation system and for the diffusion dilution system were also mounted on the stack at the ends of their respective probes. Heated lines were provided for the latter two systems and an unheated line for the reflux system. The reflux and diffusion dilution system lines were ¼-in. Teflon, while the condensation system line was ⅜-in. Teflon.

A 7 by 10-ft garden shed was erected on the platform to contain all of the analytical and recording instrumentation plus a clean air supply system and the refrigerated condenser for the condensation interface system. Calibration gas cylinders were also located on the platform.

Figure 4 shows an installation at a power plant.

Claus Unit

An eight or nine year old, unmodified, Claus sulfur recovery unit was selected, and the analytical systems were installed in similar manner as at the power plant. In this case, the installation was conveniently at ground level. The incinerator exit consisted of a 6-ft-diameter carbon steel pipe, lined with fire brick, about 6 ft long, leading directly into the base of a stack. Taps were provided in this pipe for the reflux interface system, the diffusion dilution system, and the manual sampling probe. The probes were all shortened appropriately, and the trolley was not necessary in this case for the manual sampler. Otherwise the installation was essentially the same as at the power plant.

Figure 5 shows an installation at a Claus unit.

Test Procedures

EPA has proposed performance specifications and test procedures for monitors of SO_2 emission sources required by Part 60 of Chapter I of

FIG. 4—*Photograph of installation at a power plant.*

FIG. 5—*Photograph of installation at a Claus unit.*

Title 40 of the *Code of Federal Regulations* [4]. These specifications and tests have been thoroughly evaluated for power-generating plants fired by coal [1]. It was concluded from these evaluations that the values and test procedures might be made generally applicable to other pollutant-industry combinations. Therefore, the appropriate test method from this set was selected for the purposes of the present investigation. Simply stated, the calibration gases and the stack gases were both analyzed by a wet chemical method, and the deviations in instrument determinations versus wet chemical determinations on the stack gases were used to evaluate the instrument determinations.

Clean, dry air was provided for zeroing the analyzers and gas cylinders of SO_2, blended with nitrogen, for up-scale calibrations. These gases were supplied to all analytical systems, close to the probes, ahead of filtration and drying, as described earlier. The zero air was generated by compressing, filtering, and drying ambient air. The ambient air was analyzed to determine that it contained insignificant concentrations of SO_2. The up-scale gases were analyzed by a wet chemical method to determine their concentrations, before use.

The process streams were sampled and analyzed by the same wet chemical methods as used for the up-scale standards, based on EPA Reference Method 6 [5]. This is the barium-thorin titration method.

For the 250 ppm range the method was performed as described in the reference. Sample flow through the impingers was about 1 litre/min and sampling time was 30 to 35 min. For the 5000 ppm range, the same flow rate was used but the time was reduced to 6 or 7 min. Also, the total peroxide was diluted to 250 ml prior to titrating rather than the 50 ml. Tests indicated that the sulfate collected in the second peroxide impinger was less than 10 percent of the total in both cases.

The reproducibility that was obtained with Method 6 is illustrated by the replicate determinations on cylinders (Table 2), and an indication of the accuracy may be gained by comparing the Method 6 values with the

TABLE 2—*Method 6 determinations on cylinder gases.*

	Sulfur Dioxide, ppm								
	Cylinder 1	Cylinder 2	Cylinder 3	Cylinder 4	Cylinder 5	Cylinder 6	Cylinder 7	Cylinder 8	Cylinder 9
Run 1	155	311	454	420	453	3760	5530	8810	9340
Run 2	155	302	458	425	451	3710	5540	8820	9290
Run 3	161	316	462	429	450	3780	5550		
Run 4	156	307	457						
Mean	157	309	458	425	451	3750	5540	8815	9315
Tag value	158	312	458	442	455	4000	6000	9160	9310

cylinder tag values (Table 2). Overall repeatability is estimated to be better than 3 percent at the 95 percent confidence level. Accuracy appears to be 2 to 3 percent in the 250 to 450 ppm range and around 5 or 6 percent in the 4000 to 9000 range. There is some indication that Method 6 may read low by 1 or 2 percent at the low end and up to 3 or 4 percent at the high levels.

During the manual sampling, analyzer readings were taken every 2 min at the power plant and each minute at the Claus unit. These readings were averaged for comparison with each manual sample. The analysis systems were calibrated before and between the periods of manual sampling, and average zero readings and up-scale readings for each day were used in reducing the analyzer output data to parts per million SO_2. All instruments were purportedly linear; therefore, zero corrections and calculated slopes were used in reducing the data.

TABLE 3—*Correlations of analyzers with Method 6 at a power plant.*

		SO_2, ppm		
Method 6	System 1	System 2	System 3	System 4
216	234	235	195	240
213	240	227	201	241
232	264	262	...	263
234	262	262	...	257
245	259	260	234	260
234	256	257	231	255
228	236	246	226	252
226	231	238	221	242
229	246	251	225	244
230	245	252	202	239
228	242	253	218	241
240	254	258	246	252
212	253	263	244	254
234	226	232	209	227
223	219	223	200	215
209	214	222	189	216
204	215	220	189	209
198	221	222	192	220
203	212	212	186	210
198	211	214	186	201
219	238	223	187	220
217	223	226	191	211
223	219	226	193	219
213	217	225	191	212
180	193	194	169	199
183	200	202	176	190
206	214	215	184	213
213	215	218	184	199
219	223	224	183	217
218	220	224	184	217
221	227	229	187	219
215	223	223	185	215

Results

Since the infrared analyzer and the Dynasciences SS-330 saw dry samples while the Meloy and the Dynasciences SS-310 saw wet samples, it was necessary to correct the data from the latter instruments to the dry basis in order to be comparable to the manual method determinations.

Since the power plant has wet scrubbers followed by demister whose temperature is maintained at 120°F and, in turn, followed by reheaters and the stack temperature is 150°F, the water vapor content is the saturation level at 120°F. As the barometric pressure was very constant during the test period, this water vapor value (13 percent) could be used for making the necessary corrections on data from the power plant site.

TABLE 4—*Correlations of analyzers with Method 6 at a Claus unit.*

	SO$_2$, ppm		
Method 6	System 1	System 2	System 3
4430	4380	3350	3770
4220	4190	4130	4390
4180	4240	3410	. . .
3970	4090	3130	. . .
4030	4160	3630	3680
5280	5050	4750	3510
5530	5300	4900	4840
4950	4810	4710	3600
5280	5170	5310	5560
5530	5480	4710	5500
5510	5500	5270	6290
5610	5550	5780	6260
5370	5500	6070	5810
5330	5230	5690	5490
5330	5460	5630	5660
5340	5480	4950	5810
5130	5030	4840	4740
5230	4600	4970	5380
5070	5180	5370	5040
5160	4960	5270	5090
5300	5530	6240	6430
5250	5560	6570	7690
13260	12040	12630	14590
9000	9710	10130	11320
7240	7450	8240	9220
5970	6260	6600	6440
6040	6320	6800	6650
6580	6530	6900	7750
6940	6930	8450	8560
5210	5240	5550	5850
5160	5360	6370	6490
5870	5990	6590	6770
5590	5640	6760	6540
5620	5530	5920	5280
6870	6720	7600	7990

At the Claus unit, Reference Method 4 [5] was used to determine the water vapor level each day and these values, which varied from 17 to 23 percent, were used to correct the Meloy and Dynasciences data to the dry basis.

Thirty-two valid correlations between monitor systems and manual determinations were obtained in six days at the power plant and 35 correlations in eight days at the Claus unit (Tables 3 and 4).

Following the EPA procedure, each group of correlations was divided, chronologically, into sets of nine for subsequent treatment. This gave four sets for each site with some data overlapping.

For each set, the mean of the reference method values was determined along with the mean differences and the 95 percent confidence intervals, according to the prescribed formulae which are shown in the Appendix. The sum of the mean difference and the 95 percent confidence interval divided by the mean reference value is called "accuracy (relative)." These values are shown in Tables 5 and 6 for each of the eight sets of data.

Discussion

EPA specifications require that the accuracy (relative) of a monitoring system, as determined by this test, should be no greater than 20 percent. As shown in Table 6, all four systems produced numbers well within this range at the power plant and only one exceeded it, part of the time, at the Claus unit.

TABLE 5—*Accuracy (relative) from a power plant correlation.*

	Relative Accuracy, %			
	System 1	System 2	System 3	System 4
Data Set 1	11.4	10.9	6.4	11.5
Data Set 2	10.2	13.5	11.5	9.8
Data Set 3	7.9	8.2	8.2	6.5
Data Set 4	5.3	6.3	6.3	5.3

TABLE 6—*Accuracy (relative) from a Claus unit correlation.*

	Relative Accuracy, %		
	System 1	System 2	System 3
Data Set 1	3.8	16.9	27.1
Data Set 2	5.4	10.4	10.5
Data Set 3	9.6	15.3	27.0
Data Set 4	3.0	18.7	21.2

In the EPA procedure, the wet chemical method is assumed to give the "correct value," and any deviation on the part of an instrumental monitoring system is considered to be an error. Since the manual method accuracy was estimated to have an accuracy of only 2 to 6 percent in this case, the correlations are actually remarkably good.

It seems a fair conclusion that the method of instrumental calibration used in this investigation is acceptable.

APPENDIX

Procedure for Determination of Mean Values

1. The mean value of a data set is calculated according to the following equation

$$\bar{X} = \frac{1}{n}\sum_{i-1}^{n} Xi$$

where

Xi = individual values,
$\sum$ = sum of the individual values,
$\bar{X}$ = mean value, and
n = number of data points.

2. The 95 percent confidence interval (two-sided) (CI) is calculated according to the following equation:

$$CI_{95} = \frac{t_1 - \alpha/2}{\sqrt{n}} \sqrt{\frac{n(\sum Xi^2) - (\sum Xi)^2}{n(n-1)}}$$

where

$\sum Xi$ = sum of all data points,
$\sqrt{n}$ = square root of the number of data points, and
$t_1 - \alpha/2$ = t 0.975 for n samples from a table of percentages of the t distribution (for 9 samples it equals 2.306).

References

[1] Nader, J. S., Jaye, F., and Conner, W., "Performance Specifications for Stationary Source Monitoring Systems for Gases and Visible Emissions," Technology Series EPA-650/2-74-013, Environmental Protection Agency, Research Triangle Park, N.C., 1974.
[2] Chapman, R. L., Environmental Science and Technology, Vol. 8, No. 6, June 1974, pp. 520–525.
[3] Jacquot, R. D. and Houser, E. A., Proceedings, 27th Annual Conference and Exhibit, Paper 72–730, Instrument Society of America, 1972.
[4] "Stationary Sources—Proposed Emission Monitoring and Performance Testing Requirements," Federal Register, Vol. 39, No. 177, Sept. 1974, pp. 32852–32874.
[5] "Standards of Performance for New Stationary Sources," Federal Register, Vol. 36, No. 247, Dec. 1971, pp. 24876–24895.

R. H. Dieck[1]

Gas Turbine Emission Measurement Instrument Calibration

REFERENCE: Dieck, R. H., "Gas Turbine Emission Measurement Instrument Calibration," *Calibration in Air Monitoring*, *ASTM STP 598*, American Society for Testing and Materials, 1976, pp. 16–39.

ABSTRACT: Fundamental to valid emission measurements is the proper calibration of the measurement instrumentation. This paper addresses the problems associated with instrument calibration and assesses the role of instrument uncertainty in the complete analysis of error. A review of the need for instrument calibration is included, as is a discussion of the basic methodology required, from securing the necessary calibration data to its evaluation in a statistical framework.

Topics necessary for proper instrument calibration and uncertainty assessment included are: proper choice of units, definition of terms, calibration to calibration precision and its variability, calibration curve fitting, calibration curve shifts and their evaluation, errors common to instruments in systems, comparisons to other identical instruments, and evaluation of manufacturers' statements.

In addition, a comparison of typical instrument performance with that required by the Environmental Protection Agency (EPA) is made.

Finally, the need for real-time assessment of instrument precision is discussed, and an example of how it has been achieved at Pratt and Whitney Aircraft is presented.

KEY WORDS: instruments, accuracy, gas analysis, data validity, precision, bias, calibration, statistics

The effectiveness of techniques for the reduction of pollutants from fuel burning sources is assessed by measurement of pollutant concentrations in the exhaust stream. In order to interpret such measurements, a clear understanding of measurement uncertainty is essential. In addition, a commonly agreed upon error model is required in order to compare results from various testing organizations.

In gas turbine emission measurement, it has been shown that the major source of measurement uncertainty is sampling error due to nonuniform pollutant concentrations in the exhaust stream [1].[2] It has also been shown

---

[1] Assistant project engineer, Pratt and Whitney Aircraft, East Hartford, Conn. 06108.
[2] The italic numbers in brackets refer to the list of references appended to this paper.

by several investigators that additional uncertainty in the level of pollutant measured will result if the data obtained is not corrected for the effects of ambient conditions [2–4]. It is the intent of this paper, however, to address only the uncertainty which may be attributed to the measurement instrumentation. It should be emphasized that while such a restriction to instrumental errors alone permits an in-depth review of their problems, utilizing the instrument uncertainties as estimates of emission measurement uncertainty will usually result in far too optimistic an appraisal of the accuracy of the test data.

Included in this paper will be a discussion of: the statistical framework for uncertainty assessment, the accuracy of the calibration standards used, calibration gases, the types of gas analysis instruments used at Pratt and Whitney Aircraft (P&WA), the documentation of instrument performance, establishment of instrument calibration curves, and the variability that exists in instrument precision. In addition, the present P&WA system of "on-line" accuracy assessment will be discussed, as will the way in which calibration data so obtained may be utilized.

A review of the information presented will clearly establish the need for a generally agreed upon standard method of uncertainty assessment for air pollution measurement instrumentation.

Statistical Framework

General

In making statements about the accuracy of pollutant measurements, it is essential that a consistent terminology be employed. That terminology is usually statistical in nature. Without utilizing statistics, it is difficult, if not impossible, to assess properly the significance of any measurements made and to apply the results appropriately. However, although analysis of physical measurements by statistical methods has been of recognized importance for a considerable period of time, there continues to be a bewildering variety of statistical methods in common usage and an equally bewildering lexicon of definitions. American Society for Testing and Materials (ASTM) alone, has published no less than 13 definitions for "precision" and 8 for "accuracy" [5].

Often the uncertainty of test results is reported within the framework of statistical jargon without any clear description of how the various terms were defined or applied. Many times technical clarity is sacrificed in the name of mathematical complexity. Unfortunately, this has had the effect of eroding the credibility of the statistician and the proper use of statistics, and of supporting the argument that any conclusion can be defended through use of suitable statistical analysis. Lacking faith in statistical analysis to describe properly the behavior of a data set or the significance of a measurement, many workers continue to use such meaning-less terms as "good," "excellent," "poor," etc. which, of course, cannot quantitatively define the accuracy of a test result or the precision of an instrument.

However, despite the apprehensions of some, statistical methods, properly applied, with well-defined terminology, should be used to describe variations quantitatively in test results and ascribe that variation appro-priately to the measured parameter or the instrument making the measure-ment. Statistical methods are simply a tool and should be treated as such. The methods provide a systematic approach to defining and expressing instrument accuracy but should not take the place of good engineering judgment.

Bias and Precision Errors

In general, the accuracy analysis reported in this study was based on the statistical approach outlined by Natrella [6], among others.

Two forms of error were considered—bias and precision.

Major bias errors are caused largely by calibration gas uncertainty, are systematic, and affect all measurements of a variable by the same fixed percent of reading. They remain fixed throughout the duration of a test. Bias error is a measure of the deviation of the average of a group of data from the true value. Precision errors reflect the scatter of the measurements about the biased average.

Normal statistics define bias error b as

$$b = \overline{X} - t = \left[\frac{\sum_{i=1}^{n} X_i}{n} \right] - t \tag{1}$$

and precision error $2S$ as

$$2S = 2 \left[\frac{\sum_{i=1}^{n} (X_i - \overline{X})^2}{n - 1} \right]^{1/2} \tag{2}$$

where

t = true value of parameter X,
X_i = i^{th} measurement of X, and
n = number of measurements of X made.

The effect of bias and precision errors can be seen schematically in Fig. 1. The bias is usually caused by the calibration gas uncertainty. The instrument's precision is evidenced by variation around the average.

It should be noted here that the use of $2S$ as an estimate of precision (Eq 2) is recommended. For a Gaussian-normal data set, the interval $\overline{X} \pm 2S$ will include, on the average, 95 percent of the data points. This

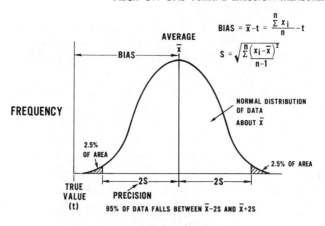

$$\text{BIAS} = \bar{x} - t = \frac{\sum\limits_{i}^{n} x_i}{n} - t$$

$$S = \sqrt{\frac{\sum\limits^{n}\left(x_i - \bar{x}\right)^2}{n-1}}$$

FIG. 1—*Effect of bias and precision errors.*

knowledge provides an instrument user a realistic estimate of the likely deviations he will see in a group of readings. Others have suggested $1S$ be used as an estimator of precision. In this case, 68 percent of data is within the interval $\bar{X} \pm 1S$. However, this results only in knowing if an observed measurement is within $\bar{X} \pm 1S$ with about the same confidence as that of heads showing after flipping a coin. Although the choice of $2S$ is arbitrary, it is felt that $1S$ is far too optimistic an appraisal of instrument precision, and, while advantageous to use from a manufacturer's point of view because it looks good, it is an insufficient estimate of instrument performance from the user's point of view.

Choice of Error Units

When terms such as precision and bias are used to assess instrument accuracy, an appropriate choice of units must be made. The error caused by a measuring device may be expressed either as percent of full scale, one absolute value to be utilized over the entire range, or percent of reading, a fixed percentage of the indicated value. The experimenter should choose those units which result in the most nearly Gaussian-normal distribution for the error data so that terms such as variance and precision will be well defined and understood, and reasonable analytical methods will be available for error analysis.

Determining whether error data are Gaussian-normal may be done in at least two ways: through the use of (a) an exacting calculation involving the Chi-squared distribution and (b) by observing the error data to be linear on probability paper.

Previously reported testing [7] has shown, through the use of probability paper, that emission instruments' errors best approximate a normal distribution when expressed in percent-of-full-scale or absolute units.

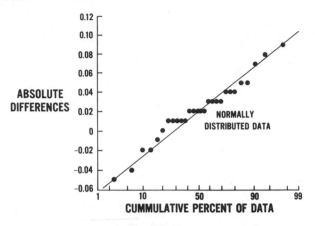

FIG. 2—*Absolute difference between two individual CO_2 analyzers (CO_2 levels varied from ∼2 to 5 percent CO_2).*

Dixon and Massey [8] have described the origin and basis for probability paper. The previously reported differences between two identical carbon dioxide (CO_2) instruments [7] analyzing the same exhaust sample are shown in Fig. 2. Note how closely the data approximate a straight line. The horizontal groupings are a result of the least-count of the measurement system, that is, no difference less than an integral multiple of 0.01 percent CO_2 could be detected with these instruments. It is apparent that absolute differences, or percentages of full scale, are the proper choice of error units for these CO_2 analyzers.

It should be noted that the presence of a small, 0.02 percent CO_2, bias between the two analyzers due to a shift in the central values of the instruments does not affect the choice of units evaluation. Central value shifts usually are not significant and, therefore, will not be treated here. The major source of instrument bias in gas analysis is error in the evaluation of the concentration of the calibration gas. Those bias errors should be expressed as relative errors since, when a calibration gas is in error by one percent relative, the entire range of the measuring instrument on which such a gas is used for calibration will be off by 1 percent relative, provided the calibration line is a precise representation of the instrument's performance. This will be in addition to the uncertainty contributed by the instrument's precision.

Calibration Hierarchy

Figure 3 shows that the accuracy of emission measurements is the result of the propagation of bias and precision errors through several levels of a calibration hierarchy. The uncertainties in the top level of the hierarchy are the bias of the National Bureau of Standards (NBS) primary standard

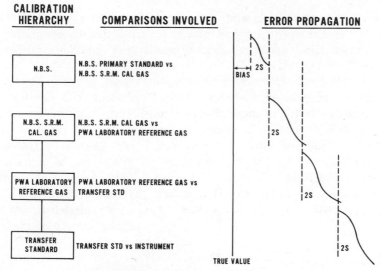

FIG. 3—*Propagation of error in a calibration hierarchy.*

and the precision with which the NBS compares the NBS standard reference material (SRM) calibration gas to that primary standard. The uncertainties of the second and third levels, respectively, are the precision errors which result from the comparisons of the P&WA laboratory reference calibration gas to the NBS SRM, and the comparison of the transfer standard calibration gas to that P&WA laboratory reference calibration gas. The precision ($2S$) of the fourth level is referred to as the calibration-to-calibration precision.

As can be seen in Fig. 3, the cumulative uncertainty at any level cannot be less than the uncertainty of the previous level.

A calibration hierarchy not only provides a method of reviewing the sources of uncertainty at each level as to which is most significant, but illustrates the traceability of a particular measurement to an NBS standard. As the date for compliance with regulations approaches, the traceability to NBS and the accuracy of calibration as demonstrated by a calibration hierarchy will become critical in reviewing the significance of compliance test results.

Combining Bias and Precision Errors

A method for obtaining a single number to express the uncertainty that results from the existence of a calibration hierarchy of the type in Fig. 3 has been dealt with in detail by Abernathy and others [9]. Very simply, the total uncertainty may be expressed as

$$U = b + t_{95}S$$

where U is the total uncertainty. The terms b and $2S$ are the quadrature sums of the unknown bias and precision errors due to calibration gas uncertainty and instrument variation, respectively. b and $2S$ are independent errors.

Dependent errors from error sources which vary to some degree with each other cannot be so easily combined. Dependent error combinations require specialized treatment, including a consideration of their correlation.

Briefly then, the place of statistics is to provide a readily understood and accepted method for estimating accuracy in as rigorous a fashion as appropriate to permit the assessment of the likelihood of a particular measurement being within a chosen tolerance band. As such, it is not the "none-will-exceed" approach often utilized by manufacturers, which is actually impossible to achieve but rather provides a probabilistic model of data variation.

Calibration Standards

The major source of test instrument bias is the calibration gas uncertainty. Table 1 shows some typical transfer standard calibration gas bottle analysis accuracies in percent of reading units. Many are within the EPA requirement of ± 2 percent [10].

These errors will apply systematically to all data obtained from an instrument calibrated on one calibration gas bottle. Some improvement may be gained in precision of the bottle analysis average with an increased number of replicate bottle analyses. In general, the precision of the average of several replicate bottle analyses decreases as the square root of the number of analyses. Note that the precision of the data does not change with more data points; the ability to describe the average improves.

The hydrocarbon (HC), carbon monoxide (CO), and carbon dioxide (CO_2) bias errors are those assigned by NBS to their standard reference

TABLE 1—*Typical transfer standard calibration gas bottle accuracies (all in percent of reading units).*

	Gas Concentration	Bias[a]	Analysis Precision	Accuracy	Present Calibration Method
CO_2	5%	1.0	0.7	1.7	chromatograph
THC	1000 ppm	1.0	0.75	1.75	chromatograph
	100 ppm	1.0	1.23	2.23	chromatograph
	10 ppm	1.0	2.4	3.4	chromatograph
NO/NO_2	200 ppm		5.8	(5.8)	phenol disulfonic acid
CO	1000 ppm	1.0	1.4	2.4	chromatograph

[a] NBS SRM uncertainty.

gases. The nitric oxide (NO)/nitrogen dioxide $(NO)_2$ data are based on triplicate phenol disulfonic acid (PDS) calibrations, though work is presently in progress to evaluate the calibration uncertainty that will result when NBS standards for NO become available.

The analysis precisions are the result of the work of the P&WA Gas Analysis Laboratory. Previous to the existence of NBS standard gases, for CO_2 for example, it was the responsibility of the P&WA Gas Analysis Laboratory to develop calibration standards. That effort has been reported elsewhere [11]. However, as more NBS gases become available, the difference between P&WA emission measurements before the NBS standards and after is not expected to be significant. This is because the P&WA analysis of calibration gases, with some exceptions, has typically compared most favorably to that of NBS. That comparison is shown in Table 2 for CO_2 where the analysis referenced to a previous P&WA standard calibration gas is compared to the analysis with the NBS gases as a reference.

Note that single CO_2 analysis, of the type shown in both Tables 1 and 2, has a precision error of 0.5 percent of reading. The 0.7 percent of reading error reported in Table 1 is the quadrature sum of the errors of Steps 2 and 3 in the calibration hierarchy previously discussed.

It can be seen that if there was any bias between P&WA and NBS it was small. Most of the errors noted could be easily accounted for by the analysis precision.

Pratt and Whitney Aircraft Emission Instrumentation

The emission measurement instrumentation utilized at P&WA currently adheres to the measurement system required by the EPA [10]. The development and utilization of this instrumentation has been described previously [12]. The measurement techniques utilized for each exhaust component are outlined in Table 3.

Although this instrumentation and its attendant sample handling system adheres in form to the Federal Register regulations, its performance in-use is typically not as accurate as the performance required by the regulations.

TABLE 2—*Analysis of CO_2 reference gases in mol percent (P&WA versus NBS).*

Analysis Referenced to Previous P&WA Standards	Analysis Referenced to NBS Standards	Error, %
0.920	0.928	−0.87
4.05	4.02	0.74
7.74	7.78	0.52
9.89	9.93	−0.40
13.90	13.83	0.50

TABLE 3—*P&WA emission measurement instrumentation.*

Component	Measurement Technique
CO, CO_2, NO^a	nondispersive infrared
$NO_2{}^a$	nondispersive ultraviolet
THC	flame inoization detector
O_2	polarographic
NO_x	chemiluminescent

[a] NO and NO_2 have been replaced by the chemiluminescent NO_x instrument.

Documentation of Instrumentation Performance

Need

It should be obvious that the simplest way to evaluate an instrument's performance is to observe its variation in calibration. The precision data are needed to provide an estimate of instrument accuracy, as well as provide a running history of the operation of the particular instrument involved. The former allows an assessment of the significance of test data to be made. The latter will often permit the operator to recognize problems during a test and take corrective action. Failing that, a well-documented instrument calibration history is the first step in assessing where a test went wrong so the same mistake will not occur in repeat testing.

Method

A major aspect of evaluating instrumentation performance is the procedure by which its performance is documented. The Instrumentation Department at P&WA, recognizing the importance of a clear and definitive understanding of instrument accuracy and the necessity for good documentation, has set up a separate group of individuals to pursue instrument documentation and accuracy assessment. Known as the data validity group, they are relieved from actual experimental testing obligations so that the viewpoint they take will be as independent of personal or emotional bias as possible. The data validity group is staffed by individuals with a background in instrumentation engineering but also with an interest in analytical work. This combination has provided for the practical application of statistics to instrument and test accuracy problems rather than the "black-box" approach often applied by pure statisticians. Out of the data validity group has grown a generally applicable accuracy assessment method which has three major theses:

1. The method should suit the needs of the test—for example, if there is only time for one quick instrument calibration, choose the most often util-

ized region of the most common instrument range. If zero is unimportant, only check the span. Sometimes, the precise needs of a test are not obvious, and as much documentation as practical is desirable. The data validity engineer must, in this case, closely follow test results to be sure that the accuracy data being gathered are sufficient both in quantity and scope.

2. "As-is" calibrations in the field, as close to testing conditions as possible, provide the best assessment of instrumentation performance obtainable.

3. The frequency of calibration should be sufficient to maintain only the desirable degree of accuracy. Some field test instruments need to be calibrated only monthly to maintain a stated accuracy, but that too needs to be documented over a suitable length of time. Simply stated, it is a waste of money to calibrate either too often or too little, and, therefore, it is important that an appropriate calibration interval be defined.

Table 4 is an illustration of the calibration form used at P&WA for the gas analysis instruments. The number and types of entries are based on normal instrument operation. Calibration data of this type are recorded during every test every time an instrument range is calibrated. The data

TABLE 4—*Calibration log gas analysis instrument systems.*

SYSTEM	☐ EEA VAN	☐ GT & CE VAN	☐ MODULE	☐ INDIVIDUAL INSTRUMENTS

ENG MODEL	ENG/RIG=	STAND=	DATE	SYSTEM OPERATORS

GAS BOTTLE PRIMARY PRESSURES

BOTTLE #	PRESS.	BOTTLE #	PRESS.	BOTTLE #	PRESS.	BOTTLE #	PRESS.	BOTTLE #	PRESS.

TIME INITIAL CAL. _____

		CO_2	CO	NO	NO_2	THC	O_2	NO_x	H_2	N_2
	SPAN GAS									
TIME _____	RANGE									
UNTOUCHED	SPAN									
CALIBRATION	ZERO									
AFTER RE-ZERO {	SPAN									
AFTER RE-SPAN {	ADJ. SPAN									

are then utilized to provide uncertainty estimates for the test results. Without these data, questions as to the significance of test results and performance of instruments would go unanswered.

One of the responsibilities of the data validity group was to standardize the methods and terminology that apply to gas turbine performance measurement uncertainty at P&WA. The major part of this effort was accomplished with the publication of the "Handbook, Uncertainty in Gas Turbine Measurements" [9]. That handbook has received wide acceptance and is the major document used to assure uniformity in measurement uncertainty estimates throughout the industry. The procedures detailed in that handbook are now being applied to emission measurement uncertainty at P&WA. However, a general accuracy assessment method, which can be utilized by all organizations participating in emission measurements, is still needed.

Problems

The institution of a calibration log of the type in Table 4, for instance, sometimes meets with considerable opposition which is frequently emotional in nature and can take one of several forms:

1. Individuals are often emotionally involved with their work and are naturally resentful of any outside agency critically reviewing the results of their effort.

2. The experimentalist might be pressed to produce results and quite often is willing to postpone considerations of accuracy until after the fact. While perhaps a valid argument for an experimental "one-shot" study, this idea is often used as a protective measure when, in fact, the appropriate time may have been reached for documenting the instrument's performance.

3. The experimenter does not feel that he has the time needed to fill out the calibration forms. While it is extra work, considerable time may be saved, should a problem develop, if careful attention has been paid to instrument performance documentation.

4. The experimenter sometimes does not really see the need for determining accuracy.

In summary, instituting a program for documenting instrument performance is often met with resistance which is frequently emotional rather than practical in nature. Although it is the presence of a separate data validity group that generates that emotional resistance, the problems thus created are usually overcome more easily than those attendant to the alternative of having each individual attempt to objectively assess his own experimental uncertainty.

Establishing Instrument Calibration Curves

The *Federal Register* [*10*] requires the establishment of the calibration curve of gas analysis instruments and the checking of those curves on a specific schedule. Because of the difficulties that may be encountered in fitting calibration curves to test data, some discussion of the methods used at P&WA to avoid the pitfalls will be useful.

Calibration Curve Fitting

Because they are nonlinear, the calibration curves for CO_2 nondispersive infrared (NDIR) instruments make excellent examples for describing the methodology utilized. The basic methods usually employed in curve fitting are that of *least squares* or *regression analysis*. Both of these techniques result in an estimate of error for a polynomial curve fit called the *standard estimate of error* (SEE). The calculation of twice the standard estimate of error is made as follows

Given functional form $Y = F(X)$

$$2\ \text{SEE} = 2 \left[\frac{\sum_{i=1}^{n} (Y_i - Y_{ci})^2}{n - (q + 1)} \right]^{1/2} \tag{3}$$

where

$2\ \text{SEE} =$ twice the standard estimate of error,
$Y_i =$ Y reading at X_i,
$Y_{ci} =$ calculated $Y = F(X_i)$,
$n =$ number of data points, and
$q =$ order of the polynomial.

As can be seen, Eq 3 is analogous to Eq 2; Eq 3 expresses the variation of the data around the curve fit, while Eq 2 expresses the variation of data around a biased average. Both are 95 percent confidence intervals such that $X \pm 2S$ contains 95 percent of the data points and $F(x) \pm 2\ \text{SEE}$ is a band about the curve that contains 95 percent of the points fitted (with due allowances for end effects). A more rigorous treatment of curve fittings and confidence intervals has been completed by Mandel and Linning [*13*].

A problem is often encountered in polynomial curve fitting by choosing the lowest 2 SEE as an indication of the best order of fit. This may be illustrated by Table 5 where the 2 SEE's for various CO_2 analyzers' calibration curves are compared with the average error associated with the calibration gases used to define the curves.

Note that the 2 SEE and average CO_2 calibration gas errors are comparable for every range but CO_2—instrument B, 0–2 percent. When the polynomial curve fits for that range are reviewed individually, Table 6 results.

TABLE 5—CO_2 calibrated curve 2 SEE.

Instrument	Range, %	Fit Order	CO_2 2 SEE, %	Calibrated Gas Avg Error CO_2, %
CO_2-A	0 to 5	3	0.028	0.044
	0 to 2	3	0.020	0.022
CO_2-B	0 to 18	6	0.101	0.115
	0 to 5	6	0.035	0.044
	0 to 2	5	0.0073	0.022

TABLE 6—2 SEE versus fit order for 0 to 2 percent CO_2 analyzer.

Fit Order	2 SEE IN CO_2, %
1	0.194
2	0.052
3	0.058
4	0.039
5	0.0073

The choice as the "best" fit was obviously fifth order, but it resulted in substantial between point errors as shown in Fig. 4 where the curve fits are plotted in detail along with the manufacturer's supplied calibration curve. As the gyrations shown by 5th and 4th order fits were not expected physically, the next best fit was the 2nd order. It too is shown in Fig. 4 for comparison purposes.

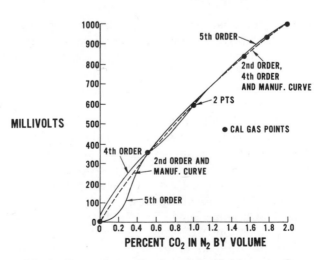

FIG. 4—CO_2 analyzer—B polynomial calibration curve fits.

It should be noted that the use of polynominal curve fits for NDIR instruments is an approximation procedure which attempts to describe the physically expected exponential shape. More recent work at P&WA has resulted in a procedure for fitting the calibration data, percent CO_2 as a function of millivolt output (mV), to an exponential curve of the form

$$\%CO_2 = A(e^{B \times mV} - 1) \tag{4}$$

where A and B are the constants of the fit. This procedure has several advantages over the commonly utilized polynomial curve fits.

1. The curve is forced through zero.
2. The curve has no inflections.
3. The curve shape is similar to that which is physically expected.
4. The curve does not have many constants, whose use may lead to substantial between-point errors.

Calibration Curve Shifts

It has been noted on several occasions that the calibration curves can shift substantially. As an example, Table 7 details the curve shifts noted at several CO_2 levels for the 0 to 18 percent range of one of P&WA's CO_2 instruments.

Only two curve shifts are reported. One shift occurred over three months and the other over seven. The change in CO_2 levels checked was due to the introduction of a new set of calibration gases between the first and second time period.

Since the time between checks is substantial, several months, the causes of the shifts are unknown as is the time they occurred. The more frequent calibration curve checks now required by the EPA should prevent much of this problem in the future. However, to ignore its significance merely because the calibration checks are more frequent may not be proper because the time scale of the shift at present is unknown and may have occurred within the one month calibration check period required by the EPA.

TABLE 7—*CO_2 calibration curve shifts.*

Jan. 1972–April 1973		June 1973–Dec. 1973	
CO_2 Calibrated Gas Level	CO_2 Shift, %	CO_2 Calibrated Gas Level	CO_2 Shift, %
4.0	0.39	1.54	0.46
6.0	0.62	3.02	0.68
8.0	0.74	8.14	0.95
10.0	0.59	13.90	0.00
12.0	0.47	15.01	−0.23

The stability of the calibration curves for the other emission instruments at P&WA is under investigation.

Instrumentation Precision Variability

Even after an instrument's calibration curve has been established, the instrument will continue to exhibit precision error in its utilization. By evaluating the precision which an instrument exhibits when analyzing the calibration gas, an estimate may be made of the instrument's precision when reading a test point. Calibration precision is utilized because the calibration gas concentration is assumed invariant for the duration of a test, thus placing all variations within the instrument. Test point concentrations vary considerably from point to point and as such cannot be easily used as a tool to measure instrument variation.

Figure 5 illustrates the considerable variability in instrument calibration precision from day to day and range to range. The source of the day-to-day variability in instrument precision is under investigation. The existence of the variability, however, requires the evaluation of the instrument precision on the day of the test for the proper assessment of emission accuracies. The precisions shown are expressed over the 95 percent confidence interval; 95 percent of replicate data will be within $\pm 2S$ of the average.

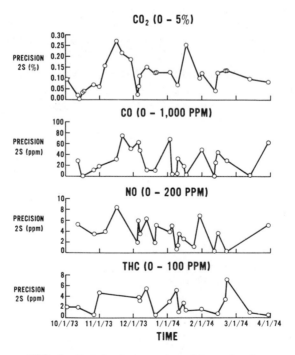

FIG. 5—*Emission instrument precision versus time.*

TABLE 8—*Variability of daily instrument precision* (2S).

Constituent	Range	Single Day Lowest Measured 2S	Six Month Pooled Avg 2S	Single Day Highest Measured 2S
CO_2	0 to 5%	0.011% CO_2	0.09% CO_2	0.170% CO_2
CO_2	0 to 2%	0.008% CO_2	0.020% CO_2	0.026% CO_2
CO	0 to 1000 ppm	1.1-ppm CO	19.6-ppm	55.8-ppm CO
CO	0 to 100 ppm	0.28-ppm CO	3.0-ppm CO	8.8-ppm CO
NO	0 to 200 ppm	0.74-ppm NO	5.0-ppm NO	13-ppm NO
NO_2	0 to 200 ppm	0.71-ppm NO_2	5.0-ppm NO	12-ppm NO_2
THC	0 to 1000 ppm	2.8-ppm CH_4	22-ppm CH_4	40-ppm CH_4
THC	0 to 100 ppm	0.28-ppm CH_4	4.0-ppm CH_4	9.9-ppm CH_4
O_2	0 to 25%	0.040% O_2	0.28% O_2	0.74% O_2

NOTE—The data were taken over six months. Several hundred calibrations were included in the pooled average 2S, while each test day typically had 6 to 8 calibrations.

Table 8 illustrates the typical variability of in-use emission instrument precisions. For most cases for which there is some comparison, typical in-use, in-day precision is poorer than that permitted by the EPA regulations where precision has been assumed to be 2S over the 95 percent confidence interval.

Note that variability even exists in long time period averages such as six months. Table 9 illustrates that variability for several such six-month averages and compares the data with the precision requirements of the EPA. For those ranges for which there is some comparison, P&WA is usually over the EPA limit. Missing precision values must take the precision for a previous evaluation or, lacking that, the precision of the next higher range. Note also that some ranges have exhibited considerable variability in precision over the time periods. The only uniformly improving instruments are the NO and NO_2 instruments no longer utilized. The rest have somewhat mixed results.

It should be noted that EPA parameters such as accuracy and precision were not well defined in their regulations. Here it is assumed that precision is 2S over the 95 percent confidence interval. It should also be noted that two "identical" instruments from the same manufacturer need not exhibit identical precision error as shown in Table 10.

The reasons for the foregoing differences in instrument performance are being investigated but are at the present time still unknown. These precision comparisons underscore the need for continued, current evaluation of emission instrument performance and the need to recognize the possible difference between typical in-use precision and that permitted by the EPA.

Correction for Precision Error

The EPA [10] recommends "backtracking" gain adjustments to improve on the test data between calibrations: that is, if, over an hour, the instru-

TABLE 9—Comparison of the EPA required instrument precisions with the history of P&WA emission instrument precisions.

Constituent	Range	P&WA Precision by Six Month Time Periods				EPA Required
		1	2	3	4	
CO_2	0 to 2%	0.22% CO_2	0.015% CO_2	0.02% CO_2	0.016% CO_2	0.02% CO_2
	0 to 5%	...	0.11% CO_2	0.09% CO_2	0.108% CO_2	0.05% CO_2
CO	0 to 100-ppm CO	...	1.81-ppm CO	3.0-ppm CO	1.4-ppm CO	1-ppm CO
	0 to 500-ppm CO	...	...	...	...	5-ppm CO
	0 to 1000-ppm CO	13.9-ppm CO	12-ppm CO	19.6-ppm CO	42.5-ppm CO	10-ppm CO
	0 to 2500-ppm CO	...	...	...	...	25-ppm CO
	0 to 10000-ppm CO	...	110-ppm CO	...	200-ppm CO	100-ppm CO
THC	0 to 10-ppm THC	...	...	...	...	0.1-ppm THC
	0 to 100-ppm THC	...	2.7-ppm THC	4-ppm THC	3.0 ppm THC	1.0-ppm THC
	0 to 1000-ppm THC	...	27.2-ppm THC	22-ppm THC	10.8-ppm THC	10-ppm THC
	0 to 2000-ppm THC	16.2-ppm THC	20-ppm THC	...	4.3-ppm THC	20-ppm THC
	0 to 10000-ppm THC	...	272-ppm THC	...	42.4-ppm THC	100-ppm THC
NO_x	0 to 200-ppm NO_x	...	...	...	...	2-ppm NO_x
	0 to 500-ppm NO_x	...	...	...	...	5-ppm NO_x
NO	0 to 200-ppm NO	13.9-ppm NO	5.1-ppm NO	5-ppm NO	4.0-ppm NO	...
	0 to 500-ppm NO	...	...	...	8.0-ppm NO	
NO_2	0 to 200-ppm NO_2	15.2-ppm NO_2	5.9-ppm NO_2	5-ppm NO_2	3.35-ppm NO_2	...
O_2	0 to 25% O_2	...	0.25% O_2	0.28% O_2	0.87% O_2	...

TABLE 10—*Comparison of precision error for "identical" emission instruments.*

Constituent	P&WA Precision—6 Month Pooled Average		
	Range	Instrument A	Instrument B
CO_2	0 to 2%	0.016%	0.007%
	0 to 5%	0.11%	0.11%
CO	0 to 100 ppm	1.4 ppm	2.0 ppm
	0 to 1000 ppm	42.5 ppm	15.6 ppm
	0 to 1%	0.020%	0.017%
THC	0 to 100 ppm	3.0 ppm	4.3 ppm
	0 to 1000 ppm	10.8 ppm	19.7 ppm
	0 to 2000 ppm	4.3 ppm	9.6 ppm
	0 to 1%	0.042%	0.014%
O_2	0 to 25%	0.87%	0.55%

ment has drifted four divisions, test data taken at 15 min may be adjusted one division, that at 30 min, 2 divisions, etc. This approach presumes a correlation for the time between calibrations and the magnitude of the gain change necessary to bring the instrument into calibration. Table 11 shows typical correlation coefficients of the time between calibrations, which varied from 15 min to 2 h, with the magnitude of the gain adjustments for CO_2, NO_2, NO, HC, and CO. None are significantly different from zero.

Table 11 indicated the lack of a specific relationship between instrument drift and time between calibrations. The lack of that relationship is further illustrated by Fig. 6. Attempts to utilize data of the type in Fig. 6 or the correlations in Table 11 for adjusting instrument data would prove most frustrating. There is apparently no advantage to the backtracking of gain adjustments; indeed, it may cause more error than it removes.

It should be noted that allowing sufficient instrument warmup time will reduce the likelihood of instrument drift with time and result in only random variation of the type in Fig. 6.

TABLE 11—*Gain change magnitude correlation with time between calibrations.*

Instrument	Correlation Coefficient
CO_2	0.00
NO_2	−0.03
NO	−0.03
THC	0.01
CO	0.06
None significant	

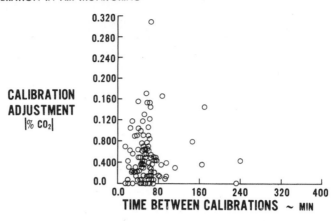

FIG. 6—*Calibration versus time between calibrations CO_2 analyzer, 0 to 5 percent range.*

Uses of Accuracy Data

Real-Time Calibration at P&WA

The emission measurement systems at P&WA now are equipped to evaluate emission levels on a real-time basis through the use of a computer interface. This interface has made it possible to keep track of every calibration of every instrument range automatically. The system operators are then provided with a running assessment of instrument precision and bias (due to central value drift which is usually negligible). When the precision or bias values obtained are greater than that typically seen in instrument operation, the data are flagged so the instrument operator may be alerted for possible instrumentation problems.

Consistency Checks

Several on-line consistency checks are available for emission testing. The use of these checks is intended to make immediately apparent to the instrument operators any serious instrument malfunction. Some of these surveillance checks and their uses are shown next.

Surveillance Parameter(s)	*Usage*
Performance F/A versus carbon balance F/A	Comparing the performance fuel-air ratio (F/A) from engine data and the carbon balance F/A from the gas sample provides an estimate of the representativeness of the gas sample, in addition to revealing some possible instrumentation problems. The differences observed should usually be less than 5 percent and will

Surveillance Parameter(s)	*Usage*
	almost always be less than 10 percent. Some of the causes of the discrepancies observed may be: CO_2 instrument malfunction, sample line leaks, CO_2 calibrated gas bias, performance F/A error, and nonrepresentative sampling.
Curve fit 2 SEE data	All the curve fit data provide an estimate of the self-consistency of the test data. The lower the 2 SEE, the better the fit, the more consistent the data. (The 2 SEE is a description of the data scatter around a particular curve.)
1. Total CO_2 versus total oxygen (O_2)	These data theoretically [*14*] yield a straight line of the form:

$$CO_2 = 0.6231\ O_2 + 0.13054$$

	The line is independent of sampling errors; thus, its 2 SEE estimates the combined precision of the CO_2 and O_2 instruments. Although the slope and intercept of the line are related, if test data have a different slope, it may indicate the carbon-hydrogen ratio of the fuel is other than 2. A different intercept may indicate a bias in either CO_2 or O_2 calibration gases, or both.
2. Log oxides of nitrogen (NO_x) versus total CO_2	These data were empirically shown to approximate a 2nd order function [*14*]. The 2 SEE here estimates the combined precision of NO_x and CO_2 instruments.
3. Log CO versus log total hydrocarbons (THC)	These data were empirically shown to approximate a 2nd order function [*14*]. The 2 SEE here estimates the combined precision of the CO and THC instruments.

Cross Checks and Data Validity

A significant advantage to possessing as-is instrument calibration data is obtaining, not only the capacity to check on the consistency of the relationships between various parameters measured, but the causes of their uncertainty as well. There are specific relationships, just described, between several of the constituents that may be utilized to detect erroneous data by severe departure from that relationship. A calibration record then permits some assessment as to the causes of the variability in the relationship that is observed. The latter may be seen by observing the correlations typical

TABLE 12—*Correlation between "instrument calibration precision" and "test data scatter[a] about relationships between constituents."*

Comparison	Order of Fit	Correlation Coefficient	Explained Variation, %
CO_2 precision versus CO_2-O_2 2 SEE	1st	0.44	19
O_2 precision versus CO_2-O_2 2 SEE	1st	0.80	64
CO_2 precision versus CO_2-NO_x 2 SEE	3rd	0.60	36
NO precision versus CO_2-NO_x 2 SEE	3rd	0.83	69
NO_2 precision versus CO_2-NO_x 2 SEE	3rd	0.42	18

[a] All data based upon ten tests.

when instrument calibration precision data are compared to data scatter, 2 SEE, about well-known constituent relationships.

Table 12 shows the results of a comparison between the instrument precisions and the data scatter — about five curve fits for ten separate tests. It is known that variations in one source of error may be explained to some degree by variations in another through the use of correlation coefficient. For example, considerable data scatter was observed when CO_2, and O_2 test data were fitted with a straight line (predicted from combustion chemistry). The scatter was greater than expected and persisted for many tests. As can be seen, the first two correlations in Table 12 indicated that, by far, the major source of the data scatter was the precision of the oxygen analyzer because the O_2 precision correlates better with the CO_2-O_2 curve 2 SEE than does the $\overline{CO}_2$ precision. Without the calibration data, the cause of the variability would have remained unknown, and no corrective action could have been taken.

Meeting Specifications or Regulations

Probably the single major benefit for securing and understanding the accuracy data pertaining to any measurement process is that the data may be used to define the relationship between (a) measurement uncertainty, (b) fraction of units failing to meet specifications due to measurement uncertainty, and (c) the value a parameter must have, in relation to the limit, to assure a given fraction meeting the specification. This relationship may be seen graphically in Fig. 7.

As an example of the utility of Fig. 7, consider a situation where, because of rebuilding, material, and testing costs, it would not be profitable for a company to have an engine exceed an emission limitation more than 1 percent of the time. If the uncertainty in that emission measurement is 15 percent, which is not unreasonable if sample error is considered, then Fig. 7 shows that the emission average for a group of engines cannot exceed 82 percent of the limit. If it is too expensive to make engines averag-

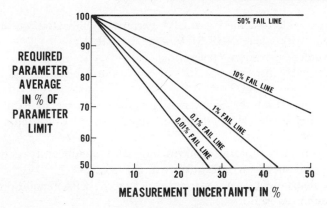

FIG. 7—*Parameter average required for given failure level as a function of measurement uncertainty.*

ing 18 percent below the emission limit, then an appropriate improvement in measurement uncertainty must be made.

It should be noted that gas turbine performance-related instrumentation uncertainties are considerably less than the 15 percent emission measurement example. Most performance measurements are well below 2 percent of reading and some only a few tenths, for example, thrust. However, Fig. 7 is still applicable, as contractual requirements usually vary in severity inversely with the measurement uncertainty of the parameter involved. All that is needed to utilize Fig. 7 is the knowledge of the limitations on the parameter of interest, its measurement uncertainty, and what failure level is tolerable.

Conclusions

1. A knowledge of measurement uncertainty is required before any assessment of the significance of a measurement can be made.

2. Instrument uncertainty would be best described through the use of a well-defined, mutually agreed upon statistical procedure, which does not presently exist for emission measurements.

3. Instrument users and manufacturers need identical methods for instrument accuracy assessment.

4. Calibration to calibration precision, obtained in the instrument's working environment, will usually provide the best estimate of instrument precision available.

5. Gaussian-normally distributed error data are the most useful in assessing instrument uncertainty.

6. The use of a separate analytical group to determine instrument uncertainty can be a valuable tool.

7. It is possible to achieve the EPA permitted calibration gas accuracies in the laboratory where NBS SRM's are available.

8. Instrument precision varies widely from day to day.

9. "Identical" instruments do not always exhibit identical precision error.

10. Assuming that the instrument calibration curve fit exhibiting the lowest 2 SEE is the most accurate might lead to substantial between calibration point errors.

11. Instrument calibration curves can shift significantly and without detection until the next calibration curve check.

12. The instrument precisions permitted by the EPA regulations are not typically achieved in normal use.

13. Backtracking gain adjustments is not an appropriate method for correcting emission instrument data.

14. Real-time analysis of instrument precision data is achievable, and the results permit the assessment of data validity while a test is in progress.

15. The existence of measurement uncertainty increases the margin needed between regulatory limitations and the average emission level of an engine type to assure complete compliance.

16. It is clear that, without an assessment of emission measurement uncertainty, any conclusions resulting from data comparisons may be erroneous, and the differences observed may be due to chance.

Acknowledgment

The author wishes to acknowledge E. E. Western and K. S. Sek, both of Pratt and Whitney Aircraft, for their efforts in obtaining most of the emission uncertainty estimates contained in this paper.

References

[1] Dieck, R. H., "Gas Turbine Emission Measurement Uncertainty," *Proceedings*, 1974 International Conference, Instrument Society of America, New York, N.Y., 28–31 Oct. 1974.

[2] Lipfert, F. W., "Correlation of Gas Turbine Emissions Data," presented at the ASME Gas Turbine and Fluids Engineering Conference and Products Show, San Francisco, Calif., American Society of Mechanical Engineers, 26–30 March 1972.

[3] Marchionna, N. R. and Diehl, L. A., "Effect of Inlet Air Humidity, Temperature, Pressure, and Reference Mach Number on the Formation of Oxides of Nitrogen in a Gas Turbine Combustor," Technical Note No. NASA-TN-D-7396, National Aeronautics and Space Administration, Oct. 1973.

[4] Western, E. E. and Dieck, R. H., "A Method for Evaluating the Effect of Inlet Humidity and Temperature on the Production of Oxides of Nitrogen in High Bypass Radio Turbofan Engines," *Proceedings*, 1974 National Conference, Instrument Society of America, New York, N.Y., 28–31 Oct. 1974.

[5] "Glossary of ASTM Definitions," *1973 Annual Book of ASTM Standards*, American Society for Testing and Materials, 1973.

[6] Natrella, M. C., "Experimental Statistics," Handbook Number 91, National Bureau of Standards, p. 1073.

[7] Dieck, R. H. and Elwood, J. H., "The Assessment of Emission Analysis Accuracy," Paper No. 74–91, presented at the annual meeting, Air Pollution Control Association, Denver, Colo., June 1974.

[8] Dixon, W. J. and Massey, F. J., Jr., *Introduction to Statistical Analysis*, 3rd ed., McGraw-Hill, New York, 1969, p. 61.

[9] Abernathy, R. B. et al, "Handbook-Uncertainty in Gas Turbine Measurements," Publication No. AEDC-TR-73-5, Arnold Engineering Development Center, Feb. 1973.

[10] "Control of Air Pollution from Aircraft and Aircraft Engines," *Federal Register*, Vol. 38, No. 136, Part II, 17 July 1963.

[11] Elwood, J. H., Robertson, D. J., Groth, R. H., and Gardner, D. G., "Problems in Establishment of Standard Reference Gases and Analytical Procedures for Use in Gas Turbine Exhaust Measurements," presented at the 68th Annual Meeting of the Air Pollution Control Association, Boston, Mass., 15–20 June 1975.

[12] Elwood, J. H. and Dieck, R. H., "Techniques and Procedures for the Measurement of Aircraft Gas Turbine Engine Emissions," presented at the 67th Annual Meeting of the Air Pollution Control Association, Denver, Colo., 9–13 June 1974.

[13] Mandel, J. and Linning, F. J., *Analytical Chemistry*, Vol. 29, May 1957, p. 743.

[14] Alwang, W. G., Campbell, N. T., and Groth, R. H., "Empirical Validation of Turbine Engine Exhaust Measurements," presented at the 68th Annual Meeting of the Air Pollution Control Association, Boston, Mass., 15–20 June 1975.

S. G. Wechter[1]

Preparation of Stable Pollution Gas Standards Using Treated Aluminum Cylinders

REFERENCE: Wechter, S. G., "Preparation of Stable Pollution Gas Standards Using Treated Aluminum Cylinders," *Calibration in Air Monitoring, ASTM STP 598*, American Society for Testing and Materials, 1976, pp. 40–54.

ABSTRACT: The use of gas cylinder calibration standards is becoming an increasingly important tool for use in pollution analysis methods requiring a known reference. There are problems, however, in the preparation of pollution gas standards using high pressure steel cylinders. Researchers have documented these problems in the literature, especially in recent months. When reactive gases such as the oxides of nitrogen, carbon monoxide, or sulfur dioxide are blended in a steel cylinder with an inert balance gas, the concentration that the cylinder delivers can vary with time, pressure, and temperature. The nature of the blend's instability is random and a function of the absorption or reaction with the walls of the cylinder. These disturbing features lead to an obvious question. Can the specialty gas industry provide a stable and accurate pollution calibration standard in a cylinder? This paper deals with that question and describes experience gained using treated aluminum cylinders as a solution to the problem. Included in the discussion are: (1) instrumental and analysis method evaluation, (2) calibration and correlation of internal standards, (3) effects of various cylinder types on the stability of reactive gas mixtures, (4) effects of preconditioning as a means of deactivating cylinder walls, (5) effects of variables such as temperature and pressure on cylinder concentrations, and (6) long-term stability data.

KEY WORDS: calibration, air pollution, gases, standards, gas cylinders

A pressurized calibration cylinder can be an intricate part of the many air pollution analysis methods requiring a known reference. Establishing this known reference is not, however, an easy matter. Researchers have documented problems associated not only with accuracy but also with the stability of certified cylinder standards [1–5].[2] When reactive gases such as the oxides of nitrogen, carbon monoxide (CO) or sulfur dioxide (SO_2)

---

[1] Development engineer, Rare and Specialty Gases Department, Airco Industrial Gases, Murray Hill, N.J. 08077.

[2] The italic numbers in brackets refer to the list of references appended to this paper.

are blended in a steel cylinder with an inert balance gas, the concentration that the cylinder delivers can vary with time, temperature, or pressure. The nature of the mixture's instability is random and dependent on the particular condition of the individual cylinder involved. The instability is partially a function of gas absorption or reaction with the cylinder walls. As mentioned, the effect is random, and the exact mechanisms involved are still not understood fully. What has been well established is the fact that reactive gas standards prepared in mild steel cylinders are of dubious value due to their inability to demonstrate stability.

Oxides of Nitrogen

The instability of nitric oxide (NO) and nitrogen dioxide (NO_2) calibration standards in steel cylinders has been reported in many references [6–9]. To exemplify the problem, refer to Fig. 1 and Table 1. Figure 1 illustrates how three evacuated cylinders of different wall composition were filled from a premixed, bulk container. The pressure from this single bulk container was equalized into the three cylinders in such a way that each cylinder received the same initial blend of 200-ppm NO_2 in nitrogen (N_2). Table 1 indicates the analysis results after periods of two months and two years.

Figure 2 represents data obtained from the National Bureau of Standards (NBS) [10]. It shows the analysis results of five lots of 53 steel cylinders, each containing NO in N_2. All cylinders were new Department of Transportation (DOT)-3AA type and unused but were conditioned by soaking with a high concentration of NO prior to use. As can be seen from Fig. 2, a substantial portion of each lot of 53 cylinders had decayed. The remaining cylinders seemed to exhibit stability and were released as the first lot of

TABLE 1—*Mixture 1: filled to be 200-ppm NO_2 in N_2.*

Cylinder Type	Analysis, 2 Months, ppm	Analysis, 2 Years, ppm
Wax lined	135	<1
Steel (Cr-Mo)	179	151
Treated aluminum	197	200

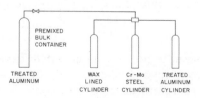

FIG. 1—*System used in filling cylinders of various wall MTL's.*

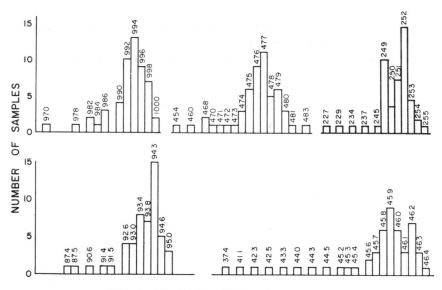

FIG. 2—*Distribution of NO in N_2 concentrations.*

NBS NO standard reference materials (SRM). These particular SRM's have been restricted in that they are not certified for more than six months, nor at cylinder pressures below 500 psig.

Carbon Monoxide

The use of CO calibration standards is another area which has generated many problems for the unsuspecting analyst [*11*]. CO concentrations in steel cylinders have a tendency to decay with time [*7,12*]. The reason for this decay is still not well understood, but it is believed to be due either to oxidation of the CO to carbon dioxide (CO_2) or the formation of iron carbonyls [*13*]. In any event, the problem is cylinder-dependent as the decay is random and shows no set pattern. Each individual cylinder seems to exhibit its own characteristics for decay (amount of rust on interior walls, etc.). To exemplify the problem, refer to Fig. 3, supplied by courtesy of the NBS. It illustrates the results of a study with CO mixtures prepared in steel cylinders (DOT-3AA). As can be seen in Fig. 3, the decline in concentration value can be quite drastic, especially at lower concentrations.

Sulfur Dioxide

SO_2 standards prepared in pressurized cylinders have a history of being unreliable for just about anyone who has ever tried to work with them. Stainless steel cylinders have been used with some success at higher concentrations, but lower levels are deemed to be virtually impossible [*14–16*].

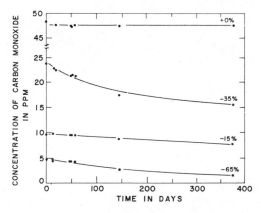

FIG. 3—*Stability of CO mixtures in steel cylinders (DOT-3AA).*

SO_2 reacts readily with moisture and has a strong tendency to be absorbed by everything, including, not only the cylinder walls but also the sampling system being used to make the measurement [*17–19*].

By referring to Table 2, the stability problem with SO_2 in steel cylinders can be seen more readily. Three cylinders of different wall compositions were filled from a single premixed bulk container using the same apparatus as in Fig. 1. The mixture was filled to be 160-ppm SO_2 in nitrogen. Table 2 indicates the analysis results after two-month and two-year periods.

The conclusions that can be reached after studying the results of Table 2 are quite evident. SO_2 in contact with a steel cylinder can be a significant problem.

Summarizing, it can be said that there are problems associated with pollution gas standards in steel cylinders, despite claims made by various suppliers. The ability to supply stable certified standards is not always as easy as it might first appear. The blending of such gases requires special and sophisticated techniques undertaken in the most stringent of conditions.

Effects of Preconditioning as a Means of Deactivating Cylinder Walls

There are many and varied methods of preconditioning being attempted to passify a cylinder wall surface. One very common method is to "soak"

TABLE 2—*Mixture 2: filled to be 160-ppm SO_2 in N_2.*

Cylinder Type	Analysis, 2 Months, ppm	Analysis, 2 Years, ppm
Wax lined	140	120
Steel (Cr-Mo)	148	132
Treated aluminum	159	157

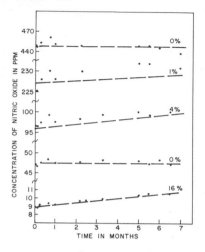

FIG. 4—*Stability of NO mixtures.*

the cylinder with a high concentration of the reactive gas of interest. The theory behind this soaking process is that all of the gas that is going to react with or be absorbed into the cylinder walls will do so during the conditioning period. When the cylinder is put into its final mixing stage, any further reaction or absorption will be supposedly precluded.

This method of preconditioning has met with only limited success. The problem arises when one realizes that what has been absorbed can also be desorbed. When the pressure or temperature of the cylinder changes, the gas that was absorbed during the soaking process can desorb, so that the concentration that the cylinder delivers can actually increase. Figure 4 illustrates analysis results obtained by the NBS on a group of preconditioned steel cylinders containing NO mixtures. Figures 5 and 6 represent analysis results on preconditioned cylinders containing 5-ppm NO in nitrogen as the temperature and pressure of the cylinder were varied. As can be seen from these figures, the cylinder concentrations tend to increase as desorption takes place [10].

Another method of conditioning involves treating the cylinder surface with a very active gas such as silane.[3] The most common procedure usually involves taking new shot-cleaned steel cylinders and alternating between treatments with silane and a high purity nitrogen bake out process. The idea here is to eliminate any traces of moisture or oxygen which may be lurking in the cylinder walls. Although this method does eliminate one problem, it does nothing to eliminate reaction with or absorption into the steel. Also, the silane conditioning agent can desorb slightly off the walls after the final mixture has been made, adding another impurity.

---

[3] Silane ($Si_n + H_{2n+2}$) is a combination of silicon and hydrogen.

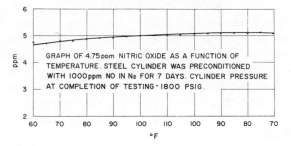

FIG. 5—*Graph of 4.75-ppm NO as a function of temperature.*

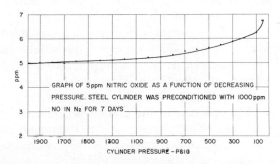

FIG. 6—*Graph of 5-ppm NO as a function of decreasing pressure.*

Still another method which can be considered a pretreatment for steel involves the actual changing of the metal surface within the cylinder. In effect, this is metal coating [20]. The one major disadvantage of this method is its cost. Different types of coatings must be used to be effective against different types of gases, and this can be quite an expensive proposition. Also, there are still some absorption effects which may be questionable.

Experimentation with Cylinder Wall Materials

The problems associated with the use of steel cylinders and the inability of pretreatment methods to be totally effective led to a search for a cylinder wall material that remained passive and would not absorb reactive gases. Experiments were conducted, initially, using a wax-lined steel cylinder. The wax coating was partially effective in controlling absorbed moisture and also demonstrated success in eliminating decay problems associated with CO. Similar success with wax-lined cylinders for use with CO mixtures has been achieved by the NBS. This type of cylinder is being used currently for the CO in nitrogen SRM's. Although the wax-lined cylinder has demonstrated definite superiority over standard steel cylinders for CO, the use of this cylinder for SO_2 or the oxides of nitrogen is not as feasible.

In some cases, the wax coating actually intensifies the decay phenomenon to a significant degree as can be seen in Tables 1 and 2. Another problem associated with wax lining involves the actual waxing process itself. Even though great care is taken in the waxing procedure, small pinholes of uncovered steel still remain. Also, a wax-lined cylinder represents a possible safety hazard. Even though the cylinders may be properly marked and tagged, there is always the danger that someone will try illegally to fill the cylinder with an incompatible gas.

Aside from wax lining, the use of various types of Teflon and organic coatings were explored. All of the methods considered, however, had specific disadvantages associated with them which rendered them unacceptable for use in a cylinder.

The extensive search for a suitable cylinder wall material led to the use of a treated aluminum cylinder which exhibited the unique properties that were required. The cylinder, after treatment, provided a highly inert sealed surface which made it quite effective in containing even subpart per million levels of very reactive gases. The special treatment referred to is actually a two part process. The first part of the process is performed by the manufacturer of the cylinder. This portion of the treatment consists of the enhancement of an aluminum oxide layer. This aluminum oxide layer then facilitates the application of the second part of the process which is undertaken by the author's firm and is proprietary in nature.

Evaluation Program for Treated Aluminum Cylinders

Preliminary experimentation and the ability of the treated aluminum cylinder to contain the reactive gases initiated an extensive evaluation program. This evaluation, now in its third year, involves the study of approximately 73 cylinders in various phases of long-term stability, temperature, and pressure testing. The gas mixtures being evaluated contain various concentrations of CO, SO_2, NO, and NO_2. The range of concentrations varies from very high to ultra-low subpart per million levels (0.023 ppm). Due to a credibility gap established through the years between suppliers and users of specialty gases, it was decided that supporting data would be of value. In order to obtain these data, evaluation cylinders were supplied to five major instrument companies, the Environmental Protection Agency (EPA), the NBS, and various competent representatives from concerned industries.

Analysis Methods and Equipment

Because of the difficulties involved with reactive gas analysis and the critical nature of the program undertaken, an extensive review of analytical techniques was required. Unfortunately, evaluations were initiated at a time in which much controversy existed as to what method of analysis could

TABLE 3—*Analytical methods used in evaluation.*

NO-NO$_2$	SO$_2$	CO
1. Saltzman phenol disulfuric acid 2. Dispersive infrared 3. Chemiluminescence[a] 4. Photometric ultraviolet[a] 5. Electrochemical cell	1. West Gaeke 2. Mass spectrometry 3. Dispersive infrared 4. SO$_2$ fluorescence[a] 5. Flame photometric detection[a] (total sulfur) 6. Gas chromatography-flame photometric detection	1. Nondispersive infrared procedure[a] 2. Dispersive infrared 3. Gas chromatography[a] (methanator)

[a] Methods which provided the best results for our specific analysis needs.

accurately measure a particular type of gas. We were forced into a position of not only performing method evaluations but also side-by-side testing of the same type of instrument from various suppliers.

Table 3 indicates the methods of analysis evaluated in the Airco study.

The wet chemical methods listed were operational early in the study but are no longer being employed. It was found that problems existed with the precision and accuracy of those methods and are probably due, at least in part, to manual techniques that were required. Access to automated apparatus may have improved results considerably. Table 4 shows the results of this evaluation.

Calibration and Correlation of Internal Standards

Accurate calibration of an instrument or the analytical method used can often be the most difficult part of a measurement. Many users of calibration standards in cylinders will rely solely on the certified value written on the tag supplied by the manufacturer. How does a calibration gas supplier calibrate the instruments he uses to certify the cylinder standard? The answer to this question can be crucial to the user of such a standard.

The best solution to this problem is for the supplier to use SRM's supplied by the NBS. The problem here is that SRM's may not always be available for a specific gas or at the concentration range desired. One of the more common methods used by specialty gas suppliers to calibrate their instrumentation is to establish some form of primary standard, such as a cylinder prepared by weight. Although this primary method is inherently very accurate, it cannot account for the reactive nature of gases. Due to reactivity or absorption into the walls of a cylinder, what is put into a cylinder very accurately by weight may not always come out with the same degree of accuracy.

It is proposed that, rather than rely on a single primary method, a series of correlations with many chemical and physical methods be undertaken to approach or verify an absolute standard. To exemplify what is meant by correlation, the following methods were correlated to establish primary standards for the oxides of nitrogen.

Two sets of standards containing six cylinders each were prepared with NO_2 concentrations, using treated aluminum cylinders. The first method of preparation was by weight, using a high precision balance (Voland Model HCE-50).

The second method was to mix the same concentrations by pressure, using a baratron manometer (MKS). The two sets of cylinders were then analyzed by chemiluminescence, looking for relative values. A correlation between the two methods was obtained to within 2 percent. The next correlation sought involved the use of an ultraviolet photometric analyzer (duPont Model 411). This analyzer is supplied with an optical calibration filter, with a simulated concentration based on known molar absorptivities for the gases being measured. When the photometric analyzer was calibrated with this filter and the cylinders analyzed, a correlation was obtained to within 2 percent of the previously determined values. At this point, two additional sets of six cylinders each, this time containing NO, were prepared again by weight and pressure. After correlation between them was completed, the chemiluminescence analyzer was calibrated with these newly prepared NO standards. The NO_2 cylinders were then analyzed going through the chemiluminescent convertor, using a NO calibration. In this way, a correlation between the two sets of NO cylinders and the NO_2 cylinders was obtained to within 2.5 percent. The higher error here was attributable, probably, to the extra step required in determining the chemiluminescent convertor efficiency by gas phase titration. The final correlation was obtained by calibrating measurement instrumentation with permeation tubes and noting analysis results. A correlation to within 3 percent was obtained using this method. In the end, it could be said that mixture concentrations were correlated with:

1. Filling cylinders by weight.
2. Filling cylinders by pressure.
3. Optical calibration correlation.
4. Conversion correlation (NO_2 to NO).
5. Permeation calibration correlation.

After correlation, the primary standard value can be assigned with confidence. This policy of correlation should be undertaken with all primary standards, rather than rely on a single method of verification which may contain inherent errors that could go unnoticed.

Effects of Temperature and Pressure on Aluminum Cylinder Concentrations

Because absorption or reaction is no longer of particular concern, calibration standards prepared in aluminum cylinders show exceptional temperature and pressure stability. See Figs. 7, 8, and 9. During tempera-

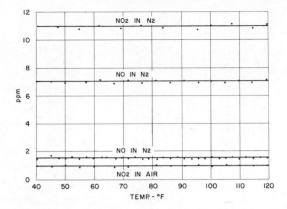

FIG. 7—*Effect of temperature on treated aluminum cylinder concentrations.*

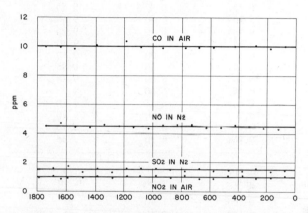

FIG. 8—*Effect of pressure on treated aluminum cylinder concentrations.*

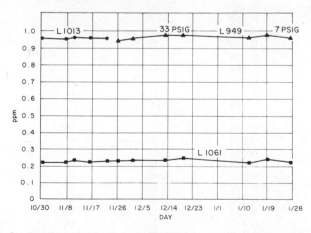

FIG. 9—*Stability of NO mixtures prepared in treated aluminum cylinders.*

TABLE 4—*Results.*

Reading Date	0.2-ppm NO in N_2	6-ppm NO in N_2	10-ppm NO in N_2	200-ppm NO in N_2
5/12/73	0.165	6.40	9.80	198
5/20/73	0.163	6.30	9.75	197
6/9/73	0.165	6.30	9.80	198
6/30/73	0.160	6.40	9.75	197
7/7/73	0.165	6.35	9.90	198
7/28/73	0.167	6.40	9.80	199
8/11/73	0.165	6.70	9.80	198
8/25/73	0.164	6.30	9.75	198
8/31/73	0.166	6.40	9.75	198
9/8/73	0.165	6.40	9.80	198
9/22/73	0.167	6.35	9.80	199
10/13/73	0.165	6.45	9.75	198
11/10/73	0.165	6.40	9.80	198
11/24/73	0.167	6.45	9.85	197
12/15/73	0.165	6.40	9.80	195
1/5/74	0.165	6.40	9.75	198
1/19/74	0.165	6.40	9.80	197
1/26/74	0.171	7.00	10.10	198
2/9/74	0.165	6.50	9.85	197
2/23/74	0.165	6.40	9.80	198
3/16/74	0.162	6.40	9.75	199
3/30/74	0.165	6.35	9.80	198
4/13/74	0.165	6.40	9.80	198
4/27/74	0.164	6.40	9.75	198
5/23/75	0.168	6.30	9.85	199

Reading Date	0.2-ppm NO_2 in N_2	2-ppm NO_2 in N_2	85-ppm NO_2 in Air	200-ppm NO_2 in N_2
5/12/73	0.180	1.40	86	197
5/26/73	0.182	1.41	86	198
6/9/73	0.185	1.45	85	196
6/30/73	0.180	1.40	86	196
7/7/73	0.182	1.39	85	197
7/28/83	0.182	1.40	87	198
8/11/73	0.182	1.40	86	197
8/25/73	0.180	1.39	86	197
8/31/73	0.178	1.40	86	197
9/8/73	0.182	1.41	85	197
9/22/73	0.180	1.40	86	198
10/13/73	0.182	1.41	86	197
11/10/73	0.180	1.40	86	197
11/24/73	0.182	1.45	85	198
12/15/73	0.180	1.41	86	197
1/5/74	0.182	1.40	86	199
1/19/74	0.180	1.41	86	197
1/26/74	0.178	1.40	86	197
2/9/74	0.180	1.40	86	198
2/23/74	0.172	1.45	85	197
3/16/74	0.182	1.40	86	197
3/30/74	0.180	1.45	86	197
4/13/74	0.182	1.35	86	198
4/27/74	0.180	1.40	85	197
5/23/75	0.183	1.43	86	196

(*Continued*)

TABLE 4—*Continued*

Reading Date	100-ppm CO in N_2	50-ppm CO in Air	25-ppm CO in N_2	10-ppm CO in Air
5/12/73	99.5	50.5	24.0	9.0
5/20/73	99.5	49.5	24.5	9.5
6/9/73	99.0	49.5	24.0	9.0
6/23/73	99.5	49.0	25.0	9.5
6/30/73	100.0	45.0	24.5	9.5
7/7/73	99.0	49.5	25.0	9.0
7/28/73	101.0	49.0	25.5	9.5
8/11/73	99.0	51.0	24.5	9.8
8/25/73	100.0	50.0	24.5	9.0
8/31/73	98.5	49.5	25.0	9.5
9/8/73	101.0	50.5	24.5	9.5
9/22/73	99.0	49.0	25.5	9.0
10/13/73	99.5	50.0	24.5	9.5
10/27/73	100.0	49.5	25.0	9.5
11/10/73	99.5	50.0	23.0	8.5
11/24/73	99.5	49.0	25.0	9.5
12/15/73	100.0	50.0	24.5	9.9
1/5/74	100.0	49.5	24.0	10.0
1/19/74	99.5	49.0	25.0	9.9
1/26/74	95.0	47.0	23.0	7.5
2/9/74	99.0	49.5	24.5	9.5
2/23/74	99.5	48.5	24.5	9.5
3/16/74	100.0	49.5	25.5	10.0
3/30/74	99.5	49.5	...	...
4/13/74	99.5	50.0	25.0	9.0
4/27/74	100.0	49.0	24.5	7.5
4/19/75	100.0	48.5	25.0	9.8

Reading Date	1-ppm SO_2 in N_2	10-ppm SO_2 in Air	25-ppm SO_2 in N_2	200-ppm SO_2 in N_2
5/12/73	1.3	10.5	26	208
5/20/73	1.4	11.5	26	207
6/9/73	1.3	10.0	25	206
6/23/73	1.3	11.5	26	209
6/30/73	1.2	11.5	27	208
7/7/75	1.3	11.0	26	208
7/28/75	1.4	11.5	26	210
8/11/73	1.6	11.5	25	208
8/25/73	1.3	11.0	26	208
8/31/73	1.3	10.5	26	210
9/8/73	1.3	11.5	26	210
9/22/73	1.2	11.5	26	208
10/13/73	1.3	11.0	26	208
10/27/73	1.3	11.5	26	206
11/10/73	1.3	11.5	25	208
11/24/73	1.4	10.0	26	208
12/15/73	1.3	11.5	26	208
1/5/74	1.3	11.5	26	208
1/19/74	1.4	11.5	25	208
1/26/74	1.3	10.0	29	210
2/9/74	1.3	11.5	26	208
2/23/74	1.4	11.5	26	215
3/16/74	1.3	11.5	26	208
3/30/74	1.3	11.0	25	210
4/13/74	1.4	11.5	26	208
4/27/74	1.3	11.5	25	208
5/23/75	1.4	11.0	25	207

ture studies, cylinders were cycled starting at room temperature, to 120°F through a low temperature cycle, and back to room temperature. The pressure testing cycle was from full cylinder pressure (approximately 2100 psig) down to 25 psig. Figure 9 represents data supplied by Beckman Instruments of Fullerton, Calif. Although no attempt was made particularly to monitor the pressure, the graph does indicate the effect of emptying the cylinder over a four-month period.

Long-Term Stability

Figures 10 and 11 illustrate the excellent stability obtained over a two-year period. Figure 11 represents data supplied by the NBS. When this

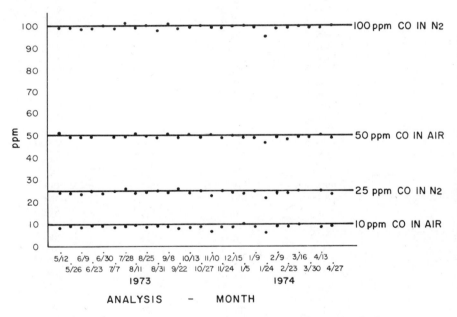

FIG. 10—*Long-term stability of CO mixtures in aluminum cylinders.*

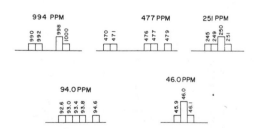

FIG. 11—*Concentration of NO mixtures in aluminum cylinders (5 samples at each concentration).*

distribution is compared with data illustrated in Fig. 2, it can be seen that aluminum cylinders offer some advantages over steel. The 25 cylinders represented were prepared at the same time and from the same bulk mixtures as the five lots of 53 cylinders represented in Fig. 2. What is particularly significant is that, among the 25 aluminum cylinders, there was not one low value.

Conclusions

Treated aluminum cylinders have the ability to contain reactive gases even at very low subpart per million levels. They show excellent temperature and pressure stability and no appreciable decay in mixture concentration, at least over a two-year period. The gases included in this study were NO, NO_2, CO, and SO_2. Data for hydrogen sulfide (H_2S), carbon sulfide (COS), and carbon disulfide (CS_2) are currently being generated and will be the subject of a future report.

References

[1] Graver, J. W., "A Basis for Accurately Reporting Component Concentrations for Gaseous and Volatile Liquid Calibration Standards," presented at the Pittsburgh Conference of Analytical Chemistry, 4 March 1974, p. 4.

[2] Souza, A. F., "A Calibration Gas Cross Reference Service," Paper 74–634, Instrument Society of America, New York, Oct. 1974, p. 3.

[3] Saltzman, B. E., Analytical Chemistry, Vol. 33, 1961, p. 1100.

[4] Elwood, J. R. and Dieck, R. H., "Techniques and Procedures for the Measurement of Aircraft Gas Turbine and Engine Emissions," Paper 74-90, Air Pollution Control Association, Denver, Colo., June 1974, pp. 19–20.

[5] Grieco, H. A. and Hans, W. M., Industrial Research, March 1974.

[6] Nelson, G. O. in Controlled Test Atmosphere, Ann Arbor Science, Ann Arbor, Mich., 1971, p. 170.

[7] McNesby, J. R. and Hughes, E. E., "Calibration Gas Standards," Paper 74-633, Instrument Society of America, New York, Oct. 1974, pp. 2–3.

[8] Saltzman, B. E. and Wartburg, A. F., Analytical Chemistry, Vol. 37, 1965, p. 1261.

[9] Adley, F. E. and Skillern, C. P., American Industrial Hygiene Association, Vol. 19, 1958, p. 235.

[10] Hughes, E. E., "Development of Standard Reference Materials for Air Quality Measurement," Paper 74-704, Instrument Society of America, New York, Oct. 1974, pp. 3–13.

[11] Mage, D. T., Journal of the Air Pollution Control Association, Nov. 1973, p. 970.

[12] "Development of Technical Specifications for Standard Gas Diluent Mixtures for Use in Measurement of Mobile Source Emissions," Report EPA-650/4-74-020, Environmental Protection Agency, June 1974, pp. 1–5.

[13] Westberg, K. and Cohen, N., Science, Vol. 171, 12 March 1971, pp. 1013–1015.

[14] Pecsar, R. E. and Hartmann, C. H., Air Quality Instrumentation, Vol. 1, Instrument Society of America, Pittsburgh, Pa., p. 99.

[15] McKinley, J. J., Air Quality Instrumentation, Vol. 1, Instrument Society of America, Pittsburgh, Pa., p. 159.

[16] Baker, G. L. and Brubaker, J. H., Analysis Instrumentation, Vol. 12, Instrument Society of America, Pittsburgh, Pa., p. 133.

[17] Slowik, A. A., "Diffusion Losses of Sulfur Dioxide in Sampling Manifolds," Paper 73-153, Air Pollution Control Association, Chicago, June 1973.
[18] Wohlers, H. C. and Newstein, H., "Carbon Monoxide and Sulfur Dioxide Adsorption on—Desorption from Glass, Plastic and Metal Tubings," *Journal of the Air Pollution Control Association*, Vol. 17, No. 11, 1967, pp. 753–56.
[19] Byers, P. L. and Davis, J. W., "Sulfur Dioxide Adsorption and Desorption on Various Filter Media," *Journal of the Air Pollution Control Association*, Vol. 20, No. 4, 1970, pp. 236–238.
[20] Goekcek, C., "Improving the Stability of High Purity Gases and Gas Mixtures in Pressure Containers," *Gas Aktuell*, Messer Griesheim, 1975.

F. J. Debbrecht[1] and E. M. Neel[1]

Application and Description
of a Portable Calibration System

REFERENCE: Debbrecht, F. J. and Neel, E. M., "**Application and Description of a Portable Calibration System**," *Calibration in Air Monitoring, ASTM STP 598*, American Society for Testing and Materials, 1976, pp. 55–65.

ABSTRACT: A newly introduced calibration system for air pollution monitors and its field use will be discussed. The system is based upon the Environmental Protection Agency's developed permeation tube technique and is fully portable, allowing intercalibration of monitors at different locations.

Two major requirements are necessary for accurate use of permeation tubes in the generation of primary standard quality calibration gas mixtures. The temperature of the permeation tube must be held within 0.1°C of the temperature at which it was calibrated to ensure accuracy within 1 percent. Also the flow rate of the gas across the permeation tube must be readable to within 1 percent accuracy.

The portable calibration system described controls the permeation tube at 35°C to well within 0.1°C. This temperature is fixed and is read out on the expanded scalemeter that is 0.4°C full scale to ensure that the permeation tube is within 0.1°C of the fixed 35°C.

The calibration system draws in ambient air through a particulate filter by an internal dual headed pump. One head provides a flow of 10 ml/min through a restriction, a charcoal scrubber, the permeation chamber, and a flow directional valve. The other head provides a diluent flow, settleable on the front panel, from 300 to 1500 ml/min. This flow is read out on a special dual ball rotameter, individually calibrated, with settleability to within 1 percent. This diluent flow can provide a fivefold change in concentration available for calibration, permitting calibration at a number of points. In addition the flow direction valve has a high concentration position in which all of the permeation effluent is mixed with the diluent air, a low concentration position in which only 20 percent of the permeation effluent is mixed with the diluent air, and a "zero" air position in which no permeation effluent is used. This last position provides only air that has passed the charcoal scrubber for the analyzer to be calibrated. The high/low concentration positions provide a 5 to 1 concentration range and when coupled with the diluent air flow range provide a 25 to 1 concentration range.

This calibration system can operate for at least 8 h from internal batteries, indefinitely from 110 V lines, while the batteries are recharging, or from an auto cigarette lighter adapter supplied as standard.

The present emphasis and concern on data correlation among the various locations and agencies involved in the air pollution effort requires the instrumentation used to be calibrated properly. A portable calibration system provides the neces-

---

[1] Director of research and Director of marketing, respectively, Analytical Instrument Development, Inc., Avondale, Pa. 19311.

sary common demoninator between a number of remote monitoring systems. This common standardization is the first crucial step before data can be compared.

KEY WORDS: calibration, monitors, instruments, air pollution, gases, permeability, standards, gases

As the need for more widespread measurement of air pollutants at greater sensitivity increases, the analytical methods used switch from wet chemical to instrumental. Thus, sulfur dioxide (SO_2) is monitored by flame photometric instruments instead of the West Gaeke method, and ozone (O_3) is measured by the chemiluminescent technique rather than the neutral KI method. In addition to the advantages of increased ease of operation, continuous real-time monitoring, and generally increased sensitivity, the instrumental techniques suffer from a disadvantage generally not associated with the wet chemical method. That is, they must be frequently standardized against an air standard containing a known amount of the pollutant being measured. The actual procedure for this calibration is rather simple, and, even in some cases, the instrument does this automatically on a time cycle. The problem posed by the needed frequency of calibration really comes from the gas standard used in the calibration.

Methods of Standard Preparation

There are two basic systems used to prepare gas standards in the laboratory. The static method involves adding known amounts of pure gases into a storage vessel where they are mixed and contained until used. In the dynamic method, pure gases at known flow rates are mixed in a flowing system as the mixture is used. There are two major advantages of the dynamic system. It avoids the adverse phenomena which can occur in the storage vessel such as contamination, fractional distillation, reaction, adsorption, leaks, diffusion, etc. Additionally, it allows great flexibility in changing components or concentration.

Static Methods

All static methods involve the addition of a known amount of gas or vapor to a known volume of clear air. The equipment and procedures are simple. However, adsorption and reaction can cause low results. They should not be used as primary standards without verification and prior experience [1].[2] Known volume bottles are used by flushing with clean air, adding a known amount of gas or vapor, and calculating concentration [2]. An additional disadvantage, especially for sampling systems, of this technique is a limited volume and depletion of the sample. Plastic bags [3]

---

[2] The italic numbers in brackets refer to the list of references appended to this paper.

overcome this problem but require the dilution air to be metered accurately. Low concentrations of reactive materials are lost even with preconditioning of the bags at the same levels of the standard [4,5]. Leaks are also a problem. Pressurized cylinders of certain gas mixtures can be used [6] for some low molecular weight hydrocarbon (HC), carbon monoxide (CO), and carbon dioxide (CO_2) in air.

Care must be used in the cleanliness of the valves and regulators used with these cylinders. Even though they can be made by weight or pressure, they are generally analyzed and thus are not primary standards. Even with the analyzed mixtures, there is some question regarding the reliability [1].

Dynamic Methods

Dynamic methods are basically flow dilution systems providing a continuous flowing calibration gas. Any losses by adsorption on surfaces occur only in the initial minutes of operation. Concentrations can be changed quite rapidly by a change of one or both flows. Two components make up the system, the dilution air flow and the source for gases and vapors. The dilution air must be good cylinder grade or must be purified according to the need of the work. An accurate flow metering device and a flow control valve are necessary for this system.

The various dynamic systems differ in the source devices for the gases and vapors. The major critical requirement for all of the source devices discussed here is the temperature control required for a constant source of gas or vapor.

The vapor pressure technique passes the diluent air through successive thermostated bubblers obtaining a mixture determined by the saturation vapor pressure of the material at the thermostated temperature [7]. Condensation and fogging are problems. Generally this gas stream is diluted by a second air flow to adjust to proper concentration. This introduces a second flow measurement error. This technique is generally not applicable in the field of air pollution, since generally the pollutants to be analyzed are gases at standard conditions. It is mentioned here to illustrate a possible approach in some specialized research in air pollution. Motor driven syringes can be used to provide a small amount of gas to a diluent air stream [8]. Generally periods no longer than an hour are used since the syringe must be refilled. Back diffusion of air into the syringe volume at low delivery rates is a source for error.

The latest development in source devices is the permeation tube. In 1966, O'Keefe and Ortman [9] of the Taft Engineering Center described permeation tubes and showed their use as primary standards in generating gas mixtures. Generally, the tubes are made by sealing a condensable vapor as a liquid in Teflon tubes. Following an initial induction period, the material in the tube (permeant) permeates through the wall of the tube at a uniform rate. A flow of clean (zero concentration of the permeant) air is passed across the permeation tube. The effluent gas then has a concentration of the permeant as determined by the following equation

$$C = \frac{R}{F} \times \left(\frac{24.45}{MW} \right) \qquad (1)$$

where

$\quad C =$ permeant concentration in ppm (volume per volume),
$\quad R =$ permeation rate in ng/min,
$\quad F =$ air flow rate in ml/min,
$\quad 24.45 =$ molar volume of gases at 25°C and 760 mm Hg, and
$\quad MW =$ molecular weight of permeant.

The quantity in parenthesis in Eq 1 converts the permeation rate from a weight per unit time to a volume per unit time. The critical point here is that the molar volume constant used be corrected by simple gas laws to the temperature and pressure of the air at the time of its flow measurement, F, or that F be converted to the volume flow at 25°C and 760 mm Hg.

The permeation rate, R, is determined by weight loss over an extended period of time with the tube being held at constant temperature. Since this is determined independently, the system can be of primary standard quality. The permeation rate is constant throughout the life of the tube as long as the temperature of the tube is held constant. This places the first requirement on any system using permeation tubes. For every 1°C change in temperature the permeation rate changes about 10 percent. This necessitates temperature control to within 0.1°C to maintain 1 percent accuracy of the concentration in the standard gas mixture. The second requirement of any permeation tube calibration system is the ability to measure and hold constant the flow of dilution air to within 1 percent accuracy.

A number of commercially available calibration systems and homemade laboratory devices have been used to incorporate the advantages of the dynamic system utilizing permeation tubes. These devices have been used in the past decade with greater or less expertise to calibrate a variety of air pollution monitors.

Description of a Portable Calibration System

In the last year or so, considerable problems have arisen in the attempt to correlate data from different monitors. The major problem is thought by many to be the fact that the monitors were calibrated by a wide variety of techniques with variable confidence levels over a wide frequency from daily to "we believe the calibration set by the manufacturer." In light of the correlation problem and the supposed reason for the problem, a fully portable calibration system using permeation tubes was devised that could be carried fully operational from instrument to instrument to calibrate them on a routine basis. This instrument (Analytical Instrument Development (AID) Model 320) provides dynamic gas mixtures with an accuracy of 1 percent in the field for a period of at least 10 h without need for external power or supplies. It has variable flow to provide variable concentration for instrument linearity check as well as calibration. A fixed temperature of 35°C was established for the permeation tube chamber. This is high enough to provide the necessary control even in warm environments. To aid the temperature control, the gas flow through the chamber was set at 10 ml/min and maintained constant.

The system was designed around rechargeable nickel-cadmium batteries as the self-contained power source. A 12 V base was chosen to permit adaptation to auto batteries for extended field operation. The battery pack was sized for 10 h of portable operation. There are two temperature sensors (thermistors) in the permeation tube oven. The first one provides the feedback for the temperature control circuit and is located in the oven heat sink with the heater. The second thermistor is located in the chamber with the permeation tube to provide amplified temperature readout on the front of the instrument. The meter is centered at 35.00°C by calibration of the readout thermistor against a certified mercury thermometer. The meter span is adjusted such that 25 percent full scale is 34.90°C and 75 percent full scale is 35.10°C. This range will maintain the permeation rate within 1 percent of that determined gravimetrically at 35.00°C. Figure 1 shows a

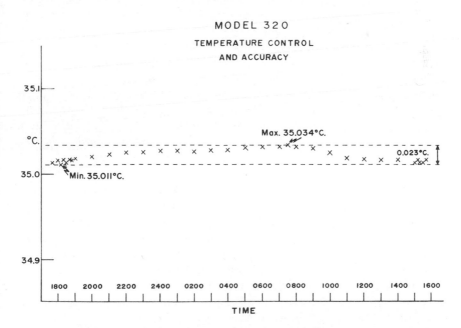

FIG. 1—*Permeation tube temperature variation over 24 h period.*

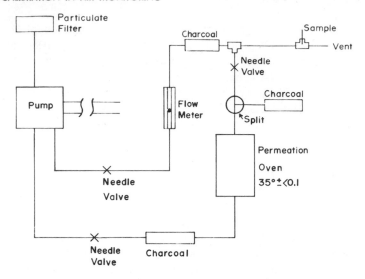

FIG. 2—*Flow schematic of Model 320.*

plot of temperature in the tube chamber for a unit over a 24 h period. This variation of 0.023°C is typical.

The entire system can best be understood by the flow diagram in Fig. 2. Ambient air is drawn through the particulate filter by a d-c operated dual-headed pump. A regulated voltage supplied to the pump ensures a constant pumping rate. Each of the two heads provides a separate air flow. The dilution air flow passes through a front panel needle valve for flow adjustment and then into a precision two-ball rotameter calibrated and readable to ±1 percent of any desired flow rate between 300 and 1500 ml/min. A charcoal filter removes any impurities from the ambient air just prior to the mixing tee where it is mixed with the effluent from the permeation tube chamber.

This chamber flow is supplied by the other head of the pump. It is adjusted by an internal needle valve to 10 ml/min and then is cleaned by a charcoal scrubber just prior to the permeation oven. In the oven a length of copper tubing provides thermal equilibrium just prior to the glass permeation tube chamber. Beyond the chamber the entire system is glass or Teflon to prevent loss of the permeant. The chamber air flow then passes to a three position split valve located on the front panel. The three positions of the split valve are shown in Fig. 3. In the high-concentration position (Fig. 3a), all of the air from the permeation oven (10 ml/min) is directed to the mixing tee to be combined with the dilution air. In the low-concentration position (Fig. 3b), only 20 percent (2 ml/min) of the chamber air is mixed with the dilution air. The remainder (8 ml/min) is dumped through a charcoal filter. In the zero air position (Fig. 3c), none of the chamber air is mixed with the diluent air. It is all dumped through the charcoal filter.

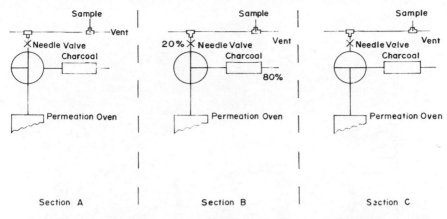

FIG. 3—*Split valve schematic of Model 320 in three possible positions.*

Following the mixing tee the combined air flow passes through a second tee providing two outputs at the rear of the instrument. One is to be connected to the analyzer to be calibrated. This allows the analyzer to draw in the calibrating gas at its prescribed rate at ambient pressure. The second outlet permits the excess calibration gas to be vented. In use the dilution gas flow through the calibration system must be greater (preferably at least 25 percent greater) than the sampling rate of the analyzer to be calibrated.

Figure 4 shows the front view of the packaged Model 320 calibration system. This illustrates the temperature readout meter with the black area indicating the range such that the permeation rate is maintained within 1 percent. Also the precision rotameter is shown. The air inlet with the particulate filter is shown in the rear view of the instrument in Fig. 5. The calibration gas exit is in the lower right hand side of the picture. The power plug on the left side is used for the line cord to recharge the batteries and to operate the instrument from line voltage. The auto cigarette lighter adapter also plugs in here to operate the instrument from the electrical system of a car. For internal battery operation, the shorting plug is used to connect the batteries to the instrument.

Figure 6 shows the access to the permeation chamber and the location of the readout thermistor in relation to the permeation tube. The tube chamber can accommodate permeation tubes 12 cm total length or 10 cm effective length. As many as three tubes of maximum length can be placed in the oven at the same time, thus increasing the concentration obtainable with a given pollutant or making a calibration gas available with more than one pollutant to make interferences studies.

Table 1 lists a number of materials of interest in the field of air pollution that are also candidates for the permeation tube approach to standardization. For each material the average permeation rate per unit length at

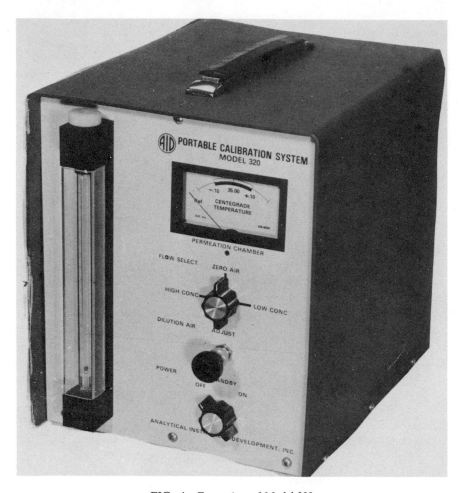

FIG. 4—*Front view of Model 320.*

TABLE 1—*Permeation tubes for Model 309.*

Material	Average Permeation Rate, ng/min/cm at 35°C	$K = \dfrac{24.45}{MW}$	Estimated Tube Life, weeks
Sulfur dioxide	420	0.382	20.4
Nitrogen dioxide	1650	0.532	6.3
Hydrogen sulfide	330	0.719	12.5
Methyl mercaptan[a]	95	0.508	300
Ammonia	262	1.439	14.5
Chlorine	1750	0.345	4.3
Vinyl chloride[a]	730	0.391	22.5

[a] Tubes are 0.25 in. outside diameter with 0.030-in. wall. All other tubes are 0.25 in. outside diameter with 0.062-in. wall.

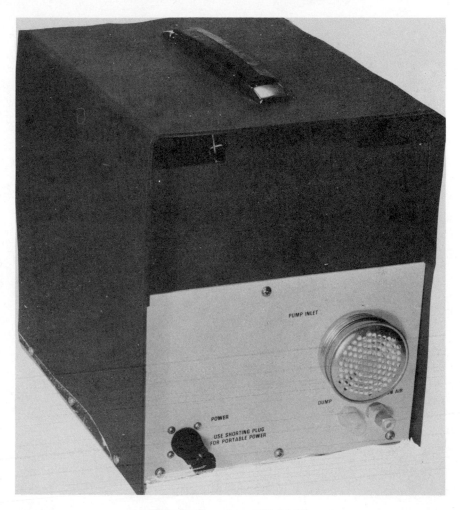

FIG. 5—*Rear view of Model 320.*

35°C is also given. The constant used in Eq 1 as well as the expected life of the tube is given.

If one assumes a tube length of 2 cm for SO_2, the permeation rate would be 840 ng/min. Using this value in Eq 1 with 0.382 as the constant and 300 ml/min as the minimum flow of the Model 320 the high concentration available would be 1.07 ppm. The low concentration of the splittler valve would provide 0.21 ppm. At the maximum flow of 1500 ml/min, the high concentration is 0.21 ppm with the low concentration being 0.042 ppm. Thus with one tube a standard span gas can be generated quickly in the field with a SO_2 concentration anywhere between 0.04 up through 1.0 ppm.

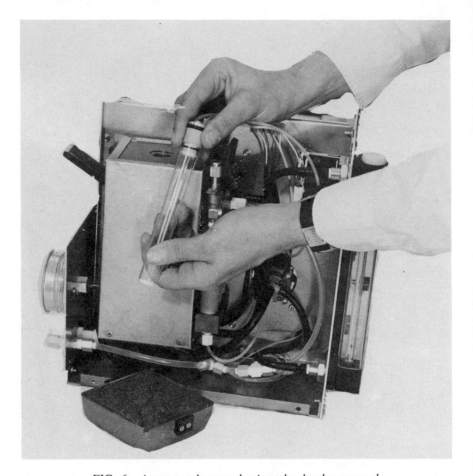

FIG. 6—*Access to tube oven showing tube chamber removed.*

A tube of maximum length (10 cm) would increase all of the above figures by a factor of five.

Performance Discussion

The following are general comments regarding the field performance of the Model 320. The unit can operate indefinitely from line voltage while the batteries are charging. It has maintained accuracy within 1 percent over a 12 h period in a fully portable mode. For a period of greater than 5 h, accuracy was maintained when the ambient air was 33°C (91.4°F). During trips in a small car totaling greater than 600 miles over a two-week period, the split flow remained constant assuring the 5:1 high-to-low concentration ratio as determined both by flow checks and analyzer checks on the calibration gas. Also during this time full temperature control was maintained off of batteries in the day and off of line at night. Control was lost during a 3 h period when the instrument was left in a closed car parked in the sun. Obviously, the interior temperature of the car significantly exceeded 35°C (95°F), thus causing a thermal upset.

Conclusion

This paper describes a new fully portable calibration system designed to produce dynamic gas standards via permeation tubes in the field. Preliminary data indicate the design specifications for flow and temperature control to maintain the accuracy of the prepared standard to 1 percent has been achieved. Field operation of the system has shown the practicality and soundness of the design.

References

[1] Saltzman, B. E. in *The Industrial Environment—Its Evaluation and Control*, National Institute for Occupational Safety and Health, U.S. Department of Health, Education, and Welfare, Washington, D.C., 1973, Chapter 12.
[2] "Preparation and Calculation of Static Gas Standards," AID Application Note 105, Analytical Instrument Development, Inc. Avondale, Pa., 1970.
[3] Schuette, F. J., *Atmospheric Environment*, Vol. 1, 1967, p. 515.
[4] Baker, R. A. and Doerr, R. C., *International Journal of Air Pollution*, Vol. 2, 1959, p. 142.
[5] Wilson, K. W. and Buchberg, H., *Industrial and Engineering Chemistry*, Vol. 50, 1958, p. 1705.
[6] Cotabish, H. N., McConnaughey, P. W., and Messer, H. C., *American Industrial Hygiene Association Journal*, Vol. 22, 1961, p. 392.
[7] Ash, R. M. and Lynch, J. R., *American Industrial Hygiene Association Journal*, Vol. 32, 1971, p. 552.
[8] Nelson, G. O. and Griggs, K. S., *Review of Scientific Instruments*, Vol. 39, 1968, p. 927.
[9] O'Keefe, A. E. and Ortman, G. C., *Analytical Chemistry*, Vol. 38, 1966, p. 760.

Qualification of Reference Methods as Fiduciary Standards

J. B. Clements[1]

Qualification of Ambient Methods as Reference Methods

REFERENCE: Clements, J. B., **"Qualification of Ambient Methods as Reference Methods,"** *Calibration in Air Monitoring, ASTM STP 598*, American Society for Testing and Materials, 1976, pp. 69–79.

ABSTRACT: A description is given of a measurement methods qualifications program used by the Environmental Protection Agency (EPA) in its reference methods activities. The first step of the two-step program is an in-depth evaluation of a method for the purpose of critically examining, in a single laboratory, a method to determine its strengths and weaknesses. The second step is an inter-laboratory collaborative test of the method whereby the method is placed in the hands of typical users for the purpose of determining important statistics on precision and accuracy. The program for evaluating methodology for ambient nitrogen dioxide in support of EPA's replacement reference method is presented as an example of this process.

KEY WORDS: air pollution, tests, standards, calibration, evaluation, measurement, emission

The Environmental Protection Agency (EPA) in setting standards dealing with ambient air quality and emissions from sources specifies the measurement methods which must be used to demonstrate that the regulatory standard is, in fact, being attained. Thus, for ambient air, the National Primary and Secondary Ambient Air Quality Standards have as a part of their regulations reference methods which must be used in measuring the pollutant concentration of the ambient air, and EPA has so far promulgated primary and secondary standards for six pollutants which are shown in Table 1 [1].[2] The reference method to be used in demonstrating compliance with these standards is shown in Table 2.

The time requirements built into the Clean Air Act did not allow for full and thorough methods development or evaluation, and the choice of the methods promulgated as reference methods was made on a best judgment

---

[1] Chief, Quality Assurance Branch, Environmental Monitoring and Support Laboratory, Environmental Protection Agency, Research Triangle Park, N. C. 27711.

[2] The italic numbers in brackets refer to the list of references appended to this paper.

TABLE 1—*National ambient air quality standards.*

| Pollutant | Standard, $\mu g/m^3$ | | Averaging Time |
	Primary	Secondary	
Total suspended particulate	75	60	annual geometric mean
	260	150	24 h max
Sulfur dioxide	80	60	annual arithmetic mean
	365	260	24 h max
		1300	3 h max
Nitrogen dioxide	100	100	annual arithmetic mean
Carbon monoxide	10[a]	10[a]	8 h max
	40[a]	40[a]	1 h max
Photochemical oxidants	160	160	1 h max
Hydrocarbons	160	160	3 h max

[a] mg/m^3.

TABLE 2—*Reference methods for ambient air quality standards.*

Pollutant	Reference Method
Total suspended particulates	high volume samples
Sulfur dioxide	pararosaniline (PRA)
Carbon monoxide	nondispersive infrared spectrometry (NDIR)
Photochemical oxidants	ozone-ethylene chemiluminescence reaction
Hydrocarbons	gas chromatographic separation of methane and flame ionization measurement of nonmethane fraction
Nitrogen dioxide	original method withdrawn; now being replaced

basis. It was recognized, at that time, that all of this methodology needed to be investigated thoroughly to be certain that the reference methods have a sound technical base. This paper will present the general program of our investigation into this methodology, paying special attention to the ambient air methods.

Reference Methods

On the basis of experience in evaluating methodology used in making measurements of ambient air pollutants and on the basis of the needs of the regulatory standards, EPA now has come to some generalizations in what it expects of reference methods. Only a single method for a pollutant will be selected by EPA and designated as its reference method. A method so designated should have acceptable accuracy and precision performance characteristics which have been scientifically and statistically validated by a multiple-laboratory collaborative test under a variety of anticipated users' conditions. The method should be readily available to prospective users, and this will likely preclude the designation of very expensive or sophisticated methods as reference methods because they might not be available to the large majority of prospective user laboratories. Obviously, most of this information was not available for the methods originally selected as reference methods, and, until recently, our evaluation and standardization program has been devoted exclusively to obtaining this type of information on the promulgated reference methods.

Equivalent Methods

Under most circumstances, it will be expected that the reference method will be the method of choice of most user laboratories to determine compliance with regulatory standards. If, however, methods other than the reference method are to be used, their equivalency to the reference method must be demonstrated to the satisfaction of the EPA administrator. Recent rules and regulations [2] present the procedures and experimental protocols one must follow in order to have a candidate ambient air method declared equivalent to a reference method.

Method Evaluation and Standardization

We use a two-step process for detailed method investigation which now serves to qualify a method as a reference method. The first step is a single laboratory investigation in which the method is examined thoroughly against reference standards to determine its efficiency and to verify interference effects. The integrity of the calibration system is examined closely. Operational details such as equipment complexity and fragility, reagent stability, variation of method as a function of pollutant concentration, and clarity of direction are all evaluated carefully. An assessment is then made to decide if the method is deserving of further testing. The decision to test further is admittedly made on a best judgment basis. Strong consideration is given to the availability and status of other methods and to agency requirements with respect to the support of air quality standards.

Those methods which survive the evaluation are then subjected to a second step which is an interlaboratory collaborative test. Our preferred procedure is to gather the test participants at a common site and have them make simultaneous measurements of ambient air using the method under test. We also supplement, or "spike," the ambient air with additional known amounts of pollutant and measure the amount recovered by each participant. This technique is similar to the procedure used in ASTM's Project Threshold and there are many common features in the two systems. We have also conducted interlaboratory collaborative tests by submitting reference materials to test participants, who then use the method to make measurements of pollutant concentrations in the test materials. Each system has its advantages and disadvantages, but our preference lies with the system where the analysts are brought to a common site.

Interlaboratory collaborative testing, of course, is a well recognized technique of method evaluation. From the results of collaborative testing, one can estimate the precision capabilities of the method, and in many cases one can estimate method bias. Also, the interlaboratory collaborative test allows one to see how the method performs in the hands of typical users and what are the weak points in the methodology which need strengthening. Occasionally, special studies, which are somewhat beyond the scope of the usual standardization activity, are conducted for the purpose of gaining additional information on the measurement processes under investigation.

Nitrogen Dioxide Methodology

Nitrogen dioxide (NO_2) is one of the ambient air pollutants for which there is a primary and secondary ambient air quality standard, and there is a reference method given in the regulations [1]. Our own investigations [3,4] and investigations in other laboratories [5,6] showed this procedure to be severely deficient, and, in June of 1973 EPA announced its intention of withdrawing the originally promulgated NO_2 reference method [4]. Our program to evaluate and test NO_2 measurement methodology for the purpose of designating a suitable reference method followed the steps outlined previously. This program serves as a good example of how we prefer to investigate measurement methodology for the purpose of qualifying it with respect to its suitability for reference methods purposes.

Original Reference Method

The original reference method is a 24-h integrated sampling procedure which passes ambient air through 0.1 N sodium hydroxide (NaOH) solution and converts ambient NO_2 to nitrite ion. The nitrite ion concentration is measured by the well-known diazotization-coupling procedure to produce a deeply colored azo dye. The amount of nitrite ion measured must be related to the NO_2 in the air sample, and, if its conversion is not 100 percent, corrections must be applied. For the reference NO_2 method, the efficiency of the removal of NO_2 from the ambient air and conversion to nitrite ion is poor, averaging about 35 percent. The most crippling drawback, however, is the lack of constancy in the correction which must be made. The collection efficiency varies with concentration from about 15 percent at 400 $\mu g/m^3$ of NO_2 to about 65 percent at about 50 $\mu g/m^3$ of NO_2. The EPA found this sufficient justification to recommend withdrawal of the originally promulgated NO_2 reference method, but EPA also decided that a new reference method must be available, and the developments that built the technical base for the choice of the new NO_2 reference method will now be presented.

Selection of Candidate Methods to Replace Original Reference Method

In developing the program for choosing a new reference method, we first considered the NO_2 methods that were available and concentrated on those we felt would have the best chance of successfully meeting the requirements we set for reference methodology. Within the limits of the resources and time available, we felt that only four or five methods could be given the thorough and in-depth study which was required. From the deliberations we chose five ambient NO_2 methods which we felt deserved investigation in our laboratory and a few words description will be given for each.

Sodium Arsenite Procedure

This is a manual 24-h integrated bubbler procedure in which ambient air is drawn through an aqueous solution of NaOH containing 0.1 percent sodium arsenite. The nitrite ion formed is determed colorimetrically by diazotization and coupling to form an azo dye in much the same manner as with the original reference NO_2 method. The procedure was first reported by Christie [7] and was also studied by Merryman et al [5].

Triethanolamine-Guiacol-Sodium Metabisulfite (TGS) Procedure

This is also a manual 24-h integrated bubbler procedure in which ambient NO_2 is collected in a solution. The absorbing reagent is an aqueous solution of triethanolamine (TEA), 0-methoxyphenol, and sodium metabisulfite. Again the NO_2 is converted to nitrite ion which is measured colorimetrically by diazotization and coupled with a slightly different combination of reagents. The procedure was first reported by Mulik et al [8].

TEA Procedure

This manual 24-h bubbler procedure uses aqueous TEA to collect NO_2 from ambient air, forming nitrite ion which is measured colorimetrically by the usual diazotization and coupling procedure. The method was first reported by Levaggi et al [9].

Continuous Colorimetric Procedure

This procedure, which is also known as the continuous Saltzman procedure, is very well known and has been widely used. The NO_2 is scrubbed from ambient air and is converted to a colored azo dye by conventional diazotization and coupling reactions. The system is so designed that a continuous measurement of NO_2 content of the air is made.

Continuous Chemiluminescent Procedure

This indirect procedure takes advantage of the light emitted in the reaction of nitric oxide (NO) with ozone (O_3). Ambient NO_2 is converted by a reduction procedure to NO. This NO, along with any NO originally present, is reacted with O_3, and the light emitted is measured by a photomultiplier tube amplified and displayed continuously. This procedure measures nitrogen oxides (NO_x) (NO + NO_2) present in the air sampled. In order to obtain a measurement of the NO_2 alone, a separate measurement of ambient NO is made by reacting the ambient air with O_3 and subtracting this value from the NO_x value.

Single Laboratory Evaluation of Candidate Methods

Each of the methods was examined in detail in our laboratory, and features such as interferences, collection efficiency as a function of NO_2 concentration, integrity of the calibration system, and complexity of the procedure were examined closely. An estimate of the precision to be expected from each method was also obtained. For each procedure we produced a detailed writeup which incorporated all of the important findings made in the laboratory investigations.

Full and complete descriptions of the results of these evaluations can be found in appropriate EPA reports and will be the subject of forthcoming publications. For this paper only the important results from each evaluation will be presented.

Sodium Arsenite Procedue [10,11]

The procedure has a constant collection efficiency of about 82 percent over the NO_2 concentration range of interest. The reported NO interference and the sensitivity to carbon dioxide (CO_2) variations were confirmed, but neither is serious enough to prevent the method's use. The method is simple to use and works well.

TGS Procedure [12]

The procedure has a constant collection efficiency of about 92 percent over the NO_2 concentration range of interest. No common air pollutants have been found which interfere with the method. There is one very critical step in the procedure. This involves the time interval between the addition of the diazotizing reagent and the coupling reagent in the analytical scheme. If the interval is greater than the specified 6 min, lower, and incorrect, analytical values will be obtained.

Triethanolamine (TEA) Procedure [13]

Fragile and expensive fritted bubblers are required in order to obtain collection efficiencies of about 85 percent. Collection efficiency using restricted orifice bubblers, which work well with the sodium arsenite and TGS manual procedures, is about 50 percent and is variable.

Continuous Colorimetric Procedure [14]

We find that dynamic calibration is essential because static calibration gives erroneous results. There is an O_3 interference to the method [15,16].

Continuous Chemiluminescent Procedure [17]

The procedure is sensitive, and pollutants which cause interferences, for example, peroxyacetylnitrate, are not wide spread in the ambient air. Calibration is somewhat complex, and the procedure is not a direct measurement of NO_2.

Interlaboratory Collaborative Tests of Candidate Methods

After evaluating the results of these investigations and considering the resources available, we chose to subject the sodium arsenite, the TGS, the continuous colorimeteric, and the continuous chemiluminescent procedures to interlaboratory collaborative testing. Each method was tested separately by having ten analysts use the method as decribed to sample ambient air simultaneously at a common site in Kansas City, Missouri. There were also provisions to supplement the air sample with known amounts of NO_2 in order to obtain an estimate of the bias suffered by each method. Simultaneous sampling was carried out for four days in each test, and the results were used to estimate within and between-laboratory precision in terms of appropriate standard deviations. Again full descriptions are given in appropriate EPA reports [18-21] and will be the subject of forthcoming publications. Table 3 presents the important results from the interlaboratory collaborative studies.

TABLE 3—*Statistical results from collaborative testing of NO methods.*

Method	Standard Deviation		Bias, %	Lower Detectable Limit, μg/m
	Within Laboratory	Between Laboratory		
Sodium arsenite	8 μg/m^{3a}	11 μg/m^{3a}	−3	9
TGS	7 μg/m^{3a}	12 μg/m^{3a}	−5	15
Continuous colorimetric	6%^{b}	12%^{b}	−15	19
Continuous chemiluminescent	6%^{b}	14%^{b}	−5	22

[a] Absolute value, not concentration dependent.
[b] Relative standard deviation, absolute value is dependent on concentration.
[c] This is an average value; bias is very collaborator dependent.

Special Study

Because of the particularly sensitive nature of the NO_2 measurement problem, we carried out a special study on the foregoing four measurement methods. The basic objective of the study was to determine the intra- and inter-comparibility of the sodium arsenite, TGS, continuous colorimetric, and continuous chemiluminescent procedures when sampling the same atmosphere under a variety of carefully controlled conditions in the hands of very competent operators. The study was carried out in Durham, North Carolina under rigorously controlled conditions, and the ambient air, or clean air with added pollutants, was sampled with necessary amount of replication to make meaningful statistical analyses. Overall agreement within and among methods was quite good, which demonstrated that each method is capable of producing good quality data when used by skilled technicians under carefully controlled conditions. Complete details on this special study, which is somewhat beyond the scope of our usual standardization activity, are reported by Purdue et al [16].

Other Reference Methods

Three of the other reference methods for ambient air pollutants have also been studied by a somewhat similar procedure. The high-volume sampler procedure for total suspended particulate matter, the pararosaniline procedure for sulfur dioxide (SO_2), and the nondispersive infrared procedure (NDIR) for carbon monoxide (CO) have all been investigated, but, in these cases, the emphasis has been on the interlaboratory collaborative test. Each of the these procedures, as described in the *Federal Register* [1], was tested according to the following general outline. The original reports can be consulted for full details.

High-Volume Procedure for Total Suspended Particulate Matter [22]

This test was carried out by having twelve laboratories simultaneously sample the ambient air at a common site in Cincinnati, Ohio, over a four day period. The following results were obtained:

(*a*) The relative standard deviation for a single analyst variation is 3.0 percent.

(*b*) The relative standard deviation for multilaboratory variation is 3.7 percent.

(*c*) The minimum detectable amount of particulate matter is 3 μg, which is equivalent to 1 to 2 μg/m for a 24-h sample.

Pararosaniline Procedure for Sulfur Dioxide [23,24]

The reference method allows two options with respect to sampling time, and both options were subjected to collaborative testing. In each test, the participants were supplied SO_2 permeation tubes and associated equipment which allowed them to generate atmospheres of SO_2 whose concentrations were known to the test coordinator. The 30-min sampling option was tested collaboratively by 14 laboratories, and the following results were obtained:

(*a*) The standard deviation for within-laboratory variation varies linearly with concentration from 15 $\mu g/m^3$ at 0 to 36 $\mu g/m^3$ at 1000 $\mu g/m^3$.

(*b*) The standard deviation for between-laboratory variation varies linearly with concentration from 29 $\mu g/m^3$ at 0 to 70 $\mu g/m^3$ at 1000 $\mu g/m^3$.

(*c*) No systematic error bias or inaccuracy was detected, and the lower limit of detection is 25 $\mu g/m^3$ (95 percent confidence level).

The 24-h sampling option prescribed in the reference method was collaboratively tested by four laboratories, and a statistical analysis provides the following results:

(*a*) The standard deviation for within-laboratory variation varies linearly with concentration from 18 $\mu g/m^3$ at 100 $\mu g/m^3$ to 51 $\mu g/m^3$ at 400 $\mu g/m^3$.

(*b*) The standard deviation for between-laboratory variation varies linearly with concentration from 37 $\mu g/m^3$ at 100 $\mu g/m^3$ to 104 $\mu g/m^3$ at 400 $\mu g/m^3$.

(*c*) The 24-h sampling method appears to have a concentration dependent bias which becomes significant at the 95 percent confidence level at about 400 $\mu g/m^3$. Observed values tend to be lower than expected SO_2 concentration levels.

A comparison between the results of the 30-min and 24-h sampling options indicates that the 24-h procedure is capable of better precision than is the 30-min procedure. However, it should be pointed up that these differences are based on collaborative tests which differed in experimental design. Although accepted statistical techniques were used to process the data, these techniques involve assumptions which preclude rigorous comparison between test results, and the exact degree of improved precision is uncertain.

NDIR Procedure for Carbon Monoxide (CO) [25]

This reference method was collaboratively tested by supplying 16 laboratories with cylinders containing carbon monoxide in air of varying concentrations which were unknown to the test participants. A statistical analysis of the data provided the following information about the procedure:

(*a*) The standard deviation for within-laboratory variation is 0.57 mg/m^3 (1 ppm CO $= 1.15$ mg/m^3 CO).

(*b*) The standard deviation for between-laboratory variation varies nonlinearly with concentration with a minimum of 0.85 mg/m^3 at 20

mg/m^3 and ranges as high as 1.4 mg/m^3 in the concentration of 0 to 60 is mg/m^3.

(c) The minimum detectable limit is 0.3 mg/m^3.

Acknowledgments

The laboratory evaluations of the NO_2 methods were carried out within the Quality Assurance Branch by a team led by J. H. Margeson and composed of M. E. Beard, R. G. Fuerst, and E. C. Ellis.

The collaborative tests of the NO_2 methods were carried out by contract with Midwest Research Institute, Kansas City, Missouri, under the direction of P. C. Constant.

The collaborative test of the high-volume sampler procedure, the pararosaniline SO_2 procedure, and the NDIR procedure were carried out by contract with the Southwest Research Institute, Houston, Texas, under the direction of H. C. McKee.

References

[1] Federal Register, Vol. 36, No. 84, 30 April 1971, pp. 8186–8201.

[2] Federal Register, Vol. 40, No. 33, 18 Feb. 1975, pp. 7042–7070.

[3] Hauser, T. R. and Shy, C. M., Environmental Science and Technology, Vol. 6, No. 10, 1972, pp. 890–894.

[4] Federal Register, Vol. 38, No. 110, 8 June 1973, pp. 15174–15180.

[5] Merryman, E. L., Spicer, C. W., and Levy, A., Environmental Science and Technology, Vol. 7, No. 11, 1973, pp. 1056–1059.

[6] Blacker, J. H. and Brief, R. S., Chemosphere, No. 1, 1972, pp. 43–46.

[7] Christie, A. A., Lidzey, R. G., and Radford, D. W. F., Analyst, Vol. 95, 1970, pp. 519–524.

[8] Mulik, J., Fuerst, R., Guyer, M., Meeker, J., and Sawicki, E., Environmental Analytical Chemistry, Vol. 3, No. 4, 1974, pp. 333–348.

[9] Levaggi, D. A., Siu, W., and Feldstein, M., Journal of the Air Pollution Control Association, Vol. 23, No. 1, 1973, pp. 30–33.

[10] Beard, M. E. and Margeson, J. H., "An Evaluation of Arsenite Procedure for Determination of Nitrogen Dioxide in Ambient Air," EPA-650/4-74-048, Environmental Protection Agency, Nov. 1974.

[11] Beard, M. E., Suggs, J. C., and Margeson, J. H., "Evaluation of Effects of NO, CO_2, and Sampling Flow Rate on Arsenite Procedure for Measurement of NO_2 in Ambient Air," EPA-650/4-75-019, Environmental Protection Agency, April 1975.

[12] Fuerst, R. G. and Margeson, J. H., "An Evaluation of TGS-ANSA Procedure for Determination of Nitrogen Dioxide in Ambient Air," EPA-650/4-74-047, Environmental Protection Agency, Nov. 1974.

[13] Ellis, E. C. and Margeson, J. H., "Evaluation of Triethanolamine Procedure for Determination of Nitrogen Dioxide in Ambient Air," EPA-650/4-74-031, Environmental Protection Agency, July 1974.

[14] Margeson, J. H. and Fuerst, R. G., "Evaluation of the Continuous Colorimetric Method for Measurement of Nitrogen Dioxide in Ambient Air," EPA-650/4-75-022, Environmental Protection Agency, April 1975.

[15] Ellis, E. C. and Margeson, J. H., "Evaluation of Gas Phase Titration Technique as used for Calibration of Nitrogen Dioxide Chemiluminesce Analyzers," EPA-650/4-75-021, Environmental Protection Agency, April 1975.

[16] Baumgardner, R. E., Clark, T. A., and Stevens, R. K., Environmental Science and Technology, Vol. 9, No. 1, 1975, pp. 67–69.

[17] Purdue, L. J., Akland, G. G., and Tabor, E. C., "Nitrogen Dioxide Methods Comparison Study," EPA-650/4-75-023, Environmental Protection Agency, April 1975.

[18] Constant, P. C., Sharp, M. C., and Scheil, G. W., "Collaborative Testing of Methods for Measurement of NO_2 in Ambient Air," Vol. 1, Report of Testing, EPA-650/4-74-019e, Environmental Protection Agency, June 1974.

[19] Constant, P. C., Sharp, M. C., and Scheil, G. W., "Collaborative Test of the TGS-ANSA Method for Measurement of Nitrogen Dioxide in Ambient Air," EPA-650/4-74-046, Environmental Protection Agency, Sept. 1974.

[20] Constant, P. C., Sharp, M. C., and Scheil, G. W., "Collaborative Test of the Continuous Colorimetric Method for Measurement of Nitrogen Dioxide in Ambient Air," EPA-650/4-75-011, Environmental Protection Agency, Feb. 1975.

[21] Constant, P. C., Sharp, M. C., and Scheil, G. W., "Collaborative Test of the Continuous Chemiluminescence Method for Measurement of Nitrogen Dioxide in Ambient Air," EPA-650/4-75-013, Environmental Protection Agency, Feb. 1975.

[22] McKee, H. C., Childers, R. E., and Saenz, O., "Collaborative Study of Reference Method for the Determination of Suspended Particulates in the Atmosphere (High Volume Method)," PB 205-891, June 1971.

[23] McKee, H. C., Childers, R. E., and Saenz, O., "Collaborative Study of Reference Method for Determination of Sulfur Dioxide in the Atmosphere (Pararosaniline Method)," PB 205-893, Sept. 1971.

[24] McCoy, R. A., Camann, D. E., and McKee, H. C., "Collaborative Study of Reference Method for Determination of Sulfur Dioxide in the Atmosphere (Pararosaniline Method—24-Hour Sampling)," EPA-650/4-74-027, Environmental Protection Agency, Dec. 1973.

[25] McKee, H. C. and Childers, R. E., "Collaborative Study of Reference Method for the Continuous Measurement of Carbon Monoxide in the Atmosphere (Non-Dispersive Infrared Spectrometry)," PB 211-265, May 1972.

J. E. Howes, Jr.,[1] and R. N. Pesut[1]

Qualification of Source Test Methods as Reference Methods

REFERENCE: Howes, J. E. Jr., and Pesut, R. N., **"Qualification of Source Test Methods as Reference Methods,"** *Calibration in Air Monitoring, ASTM STP 598*, American Society for Testing and Materials, 1976, pp. 80–95.

ABSTRACT: Air pollution measurements require test methods that have a demonstrated capability to yield reliable data when the procedures are carried out by people with different backgrounds and experience. Collaborative testing can provide "real world" situations in which the performance of test methods can be evaluated and useful measures of the accuracy and precision of data obtained by a given method can be obtained. For methods designed to measure emissions from stationary sources, this form of round robin approach requires that the samples be collected on-site and simultaneously by the various teams involved. Laboratory analyses of the samples can then be performed on an individual basis. Statistical analysis of the collaborative test data from properly designed experiments should yield estimates of within-laboratory and between-laboratory precision and accuracy of the method under test. It should also be possible in some cases to separate the overall accuracy and precision into the individual components due to sampling techniques and laboratory analytical procedures.

This discussion is concerned with measurement methods for gaseous emissions from stationary sources. The circumstances and data cited are based on experience with the American Society for Testing and Materials Project Threshold test program. Collaborative testing of methods for sulfur oxides and nitrogen oxides is discussed specifically; however, the considerations involved with the experimental design, conduct of the testing, and data analysis are applicable to testing of other methods. Collaborative sampling was performed at both an oil- and coal-fired power station, a foundry, a cement plant, and using a pilot-plant furnace unit with gas and oil firing. Samples which were spiked with known amounts of the pollutant gases were included at the pilot plant site to provide a measure of the accuracy of the methods.

Sampling for sulfur oxides was accomplished by a continuous method in which the sulfur trioxide was condensed from the gas stream and the sulfur dioxide was absorbed and reacted with a hydrogen peroxide solution. Both sulfur oxides were then determined by the barium chloranilate method. The nitrogen oxides were samples by a "grab" technique in which an evacuated bulb was used to collect the gas sample. The nitrogen oxides were reacted with acidified hydrogen peroxide in the bulb, and then determined by the phenol disulfonic acid method.

[1] Associate section manager and researcher, Statistical and Mathematical Modeling, respectively, Battelle-Columbus Laboratories, Columbus, Ohio 43201.

Statistical analysis of the collaborative test data provides equations which express the accuracy and precision of the methods as functions of the gas concentration. Accuracy and precision of the analytical procedures also were measured from analyses of standard reference materials by the participating laboratories.

KEY WORDS: calibration, air pollution, emission, standards, gases

The control of pollutant emissions from stationary sources is a vital part of the program to improve the air quality in the United States. In order to conduct an effective control program, reliable, established methods are required to measure various species in source emissions. These methods are needed to determine the necessity for emission controls, to permit selection of the proper control equipment, and, ultimately, to demonstrate compliance to performance standards. That a significant sum of money rests on such decisions is evidenced by recent estimates that the steel industry will need to spend 12 to 14 billion dollars on control equipment to meet 1983 pollution limits and that in the United States, 194.8 billion dollars will be required to control pollution to meet 1982 Federal legislation.

Over the past few years, Committee D-22 of the American Society for Testing and Materials (ASTM) has conducted a program, Project Threshold, to evaluate "standard" or "reference" methods for the determination of pollutants in source emissions. The object of this program has been to demonstrate that selected test methods are inherently reliable and to obtain quantitative measures of their reliability in terms of the accuracy and precision of the results which the methods yield.

The Threshold program has applied the collaborative testing approach to the evaluation of source test methods. However, due to the unstable, dynamic nature of source emissions, it is necessary to add a new twist to the traditional round-robin test. Since the methods cannot be satisfactorily evaluated by sending source samples to the test participants, it is necessary to assemble the participants at a source site for concurrent testing. This type of collaborative test is considerably more complex than the usual round-robin method. Many additional factors must be considered in planning and conducting the on-site collaborative test. Improper attention to the many elements of the test can lead to perturbation of the final results by the testing procedures and techniques themselves. As a result, the outcome may be accuracy and precision estimates which are not truly representative of the method being evaluated. However, it is felt that a properly conducted collaborative test can accurately characterize the performance of a test method.

The ASTM Project Threshold program has used the on-site collaborative testing approach to validate a total of ten methods for measurement of pollutants in ambient air and in source emissions. The discussion in this paper is centered on the collaborative testing procedures used and experience gained in the Threshold study. The results of these studies have been published by ASTM [1–10].[2]

Role of Collaborative Testing in Establishing Reference Methods

A reference or standard method is an established test method which possesses a demonstrated ability to produce reliable results in specified applications. In considering ways to demonstrate and quantify the reliability of source test methods, on-site collaborative testing appears to be the best, if not the only option.

Youden [11] discusses the role of a collaborative test and considers it a kind of final inspection of a test or reference method. He describes the test as an "indispensable scrutiny of an analytical procedure to ensure (a) that the description of the procedure is clean and complete and (b) that the procedure does give results that are in accord with any accuracy claims." In line with this aim, the product of the collaborative test should be final measures of the worthiness of a test method to be called a "reference method." These final measures are the method's accuracy and precision, since any deficiencies in the method will very likely degrade these characteristics.

The precision of a reference method serves to characterize the method with respect to the agreement within a set of observations or test results obtained when using the method. ASTM Tentative Recommended Practice for Statements on Precision and Accuracy (D 2906-74) provides definitions of basic components which are used frequently to describe the precision of a test method. The three measures defined are the following:

Single-Operator Precision—the precision of a set of statistically independent observations, all obtained as directed in the method and obtained over the shortest practical time interval in one laboratory by a single operator using one apparatus and randomized specimens from one sample of the material being tested.

Within-Laboratory Precision—the precision of a set of statistically independent test results all obtained by one laboratory using a single sample of material and with each test result obtained by a different operator with each operator using one apparatus to obtain the same number of observations by testing randomized specimens over the shortest practical time interval.

Between-Laboratory Precision—the precision of a set of statistically independent test results, all of which are obtained by testing the same sample of material, and each of which is obtained in a different laboratory by one operator using one apparatus to obtain the same number of ob-

---

[2] The italic numbers in brackets refer to the list of references appended to this paper.

servations by testing randomized specimens over the shortest practical time interval.

The preceding measures can be used to obtain other measures of precision. For example, ASTM Recommended Practice D 2906-74 calculates the standard error of specific types of averages as follows:

Single-operated standard error

$$S_T \text{ (single-operator)} = (S_S^2/_n)^{1/2}$$

Within-laboratory standard error

$$S_T \text{ (within-laboratory)} = [S_W^2 + (S_S^2/_n)]^{1/2}$$

Between-laboratory standard error

$$S_T \text{ (between-laboratory)} = [S_B^2 + S_W^2 + (S_S^2/_n)]^{1/2}$$

where n is the number of observations by a single operator averaged into a determination. The standard error can be used to place confidence limits about a true unknown value, to make probability statements about the process being measured, etc.

It should also be noted that other terms are used frequently to describe precision. For example, Mandel [12] uses the terms "repeatability" and "reproducibility." By appropriate manipulation, within-laboratory and between-laboratory precision as defined in ASTM Recommended Practice D 2906-74 can be translated to these other terms.

The other important characteristic of a reference method is its accuracy. Accuracy is defined in ASTM Recommended Practice D 2906-74 as "the degree of agreement between the true value of the property being tested (or an accepted standard value) and the average of many observations made according to the test method, preferably by many observers." Disagreement between the true value and test results may occur as a systemic difference or error which is called bias.

Elements of the Collaborative Test

Proper planning for a collaborative test of a reference method should include consideration of a number of elements which can strongly influence the results of the test. Prior consideration of these facets of the test plan can enhance the likelihood of the collaborative test becoming a meaningful assessment of the reference method. The elements of the plan that should be considered include the following:

(*a*) method readiness,
(*b*) cooperating laboratory familiarization,
(*c*) test site selection,

(d) statistical test design,

(e) on-site test preparation and conduct,

(f) data collection and analysis, and

(g) statistical analysis and presentation of results.

Each of these elements of the test are discussed in the following sections.

Method Readiness

As indicated previously, the on-site collaborative test should serve as a final evaluation of a test method. Therefore, an important prerequisite is that the method be fully developed and evaluated with respect to the following aspects.

1. The text of the method should be concise and complete.

2. Significant variables in the test method and in source emissions for which the method is intended which may affect the results must be under control.

3. Preliminary estimates should show satisfactory accuracy and precision.

Variables or options which may potentially affect the method's performance should be investigated prior to the collaborative test through the use of statistically designed experiments.

Cooperating Laboratory Familiarization

In preparation for collaborative testing, all cooperating laboratories should have a good familiarity with the test method but should not be unduly trained in the method. Lack of acquaintance with a method can lead to procedural errors which render the test results useless. On the other hand, a highly practiced, orchestrated group of test teams may yield results which are not representative of the general user population. The approach taken in the Threshold study was to instruct the cooperating laboratories to study and practice a test method until they felt that they were competent in its performance. The rehearsal procedure and the number of times a method should be practiced were not dictated.

Experience has shown that a check is required to assure that all cooperating laboratory teams have developed an acceptable level of competence in the performance of the test method. After the study and practice period, appropriate standard solutions and standard reference materials should be supplied to each cooperator for analysis using the test method. The results of the standards analysis provide a basis for detecting those laboratories having problems with a method and permits resolution of their problems or, if necessary, modification of the test method prior to the collaborative test. Ultimately, the results provide a measure of the readiness of the laboratories for on-site testing. In addition, the results of these standards and others throughout the testing program provide a quality control measure.

Visits with the cooperators should be made at the end of the familiarization phase to discuss individual laboratory difficulties and answer any additional questions which may have arisen during the familiarization program. Also the visits should verify that the cooperator's sampling and analytical laboratory equipment complies with the test method requirements and that they have a sufficient quantity of equipment (and spares) to meet the demands of intensive on-site testing.

Test Site Selection

One might think that selection of a test site is of lesser importance when compared to the other elements of the collaborative test. However, unless several site factors are considered, the quality of the test data or the applicability to the results or both can be significantly impaired. These factors include:

(*a*) adequate space to perform sampling,
(*b*) adequate utilities, particularly electrical power,
(*c*) representativeness of sampling location,
(*d*) representativeness of emission characteristics,
(*e*) space for laboratory work, for example, sample recovery.

Most sampling sites are designed for sampling by one team; consequently, space and electrical power supplies are limited. It is usually necessary to modify the test site facilities to accommodate collaborative testing involving four or more teams.

Representativeness of the sampling conditions and source emissions is also an important consideration. It must be kept in mind that the test results will be most useful when applicable to a general class of sources. Performance of testing at a particular site with unique characteristics may not give data which is generally applicable to the entire source class.

Statistical Test Design

The statistical design for the collaborative test should consider a number of factors, among which are the number of sites to be used for testing, the number of collaborating laboratories, the number of experimental runs, and the number of measurements to be made by each laboratory in each run. Compromises are inevitable. The number of test sites to be used will be limited by the logistics of preparing for and conducting the tests. Likewise, the number of collaborating laboratories will be limited, although it is advisable to keep the number large enough so that these laboratories will be representative of the variability to be expected in general. The number of measurements to be made by each laboratory will be limited by the burden of work each laboratory can assume for the test.

In order for a statistical design to accommodate the limitations imposed, it should seek to provide as much information as possible with a minimum number of experimental determinations. Using an analysis of variance approach, the design could allow for a minimum of two measurements for each collaborating laboratory participating in an experimental run. Such a design would achieve an acceptable balance between the number of laboratories and the number of measurements for each laboratory so that both the within- and between-laboratory components of variance can be satisfactorily estimated. By appropriate blocking of the runs to separate variation due to uncontrollable sources (such as source variation), balanced designs can be constructed so that a subset of laboratories participates on a given run, and each laboratory participates on an equal basis. The analysis of variance designs can be used to assess the impact of various levels of replication by considering the effect of additional experimental blocks to detect significant factors.

In the Threshold program, blocks which were to be used for estimation of within- and between-laboratory precision consisted of two determinations performed concurrently by all laboratories. These experiments were performed using a laboratory furnace arrangement.

In field tests, where space was limited, each laboratory concurrently performed a single measurement to provide an estimate of between-laboratory standard error. Since only one determination was performed, the data could not be resolved into the within- and between-laboratory precision components.

Probably one of the most difficult characteristics of the test method to estimate in the on-site collaborative test is its absolute accuracy. Estimation of accuracy requires knowledge of the "true" concentration of the species being determined in the source emissions—a value which is difficult if not impossible to obtain.

In the Threshold program, accuracy of the nitrogen oxide (NO_x) and sulfur oxide (SO_x) methods has been estimated in pilot plant tests in which the emissions from a multifuel furnace could be spiked with known quantities of nitric oxide (NO) and sulfur dioxide (SO_2). In the test blocks used to estimate accuracy, each laboratory concurrently made one determination from a line carrying the unspiked emissions and one determination from a line carrying the emissions spiked with known levels of NO or SO_2.

The test design should also include several sets of unknown standard reference materials to be analyzed with the test sample. These sets provide quality control information and yield independent estimates of accuracy and precision of the sampling and analytical portions of the procedure.

Finally, the statistical design for the experiments should also include appropriate randomization of the order in which measurements are taken. Randomization reduces the chances that uncontrolled systematic affects will disturb the experiment and also makes it legitimate to analyze the resultant data as if they were independent observations. With a well-planned design, several levels of randomization can be executed. The blocks of experimental runs should be randomly ordered. The assignment of laboratories to sampling ports for each run should also be randomized. For tests involving a spiked and unspiked sample, the order in which the spike is introduced, either on the first or second sample, should be randomized.

Preparation and Conduct of On-Site Tests

The collaborative testing routine requires that the sampling teams function in a slightly different manner than they might in normal practice. Instead of operating at their discretion, the teams must adhere to at least an informal schedule to assure that testing is completed in an efficient manner. Of course, allowances must be made for unexpected events which occur during testing.

The Threshold work suggests that a practice period should be conducted at the start of testing to acclimate the teams to the collaborative testing routine. In the tests of the phenol disulfonic acid (PDS) NO_x method for example, a high incidence of outlying observations and procedural errors were noted during the first two days of testing, with significant reductions afterwards. The implication is that procedural errors were committed in attempting to conform to the test routine. After adaption to the routine, the teams were able to perform in a normal manner.

In establishing a schedule for conduct of the collaborative test program it is essential to allow an adequate time between tests to permit sample recovery and preparations for subsequent tests. The temptation to perform as many tests as possible in the alotted time to obtain more data must be resisted. Inevitably, this will lead to an increase of procedural errors which will render some of the data useless.

Data Collection and Analysis

The data collection process can be facilitated by the use of standardized data collection forms for on-site work. The forms should be designed so that the collaborating laboratories can directly record all the raw data from the method as they are generated. The forms should also allow for the recording of any pertinent intermediate calculations and final results.

A computer program has been found to be useful to check the calculations of the collaborating laboratories independently. From this, an indication of the potential for making errors in the reference method's calculations can be obtained, and corrections in the test data can be made.

After the results have been checked for calculational errors, they should also be reviewed for outlying measurements, where some determinations may be sufficiently far-removed in magnitude from the remaining determinations that they become suspect. It may be that errors were committed in recording the raw data from which subsequent calculations are made or by some assignable but unascertained cause which is not due to the reference method itself.

The manner in which such outliers are identified and handled varies. Some investigators would not exclude any observed measurements from a calculation of precision while other investigators would be inclined to exclude them. If the decision is to reject observations tagged as outliers, a method for detecting the outliers must be adopted. Natrella [13] describes several criteria for declaring observations as outliers, and presents tables for their application. Additional procedures for detecting outliers and dealing with them are described in ASTM Recommended Practice for Dealing with Outlying Observations (E 178-75). These procedures include statistical tests which provide justification for declaring observations as outliers. They are most effective when combined with the experienced judgement of an investigator who is thoroughly familiar with the reference method being evaluated.

Statistical Analysis of Results

The primary objective of the statistical analysis is to characterize the reference method with respect to its precision and accuracy. As discussed earlier, one approach for expressing the precision of the reference method is to provide estimates of the components of variance as determined through the use of analysis of variance techniques. This approach is recommended since it provides estimates which in turn can yield various other commonly reported measures of precision. One measure of the accuracy of a reference method is in terms of the average percentage deviation of measurements from the true standard values.

In using the components of variance estimates to measure precision, the two major components are the within-laboratory standard deviation and the between-laboratory standard deviation. If the operator within the laboratory is also a factor in the experimental design, an additional component of variance can be isolated. Brownlee [14] discusses the use of analysis of variance for partitioning the observed variation within a block of simultaneous determination. Basically, this method partitions the total sum of squares of deviations associated with the determinations into "within" and "between" sum of squares of deviations, used to develop variance estimates. These are divided by their corresponding degrees of freedom to yield mean square deviations, from which the components of variance are derived. This calculation should be performed for each block of simultaneous determinations made during the course of the collaborative test.

In the Threshold experiments, data from concurrent duplicate analysis by the participating laboratories were resolved into within- and between-laboratory components of variance using the conventional analysis of variance techniques.

To establish a relationship between the mean concentration and the precision measures, a scattergram of the measures estimated for each block of simultaneous determinations at various concentration levels can be plotted. Examples of these plots for data obtained from the collaborative test of ASTM Test for Oxides of Nitrogen in Gaseous Combustion Products (Phenol Disulfonic Acid Procedure) (D 1608-60) for determining oxides of nitrogen [9] are shown in Figs. 1 and 2. Weighted regression methods may be used to relate the precision measures to concentration levels. For this example, best results were obtained using a linear function relating variability to the square root of mean concentration. The least squares solutions are given in the figures.

Other studies [15,16] have used the coefficient of variation to express precision measures as functions of concentration level. For this approach, relationships of the form $S_W = bm$ and $S_B = cm$ are used to estimate the within- and between-laboratory standard deviation components where m is the mean concentration level.

Once functional relationships have been established relating the precision estimates to concentration level, they can be used in a number of ways to characterize the method. Their use to calculate repeatability and reproducibility measures and standard errors has already been mentioned. They can be used in conjunction with analysis of standard solutions to proportion out variability due to analysis as distinct from variability due to sampling. As an example, the total variability associated with a determination of a standard of known concentration can be estimated as $S = \sqrt{S_B^2 + S_W^2}$. The observed variability in the cooperating laboratories' analyses of the standard samples can be assumed to represent the variability due to analysis since the standard solutions are supplied by the coordinating laboratory and thus involve no sampling. The difference between the estimated total variability and this observed variability due to analysis could then be taken to represent variability due to sampling with the method.

Data from the experimental runs or blocks in which both spiked and unspiked sample determinations were performed are used to estimate the accuracy of a reference method. The difference between the spiked sample determination and the unspiked sample determination, for a given block and a given laboratory, is a measure of the controlled amount of materials added to the test samples. These differences, obtained by each laboratory, form the basis for the analysis of accuracy. For this approach, accuracy is measured as a percentage difference from the true value as calculated by the equation

accuracy

$$= \frac{(\text{estimated spike concentration} - \text{true spike concentration}) \times 100\%}{\text{true spike concentration}}$$

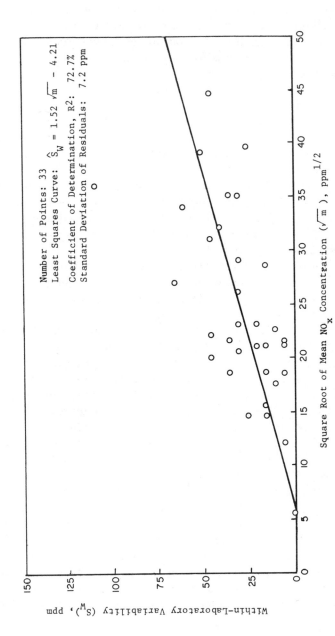

Number of Points: 33
Least Squares Curve: $\widehat{S}_W = 1.52 \sqrt{m} - 4.21$

Coefficient of Determination, R^2: 72.7%
Standard Deviation of Residuals: 7.2 ppm

FIG. 1—Scattergram and least squares curve relating within-laboratory variability to the square root of the mean NO_x concentration.

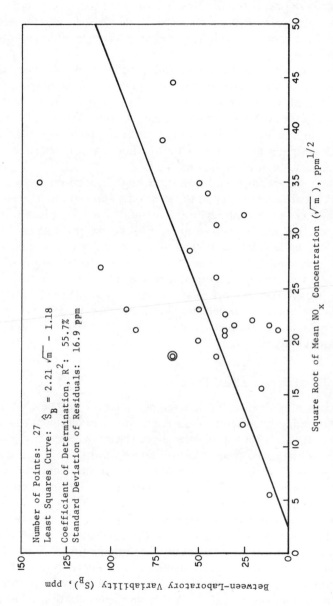

Number of Points: 27
Least Squares Curve: $\hat{S}_B = 2.21 \sqrt{m} - 1.18$
Coefficient of Determination, R^2: 55.7%
Standard Deviation of Residuals: 16.9 ppm

Between-Laboratory Variability (S_B), ppm

Square Root of Mean NO_x Concentration $(\sqrt{m})$, $ppm^{1/2}$

FIG. 2—*Scattergram and least squares curve relating between-laboratory variability to the square root of the mean NO_x concentration for pilot plant data.*

The estimated spike concentration is the difference between the laboratories' determinations of the spiked and unspiked samples. A histogram of these percentage differences can be used to indicate the accuracy of the reference method. Furthermore, if the distribution of these percentage differences appears to be approximately normal, the student's t distribution can be used to test the hypothesis that the mean percentage difference is not different from zero.

If it is not possible to spike the sampling system, the accuracy of the analytical portion of a reference method could be investigated through the use of standards of known concentrations. The cooperating laboratories' determinations of the concentration levels can be compared with the known standard value in a manner similar to that outlined previously. However, the effects of sampling according to the method are not reflected in the accuracy estimates obtained by this method.

The measures of accuracy and precision may also be related to other conditions which are free to vary in the method's application. The effect of varying conditions on the accuracy of the method—for example, alternative ways of storing the samples before analysis—can be investigated by estimating accuracy under each condition and comparing the results. In the estimates of precision, if the varying conditions can be designed into the experiment as levels of an experimental factor, their effect may be tested for statistical significance as part of the analysis of variance. In this situation, the variance observed in determinations attributable to varying these conditions would be partitioned from the total observed variation in the data and subsequently tested.

Application of Collaborative Test Data

The estimates of precision for a reference method can be useful as a means of quantifying uncertainty associated with measurements taken by applying the method. They enable the investigator to place various confidence intervals about the true unknown concentration level being measured. For example, if the measurement of concentration resulting from the reference method is assumed to be unbiased (that is, accurate), and further that the distribution of measurements is normal, a 95 percent confidence interval for the true unknown concentrations is determined as $m \pm 1.96\ S$, where m is the observed determination of the concentration and S is the appropriate estimated standard deviation. The calculation of S will depend upon the manner in which the determination of concentration level is made. If the determination of m is a single measurement by any laboratory, the appropriate form for S is $\sqrt{S_B^2 + S_w^2}$. If the determination of m represents an average of n observations by any given laboratory, the proper calculation of S is $\sqrt{S_B^2 + S_W^2/n}$.

Curves can be prepared as aids to determine if a source emission exceeds a prescribed level. For example, the Threshold study of the method for determining levels of oxides of nitrogen yielded relationships for within- and between-laboratory standard derivatives of the form

$$S_w = 1.52 \sqrt{m} - 4.21, \; S_B = 2.21 \sqrt{m} - 1.18$$

From these, 95 percent confidence limits can be plotted as a function of the mean concentration. Figure 3 represents this relationship for the case of a single measurement by any given laboratory. Such a curve can help to decide whether or not emissions from a source exceeds a prescribed level.

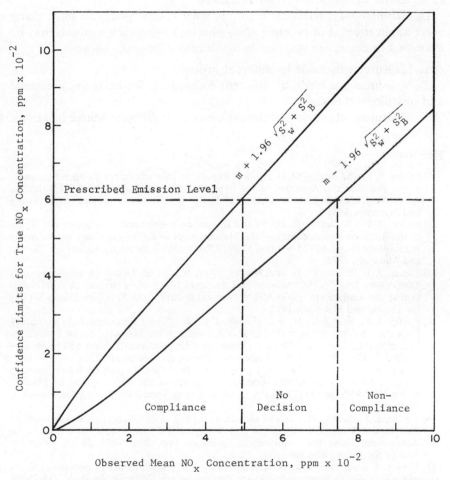

FIG. 3—*Ninety five percent confidence limits for true NO_x concentrations based upon a single measurement.*

If the measured concentration yields a lower confidence limit which exceeds the level, it is fairly certain that the source emissions are in excess of that level. If the upper confidence limit is below the level, the source emissions are almost certainly below the prescribed level. If the prescribed level lies within the confidence limits, it is uncertain whether or not the concentration exceeds the prescribed level. For example, if it is desired not to exceed a NO_x level of 600 ppm, Fig. 3 shows that for an observed single measurement that falls below about 490 ppm, the source emissions can be considered in compliance, while a measurement greater than 740 ppm would result in a decision of noncompliance. Values between these two points indicate measurements where it cannot be stated with certainty that the source is either above or below the prescribed level.

In a similar way, reference methods with known precision have many other applications. For example, data obtained using such methods may be examined to determine statistically significant differences between

1. Measurements made by different groups.

2. Measurements made by different techniques, for example, a manual and instrumental method.

3. Measurements made at different times or at different source locations.

References

[1] Foster, J. F. and Beatty, G. H., "Final Report on Interlaboratory Cooperative Study of the Precision and Accuracy of the Measurement of Nitrogen Dioxide Content in the Atmosphere Using ASTM Method D 1607," DS 55, American Society for Testing and Materials, 1974.

[2] Foster, J. F. and Beatty, G. H., "Final Report on Interlaboratory Cooperative Study of the Precision and Accuracy of the Measurement of Sulfur Dioxide Content in the Atmosphere Using ASTM Method D 2914," DS 55-S1, American Society for Testing and Materials, 1974.

[3] Foster, J. F., Beatty, G. H. and Howes, J. E., Jr., "Final Report on Interlaboratory Cooperative Study of the Precision and Accuracy of the Measurement of Total Sulfation in the Atmosphere Using ASTM Method D 2010," DS 55-S2, American Society for Testing and Materials, 1974.

[4] Foster, J. F., Beatty, G. H., and Howes, J. E., Jr., "Final Report on Interlaboratory Cooperative Study of the Precision and Accuracy of the Measurement of Particulate Matter in the Atmosphere (Optical Density of Filtered Deposit) Using ASTM Method D 1704," DS 55-S3, American Society for Testing and Materials, 1974.

[5] Foster, J. F., Beatty, G. H., and Howes, J. E., Jr., "Final Report on Interlaboratory Cooperative Study of the Precision and Accuracy of the Measurement of Dustfall Using ASTM Method D 1739," DS 55-S4, American Society for Testing and Materials, 1974.

[6] Foster, J. F., Beatty, G. H., and Howes, J. E., Jr., "Final Report on Interlaboratory Cooperative Study of the Precision and Accuracy of the Measurement of Lead in the Atmosphere Using the Colorimetric Dithizone Procedure," DS 55-S5, American Society for Testing and Materials, 1975.

[7] Howes, J. E., Jr., Pesut, R. N., and Foster, J. F., "Interlaboratory Cooperative Study of the Precision of Sampling Stacks for Particulates and Collected Residue," DS 55-S6, American Society for Testing and Materials, 1975.

[8] Howes, J. E., Jr., Pesut, R. N., and Foster, J. F., "Final Report on Interlaboratory Cooperative Study of the Precision of the Determination of the Average Velocity in

a Duct (Pitot Tube Method) Using ASTM Method D 3154-72," *DS 55-S7*, American Society for Testing and Materials, 1974.

[9] Howes, J. E., Jr., Pesut, R. N., and Foster, J. F., "Interlaboratory Cooperative Study of the Precision and Accuracy of the Determination of Oxides of Nitrogen in Gaseous Combustion Products (Phenol Disulfonic Acid Procedure) Using ASTM Method D 1608-60," *DS 55-S8*, American Society for Testing and Materials, 1975.

[10] Howes, J. E., Jr., Pesut, R. N., and Foster, J. F., "Final Report on Interlaboratory Cooperative Study of the Precision and Accuracy of the Determination of the Realtive Density of Black Smoke (Ringelmann Method) Using ASTM Method D 3211-73 T," *DS 55-S10*, American Society for Testing and Materials, 1974.

[11] Youden, W. J., *Journal of the Association of Official Agricultural Chemists*, Vol. 46, No. 1, 1963, pp. 55–62.

[12] Mandel, J., *Materials Research and Standards*, Vol. 11, No. 8, Aug. 1971, pp. 8–16.

[13] Natrella, M. G., *Experimental Statistics*, Handbook 91, National Bureau of Standards, 1963, Chapter 17.

[14] Brownlee, K. A., *Statistical Theory of Methodology in Science and Engineering*, Wiley, New York, 1960, Chapter 10.

[15] Hamil, H. F. and Camann, D. E., "Collaborative Study of Method for the Determination of Nitrogen Oxide Emissions from Stationary Sources (Fossil Fuel Fired Steam Generators), Southwest Research Institute Project No. 01-3487-001, EPA Contract No. 68-02-0623, 5 Oct. 1973.

[16] Hamil, H. F. and Thomas, R. E., "Collaborative Study of Method for the Determination of Nitrogen Oxide Emissions from Stationary Sources (Nitric Acid Plants), Southwest Research Institute Project No. 01-34 2-004, EPA Contract No. 68-02-0626, 8 May 1974.

W. L. Bonam[1] and W. F. Fuller[1]

Certification Experience with Extractive Emission Monitoring Systems

REFERENCE: Bonam, W. L. and Fuller, W. F., "Certification Experience with Extractive Emission Monitoring Systems," *Calibration in Air Monitoring, ASTM STP 598*, American Society for Testing and Materials, 1976, pp. 96–106.

ABSTRACT: The relative influences of the absolute mean value error, the confidence interval value, and the instrument calibration accuracy is examined using on-site instrument certification data acquired in the past three years. Confidence interval has strong influence based on existing certification data. The trend emphasizes the importance of the sampling technique. Properly calibrated instruments provide low values of absolute mean value error. An induced error related to calibrating instruments to 1.5 times the applicable emission standard for full scale has been observed when the relative mean value (reference average of sampling values) is low. The effect of the induced error will be amplified when the instrument calibration is performed improperly. Extractive emission monitoring systems using ultraviolet visible absorption detection techniques have successfully met the performance criteria proposed by the Environmental Protection Agency based on evaluations conducted in power plants, nitric acid plants, and sulfuric acid plants.

KEY WORDS: calibration, instruments, emission, monitors, standards

The recent experience of certifying extractive source emission monitoring systems to Environmental Protection Agency (EPA) performance criteria [1][2] indicates that accuracy and precision of the reference source test methods, the written certification procedures and calculations, and instrument calibration all have an important effect on the certification result. Experience in EPA sponsored and private evaluation programs indicate that extractive emission monitoring systems will certify successfully [2–6]. Relative accuracy, drift, and calibration error results have been particularly consistent. The performance specifications have been met despite the usual difficulties in working to a new detailed specification.

---

[1] Applications chemist and product manager, respectively, Instrument Products Division, E. I. duPont de Nemours and Co., Inc., Wilmington, Del. 19898.

[2] The italic numbers in brackets refer to the list of references appended to this paper.

FIG. 1—*Ultraviolet visible absorption instrumentation emission monitoring system.*

The recurring problem areas that have been identified include: interpretation of the procedures, improper calibration system design and materials selection, generation of large confidence intervals through the influences of sampling technique and reference method accuracy, and improper or lack of reference method analysis of standard calibration gases as required by procedures. This paper examines the potential trouble spots and representative performance specification data obtained with the certification procedures [1]. All data presented were acquired with ultraviolet visible absorption instrumentation (du Pont Model 460, 461, and 460/1 emission monitoring systems) such as shown in Fig. 1. Three types of plants have been investigated; power plants (majority of data), nitric acid plants, and sulfuric acid plants.

Method

Performance during the certification process is determined by various series of tests that examine the analyzer response to a known standard. Figure 2 illustrates the various tasks that must be performed. Following a 168-h checkout period, the certification testing is generally split into two categories: calibration and drift accuracy, and relative accuracy of the analyzer to the process emissions levels. Experience indicates that, with

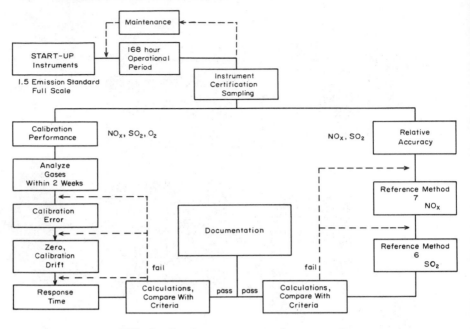

FIG. 2—*Certification process performance tasks.*

proper logistics planning, both categories of tests can be accomplished concurrently.

The performance specifications for sulfur dioxide (SO_2), nitrogen oxide (NO_x), and oxide (O_2) analyzers are shown in Fig. 3. All values listed are the "sum of the absolute mean value and the 95 percent confidence interval" of the series of tests divided by an appropriate reference value.

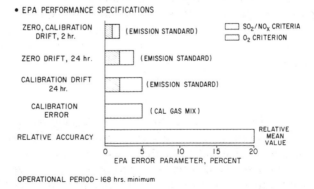

FIG. 3—*Performance specifications for SO_2, NO_x, and O_2 analyzers.*

EMISSION MONITORING REQUIREMENTS

I) SUM OF ABSOLUTE MEAN VALUE PLUS
   95 PERCENT CONFIDENCE INTERVAL

• DATA FROM CERTIFICATION PROGRAM ON-SITE

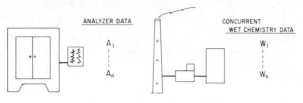

Fig. 4—*Relative accuracy calculation using the sum of the absolute mean value plus 95 percent confidence interval.*

The absolute mean value corresponds approximately to the usual definition of analyzer error.

The calculations required are performed according to the example outlined in Figs. 4 and 5 (relative accuracy calculation is shown). Most confusion about the calculations that are required in certification testing arise from the fact that the absolute error and the absolute value of the confidence interval must be added together before calculating each performance parameter. This requirement, and the use of various reference values, influences the performance values obtained. The key influences contained on the method are discussed individually.

EMISSION MONITORING REQUIREMENTS

• ABSOLUTE MEAN VALUE

$$AMV = \frac{1}{n} \sum_{i=1}^{n} (A_i - W_i)$$

A_i = Analyzer Data
W_i = Concurrent Wet Chemistry Data

• "95 PERCENT CONFIDENCE INTERVAL"

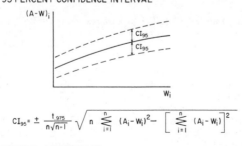

$$CI_{95} = \pm \frac{t_{.975}}{n\sqrt{n-1}} \sqrt{n \sum_{i=1}^{n} (A_i - W_i)^2 - \left[\sum_{i=1}^{n} (A_i - W_i) \right]^2}$$

• REQUIRED COMBINATION

$$\left| AMV + | CI_{95} | \right|$$

FIG. 5—*Relative accuracy calculation using absolute mean value, 95 percent confidence interval, and required combination.*

Certification Procedure Results

A substantial quantity of data using certification procedures similar to the published EPA approach has been obtained with du Pont emission monitoring systems [2–6]. The analyzer detection principle was ultraviolet visible absorption by a photometer for both SO_2 and NO_x. The majority of the data was obtained in operating power plants, nitric acid plants, and sulfuric acid plants using varying technologies. The period of data acquisition coincides generally with preparation of proposed continuous monitoring requirements.

Relative Accuracy Data

Relative accuracy results are perhaps the most important from the certification procedures since compliance data directly reflect this parameter. Table 1 contains relative accuracy data for both SO_2 and NO_x measurements obtained with the certification procedures. The data are the sum defined by EPA of analyzer error and the confidence interval associated with test procedures.

The SO_2 relative accuracy was very good giving a composite average of 8.8 percent. In each case certification specifications were met. The relative accuracy results at or below 5 percent are exceptional considering that summed values are shown. The data for Generator B are for two series of samples; one of 9 data points (B) and one of 20 individual tests including the first 9 points (B_1). As expected, the larger number of samples provides better results.

The NO_x data show a composite average of 15.2 percent which is comfortably within the EPA relative accuracy performance requirement of 20 percent for the summation. Higher values of NO_x relative accuracy than for SO_2 should be expected due to the inherent accuracies of Methods 6 and 7. This average does not include a point where certification was not

TABLE 1—*Relative accuracy result (EPA procedures with du Pont emission monitoring systems.)*

	SO_2, %	NO_x, %
Fossil-fueled Steam Generator A	11	20.4
Fossil-fueled Steam Generator B	6.7	4.3
Fossil-fueled Steam Generator B_1	2.5	1.3
Fossil-fueled Steam Generator C	17	13.3
Fossil-fueled Steam Generator D	12	26[a]
Sulfuric Acid Plant A	1	. . .
Sulfuric Acid Plant B	5	. . .
Nitric Acid Plant A		12
Composite average excluding B_1	8.8	15.2

[a] 1 percent absolute mean value + 25 percent confidence interval.

achieved the first time and one marginal point. The outlier illustrates the impact of adding the two required terms in the error calculations. In this case, the absolute mean value was only 1 percent, and the confidence interval was 25 percent. (The general influence of the confidence interval is discussed later.) The NO_x and SO_2 measurements from this system are guaranteed to the EPA specifications as a result of the demonstrated performance.

Drift and Calibration Error Data

Representative data for the various drift and calibration error parameters, taken on the same emission monitoring systems as in relative accuracy, are shown in Table 2. These data are influenced generally by different factors contained in the certification procedures than relative accuracy data. Sample size and reference values employed vary considerably. Misinterpretation of how to acquire the drift data has also been encountered frequently.

The data in Table 2 illustrate that, with proper attention to detail, good certification results will be obtained. The zero drift values are outstanding for this particular emission monitoring system, primarily because the instruments have an automatic zeroing sequence which continually updates accuracy through the day. The calibration error data shown meet criteria very well despite the use of varying concentration of standard gases, and often less than 50 percent full-scale levels, in the performance of the tests. Since the absolute concentration of standard gas is the prescribed reference value, the instrument performance can be penalized when other than 90 percent of full-scale levels are used. One 24-h calibration drift value did not meet the criterion in the first test. The usual case with all 24-h drift data is that the sample size is too small, and the confidence interval consequently swamps the absolute mean values in the prescribed summation.

TABLE 2—*Drift and calibration error results by EPA procedures (sum of absolute mean values and confidence interval).*

	Zero Drift, %		Calibration Drift, %		Calibration Error, %	Specie
	2 h	24 h	2 h	24 h		
Fossil fuel-fired steam generator	0.1	0	1.7	2.2	1.4	SO_2
Sulfuric acid plant	0.1	0.1	0.6	1.1	2.4	SO_2
Fossil fuel-fired steam generator	1.8	1.8	2.4	4.8	2.5	NO_x
Nitric acid plant	0	0	0.8	10.3[a]	0.3	NO_x

[a] IC component drifted with temperature.

Effect of Procedures on Certification Results

The procedures for certification testing specify three actions which have an important effect on the performance data obtained: method of calculation of the error, sample size for individual criteria, and initial setup of the measurement system. In most cases, the ability of good instrumentation to be certified is not hampered by these effects if they are understood by the vendors and sampling personnel. Marginal results can be obtained, however, for the various reasons described next.

Method of Calculation

Each performance criterion is determined using a formula of the form $(|X| + |Y|)/Z$ where x is the average mean difference of the test series, y is the confidence interval (95 percent) for that test series, and z is a selected reference value. Analyzer vendor performance specifications are most often determined by $|x|$ (full-scale value). Adding the confidence interval y has the advantage of broadening the acceptable error interval. Instruments slightly over on x can make up the difference in y, for example. Experience with this approach is generally favorable. However, the confidence intervals encountered have been unexpectedly large. In some cases this is due to small sample size, but sampling errors and inherent accuracy of Reference Methods 6 and 7 can be suspected as well.

Equally important is the variation in reference value chosen, z. In determination of relative accuracy, for example, z is the average of the reference method sampling. When a plant is operating well, the reference value will be low and lever the performance value up. In essence, the instrument is being tested for accuracy on a sliding scale. An accurate estimate of the emission standard of the plant is required for the period of sampling to minimize this effect. Such an estimate permits setting the instrument full scale to a more representative value of actual operation.

A second example of the effect of varying z occurs in calibration error determination. Since, for this performance, criterion z is the value of the known calibration standard, increasing values must be expected with use of standards having low values relative to the full-scale set point. Experience thus far indicates that required calibration error will be obtained without difficulty when the standard is nominally 90 percent of full scale. When standards at 50 percent or less of full scale are used, the rate of initial success drops approximately to 50 percent.

Sample Size

The confidence interval portion of the error calculations is strongly dependent on sample size. The formula, previously shown in Fig. 5, can be considered to be the product of two terms; a prefactor $(t_{0.975}/n\sqrt{n-1})$

and the radical in which the contribution of experimental scatter is calculated. Adding sample points reduces the value of CI_{95} primarily by reducing the prefactor. The large swing in the prefactor with sample size can be judged in Fig. 6 which also indicates the various sample sizes selected in the certification procedures for each performance criteria.

The current certification procedure experience follows the trend seen in Fig. 6. Larger confidence intervals occur for 24-h zero drift and calibration drift than for 2-h drift values. The data in Table 2 for calibration drift show larger values for the 24-h interval, and most of the increase is related to the confidence interval portion. Note that zero drift values are excellent for both intervals on this emission monitoring system because of the automatic zero correction feature. Normal sampling logistics make it difficult to increase the sample size for the 24-h drift determinations since only one point can be obtained per day. As a result, programs performed with this equipment have emphasized starting the 24-h interval data (and the 2 h as well) as soon as practicable after arrival on site.

The required number of samples to determine relative accuracy is nine which Fig. 6 would indicate drops the influence of the confidence interval a great deal. Unfortunately, the relative accuracy experience is that the sampling accuracy, which shows up in the radical, is frequently enough to outweigh the drop in the prefactor of CI_{95}.

Measurement System Setup

The certification procedures give instructions to set the measurement system full scale to approximately 1.5 times the emission standard for the operation. For most instruments, the full-scale value establishes reading error at all points on the scale. Relative accuracy, however, is determined using the average of Method 6 or 7 tests as the reference value. In many of

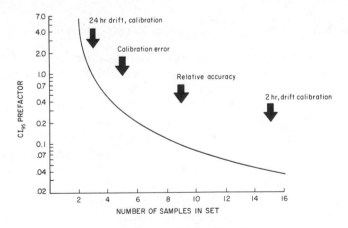

FIG. 6—*Influence of defined sample set.*

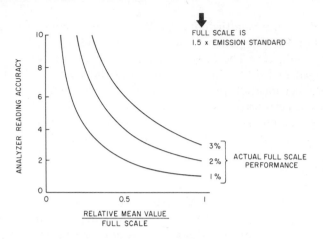

FIG. 7—*Influence of certification procedure.*

the cases shown in Table 1 the plant actually operated at emission levels well below the emission standard during the sampling period. Average readings of 10 to 20 percent full scale occurred often. It is possible to encounter a large induced error this way.

Figure 7 shows the potential influence of setting up to large full-scale value relative to the emission levels experienced. Most instrumentation will perform better than the published product literature states, but the potential to experience certification problems as described suggests the following point. Whenever a plant can be expected to deliver low emissions, for example, a new source designed to abate emissions, requesting permission of the regulatory agency to test in a more sensitive range should be considered.

Effect of Reference Method Accuracy and Sampling Errors

Certification procedure results for relative accuracy have shown that absolute mean value error will be a value near the published accuracy for the product. Confidence intervals are larger than absolute mean value error in a majority of cases and can be more than ten times larger. Even experiencing five times as much confidence interval error as absolute error can produce marginal certification results, as Fig. 8 shows.

Qualitatively, it appears that the large confidence intervals experienced to date are the combined result of reference method accuracy and sampling techniques. Both factors would be expected to increase scatter in the data which is then magnified by summing the squares in the CI_{95} calculation. (Consistent low or high bias is compensated in the calculation and not a consideration.)

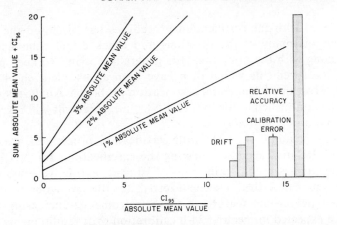

FIG. 8—*Influence of confidence interval.*

A series of collaborative studies [*7,8*] are now available which establish within- and between-laboratory precision of Reference Methods 6 and 7.

	Between Laboratory Precision, % true mean	Within Laboratory Precision, % true mean
Method 7 (NO_x)	9.5	6.5
Method 6 (SO_2)	18.5	15.0

Intuition and the certification results would predict larger scatter for the NO_x tests than indicated in the collaborative studies. The level of precision shown in the collaborative tests will increase CI_{95} but probably does not account for all the large values experienced. The potential effects of sampling technique can be examined as more certification procedure experience is acquired.

Summary and Conclusions

The experience with certification procedures so far suggests that obtaining successful results will depend on the amount of planning done by the analyzer vendor and the stack sampling contractor before the sampling starts. Training of the sampling contractor in basic analyzer operation will be very important. This may be done by on-site support at the time of tests or a comprehensive instruction manual that addresses the added requirements of certification testing. The instrument's set-up instructions and calibration procedure must be made very clear.

Experience with the certification procedures has disclosed the value of performing as many of the titrations and check calculations as possible on-site along with the sampling. It is generally possible to keep pace with the SO_2 measurements which then have been an excellent checkpoint on sampling problems or potential certification problems. Analyzers using the same detection principle for SO_2 and NO_x measurement will rarely fail to certify NO_x along with SO_2.

The data acquired thus far with certification procedures are very encouraging. Relative accuracy meeting the specifications for NO_x and SO_2 measurements has been obtained easily using the extractive emission measurement system described. Excellent zero drift values were obtained through the automatic zeroing feature of these instruments. Increasing difficulty should be expected in meeting 24-h calibration drift requirements and perhaps calibration error. The problem areas in the certification are identified and, with planning and education programs, can be avoided.

References

[1] "Proposed Emission Monitoring and Performance Testing Requirements," *Federal Register*, Vol. 39, No. 177, 11 Sept. 1974, p. 32852.
[2] Fuller, W. F., Apple, G. D., Reader, J. R., Jr., and Seago, J. L., "Combined Measurement of SO_2, NO_x, and O_2 for Power Plant Applications," 21st Annual Instrument Society of America Analysis Instrumentation Symposium, Philadelphia, du Pont Instruments, May 1975.
[3] Bonam, W. L., Fuller, W. F., and Williamson, J. A., "Emission Analyzer Certification to EPA Continuous Monitoring Requirements," Annual Meeting, Air Pollution Control Association, Boston, June 1975, pp. 75–60.1.
[4] Fuller, W. F., and Quick, D., "Instrumentation System Qualification for Continuous of Nonferrous Smelter Emissions," ISA Conference, Instrument Society of America, Pittsburgh, Pa., May 1974.
[5] McRanie, R. D., Craig, J. M., and Layman, G. O., "Evaluation of Sample Conditioners and Continuous Stack Monitors for the Measurement of Sulfur Dioxide, Nitrogen Oxides, and Opacity in Flue Gas from a Coal-Fired Steam Generator," Final Report, Southern Services, Inc., Feb. 1975. (Due to printing limits du Pont has made special arrangements to offer reprints.)
[6] National Bureau of Standards Handbook 91, Department of Commerce, 1963, pp. 3–31, paragraphs 3-3.1.4.
[7] "The Collaborative Study of EPA Methods 5, 6, and 7 in Fossil Fuel-Fired Steam Generators Final Report," EPA-650/4-74-013, Environmental Protection Agency, May 1974.
[8] Hamil, H. F. and Thomas, R. E. "Collaborative Study of Method for the Determination of Nitrogen Oxide Emissions from Stationary Sources (Nitric Acid Plants)," 01-3462-004, Southwest Research Institute, Houston, Tex., May 1974.

H. C. Lord[1]

Verification of *In Situ* Source Emission Analyzer Data

REFERENCE: Lord, H. C., "**Verification of In-Situ Emission Analyzer Data,**" *Calibration in Air Monitoring, ASTM STP 598*, American Society for Testing and Materials, 1976, pp. 107–117.

ABSTRACT: The accuracy of analytical measurements is controlled by a variety of factors. One of the most significant is the calibration technique utilized for the interpretation of the instrument output. Others are the presence of interfering species or the presence of random errors due to environmental, instrumental, or operator changes. The calibration of *in situ* analytical systems poses new requirements for the instrument manufacturer and user. Calibration techniques and verification of their authenticity in providing accurate *in situ* data are discussed in this paper.

KEY WORDS: accuracy, emission, monitoring, calibration, interferences, standards, chemiluminesence, phenol disulfonic acid, stratification, response time, dilution, comparators

System Description

Emissions measuring instrumentation, operating on the stream in place without extracting a sample, has come to be known as an *in situ* type. *In situ* operation includes installations which measure a local sample inside the stream, as well as systems that provide an average value across the diameter of the stream. For stratified streams, the latter situation provides a more representative average of the total emissions. *In situ* analyzers are characterized by fast response times (since there are no sampling system delays) and integrated optical path analyses of the actual gas stream that is passing the analyzer.

To discuss the relative accuracy, as well as the verification of that accuracy for *in situ* systems, we need to understand better their strengths and limitations.

Most *in situ* gas analyzers utilize absorption spectroscopy as the analytical technique [1].[2] With differential absorption spectroscopy, the absorption

---

[1] Vice-president, Environmental Data Corporation, Monrovia, Calif. 91016.

[2] The italic numbers in brackets refer to the list of references appended to this paper.

signal is directly proportional to the number of molecules in the path. (The perturbations which might affect that are discussed next.) Thus, one has an exact instantaneous mass emission measurement. With knowledge of the gas stream temperature and pressure, the total volume can be determined, and thus the parts per million of measured gas are known. Furthermore, with a simultaneous determination of oxygen (O_2) and water (H_2O), or carbon dioxide (CO_2) alone, parts per million dry at 3 percent O_2 can be computed. For combustion processes, that information plus fuel type and the appropriate fuel factor, F_c, pounds per million British thermal units can be automatically computed and read out [2].

The correlated *in situ* across stack measurement is an optically traversing analysis which averages the variations in spatial concentration, eliminates correlation differences from temporal variations, and, finally, provides an analysis independent of variations in dilution and also gas stream temperature. This is accomplished by measuring the emission parameter (that is, nitrogen oxide (NO_x), sulfur dioxide (SO_2), etc.) simultaneously with the measurement of the dilution parameter (CO_2), in the same optical path, and thus on the same sample. For a calibrated system, with no (or insignificant) interferences, the measured mass emission is exactly that which passed through the optical path.

It is important to realize that with an *in situ* system, it is not necessary to manipulate the sample gas temperature, the sample gas water vapor or moisture content, or the sample gas aerosol or particulate content. Also, one does not require careful isokinetic sample withdrawal.

Operation

Light from a source mounted external to the gas stream is collimated and sent through the gas stream. A single pass or folded path optical system may be used [3–5]. A focussing mirror in the analyzer compartment collects that collimated beam and focusses it onto the detection module. This module separates the wavelengths, and a single detector alternately measures the intensity at a wavelength where the gas uniquely absorbs (I) and at a nearby wavelength where the gas is nonabsorbing (I_o). Each of these regions may contain several wavelengths which are combined to form I and I_o. The relationship between I and I_o determines the gas concentration. Most gases approximately obey Beer's law where

$$I = I_o e^{-\alpha c l}$$

where

α = absorption coefficient,
c = sample concentration, and
l = path length.

The electronics divide I by I_o, providing an output independent of overall signal strength due to source aging, window darkening, particulate or water drop scattering, etc. The output of the divider, I/I_o, is operated on with a zero and span setting circuit, so that

$$\text{instrument output} = a(b-I/I_o)$$

where

a = span factor and
b = zero setting.

By selecting the two wavelengths (or sets of wavelengths) close together or intermingled, differential scattering, differential transmission through the calibration cells, or differential reflection from the mirrored optics are all eliminated.

Calibration

Calibration of *in situ* analyzers can be performed in several ways. If the source and detector are on opposite sides of the sample stream, an auxiliary source in the analyzer compartment can be used to bypass the sample. If the source and detector are both on the same side of the gas stream, a mirror can be used to bypass the absorption by the gas stream. The instrument zero can now be set. Span is set by placing a known concentration of gas into the light beam. In some situations, optical filters, equivalent to a known gas concentration, are used. However, the most meaningful calibration is a dynamic calibration wherein the standard instrument source is used, with the light beam passing through the sample. A typical dynamic calibration procedure is detailed here. The known concentration calibration gas samples are prepared by the partial pressure method [6].

This calibration procedure is a multistep process beginning with the preparation of standard, verified sealed cells of precisely known concentration, followed by the incremental addition of these cells to an operating field instrument. By forcing these known concentrations incrementally added to the unknown stack concentration to match the nonlinear calibration curve, the instrument zero, span set points, and the operating curve are all determined precisely.

In all cases, since absorption of radiation is directly proportional to the number of molecules in the light beam, one can utilize $c_1l_1 = c_2l_2$ where 1 refers to the sample stream and 2 refers to a small gas cell. This requires that the total pressure in the gas cell be the same as that of the sample stream, and that the calibration gas be prepared at the same temperature as that used for the calibration curve.

Calibration Gas Preparation

Normally, five cells are used for a complete instrument calibration. The specific cell concentrations are selected to be equivalent to the instrument span and four other equally spaced intervals less than the span, that is, 200, 400, 600, 800, and 1000 ppm. The calibration curve for that installation is the instrument response (0 to 1 V) as a function of millimeters of pure gas, determined for the appropriate full-scale sample concentration, optical pathlength, stack gas temperature, and absolute pressure.

The calibration gas cells are pumped out on a vacuum system to below 10^{-4} atm pressure. Each cell is then placed into the collimated beam of a standard instrument in the laboratory used as a reference source, so as to ensure that the blank is zero. The cells are now filled with pure gas (that is, 100 percent nitric oxide (NO), to the appropriate pressure (mm Hg) measured on an 8-in. Heisse gage, 0–760 mm, with 0.5 mm scale divisions. The gage readability and reproducibility are better than one half of a scale division. The instrument is calibrated periodically and certified accurate within ±0.1 percent of full scale across the entire scale. One thousand ppm of calibration gas in a standard calibration cell for a 10-ft path is approximately 150 mm pressure. One hundred ppm would then be approximately 15 mm. This could be reproducibly measured and prepared to better than 15 ± 0.25 mm or 100 ± 2 ppm. Higher concentration cells can be prepared more precisely. Each cell is now back filled with nitrogen (N_2) to a total pressure of 1 atm.

Each of these cells are now read on the standard laboratory instrument, and the response is checked. If there is more than a 10 mV deviation, the gas is remade. If the deviation is less than 10 mV, the deviation is noted, and the gas is relabelled, for example, 197 ppm instead of 200.

Field Calibration

With a field mountable auxiliary source and collimating mirror inserted into the analyzer module, the instrument zero is checked. Then each gas cell prepared in the laboratory is read and rechecked on this zero jig. The auxiliary source is removed, and the stream gas concentration is determined from the calibration curve. The known concentration calibration cells are incrementally added to the gas stream value. If each incrementally added gas cell plots exactly on the nonlinear calibration curve, the instrument is properly calibrated with a precisely set zero and span. For those situations where the full-scale gas concentration is so low that the calibration curve is essentially linear, an extended calibration curve is utilized which includes considerable nonlinearity.

If the low concentration cells plot reasonably well, but the higher concentration cells fall progressively off the calibration curve, the span is improperly set. If the higher concentrations fall below the curve, span is set low, and vice versa. Each cell is required to match the calibration curve within 5 ppm or 0.5 percent of full scale, whichever is larger. A forced addition of each calibration gas increment precisely determines the zero and span set points. The equation for span adjustment is

$$R = a(b - I/I_o)$$

where

a = span factor and
b = zero set point (for 500 ppm full scale) reading + 500 ppm.

$$150 + 500 \text{ reads } 700$$
$$\text{should be } \underline{650}$$
$$\text{therefore } 50 \text{ high}$$

Then, with the span adjust pot, reduce reading by 5/70 or 7.1 percent to 139 ppm, and repeat calibration check.

If the high concentration cells plot reasonably well, but the lower concentration cells fall progressively off the calibration curve, zero is improperly set. The zero adjustment is reading + 100 ppm

that is

$$150 + 100 = 225$$
$$\text{should be } \underline{250}$$
$$\text{therefore } 25 \text{ low}$$

Then raise reading 25 ppm with zero adjust pot, and repeat calibration check.

Automatic Calibration

The dynamic calibration procedure using sealed cells of known concentration can be performed automatically. Optically transparent cells, such as quartz, are filled in the laboratory, sealed, and then mounted in the instrument on a timer actuated solenoid arm. At the preset time, the cell moves into the beam and incrementally adds a known concentration of gas to the unknown sample. One cell provides a calibration check. Two cells, one of low concentration and one of higher concentration, allow instrument recalibration. A push button can be used for an override on the timer to provide an on-demand calibration check.

Comparison Data

The comparison of data from an *in situ* analyzer with data from an extractive analysis requires in-depth system understanding and test planning. The *in situ* and extractive analyses are not measuring the same samples.

The extractive systems will average some finite number of *in situ* analyses. This is because of the sample system's mixing and delay times, and the slower response time of the extractive system. The extractive systems will measure gas concentrations at one or more discrete points in the gas stream, while the *in situ* optically traverses the gas stream, averaging an infinite number of points traversed by the optical beam. Extractive systems typically manipulate the gas sample with water removal, particulate removal, interference gas removal, or sample heating or cooling, etc., while the *in situ* units analyze the sample as it passes through the instrument completely unchanged. For the comparison of data from an *in situ* analyzer with any extractive technique, instrumental or wet chemical, these various areas must be considered.

Stratification

The measured path of the *in situ* analyzer may be all or part of the inside diameter of the gas stream. Most gas streams will show some concentration or mass gradients across the stream. For particulates, this is especially true after bends, turning vanes, orifices, etc. For gases, the variations may be solely due to increased leakage and decreased gas velocity near the edges. However, for some gases such as carbon monoxide (CO) from a utility boiler, individual CO streams emanating from each burner can often be detected. There may be as much as a 100 percent change in concentration in less than 1 ft. So as to ensure a representative comparison of the *in situ* and extractive results, it is necessary to traverse the gas stream with the sample probe being used for the extractive analysis. This traversal should be done in the same plane as the *in situ* analyzer. Samples should be taken at spacings close enough to profile representatively the concentration gradients. Typically, this may be 1 ft intervals, unless experience indicates shorter or longer intervals are required. For continuous extractive monitoring, a multipoint sampling system can now be constructed which will provide a representative analysis.

Response Time

Most *in situ* analyzers, with no sampling system, etc. involved, will respond rapidly to a change in sample concentration in the gas stream. Typically, this response time will be of the order of a few seconds. An extractive reading always provides a time integration analysis. For instrumental techniques, the time integration is determined primarily by mixing in the sampling system. For many manual techniques, the sample to be analyzed later in the laboratory is collected over an extended period of time. In a gas stream with rapidly varying concentrations, it is necessary to average the continuous *in situ* data over the sampling time for the extractive data.

Sample Condition

The *in situ* analysis measures the mass or parts per million flowing past the instrument at each instant. Normally, the gas stream will contain water vapor from combustion of fuel hydrogen, water injection, wet scrubbing, etc., which acts as a diluent. Extractive systems may use heated lines to maintain the water vapor content, or may dry the sample before the gas is passed through the analyzer. If the line is heated, all of the valves, connectors, etc. must also be heated so as to prevent water condensation and thus a change of the water vapor content of the gas stream. The temperature must match the sample gas temperature, or else entrained water drops may evaporate and increase the water vapor content of the sample gas stream.

If the extracted sample is dried, the amount of removed water is needed for a comparison of the data to the fully diluted wet analysis. This can be performed in several ways, by means of a secondary CO_2 or O_2 dilution analysis and calculation. If the water vapor is removed, it is essential to ensure that no sample is removed at the same time. SO_2 is quite soluble in water, forming sulfurous acid, and would be partially removed by drying. NO_2 is also quite soluble in water.

Air leakage will also affect any direct data comparison. Sampling points near the walls are apt to show lower concentrations than the central area of the gas stream. Multipoint sampling as discussed under stratification is required to compensate for this effect. Leakage into the sampling system is another possibility. Standard operating procedure should include a leak check of the entire sampling, clean-up and analytical system, preferably by blocking the probe tip, turning the sample pump on, and checking the flow meter for a flow response.

Laboratory Test

A typical test was one performed by an independent laboratory comparing an *in situ* NO analyzer with a chemiluminescence NO analyzer. For simplicity of comparison, the *in situ* type analyzer was set up in the laboratory with a flow-through sample cell in the collimated optical beam, and this sample cell connected to a sampling system with flowmeters, pump, etc.

Both the *in situ* type and the chemiluminescence analyzers were tied into the same sample line, but each had their own flow meter and pump. A comparison by the laboratory of 28 different pairs of samples is listed in Table 1, with the actual sample concentrations ranging from 8 to 70 ppm. This table shows that at least under the condition of the test, and for the concentrations studied, the agreement was very good.

Interference Check

In a laboratory test similar to the one just mentioned, known concentrations of potential interferences were passed through the analyzer sample

TABLE 1—*Comparison of* in-situ *and chemiluminescence analyses.*[a]

	In situ		Chemiluminescence
$\bar{x}$	30.48		30.51
s	17.25		19.00
r		0.982	

[a] Wilcoxon's signed ranks test (Biometrics Bulletin, 1945, pp. 80–82).

TABLE 2—*Typical interference check.*

Potential Interferences Tested	
50% opacity	7000 ppm propane
12% carbon dioxide	1000 ppm methane
3% water vapor	150 ppm ethylene
2% carbon monoxide	107 ppm acetylene
500 ppm sulfur dioxide	100 ppm formaldehyde
500 ppm ammonia	59 ppm benzene
200 ppm nitrogen dioxide	

cell. The instrument was spanned so that the minimum sensitivity was 0.5 percent of scale, or 3.5-ppm NO. There was no instrument response from any of the items listed in Table 2.

Field Tests

In these tests, data from an *in situ* NO analyzer operating on an oil-fired power plant was compared to the data from a series of wet chemical phenol disulfonic acid (PDS) tests according to ASTM Test for Oxides of Nitrogen in Gaseous Combustion Products (Phenol-Disulfonic Acid Procedure) (D1608-60). This is essentially the same test as the Environmental Protection Agency's (EPA) reference method, Method 7 [7]. Table 3 lists several comparisons of an average PDS result for three samples, each at three different points across the gas stream with the simultaneous *in situ* reading raw, at stack O_2 and H_2O vapor concentrations.

TABLE 3—*Average PDS and* in situ *NO analysis* [4].

Load, mW	Boiler O_2, %	CO_2, %	O_2, %	H_2O, %	PDS, ppm	In situ, ppm
196	3.8/3.9	10.7	6.7	10.4	201	200
183	4.0/4.0	10.3	7.2	8.3	171	175
215	4.3/1.2	10.7	6.5	8.5	203	200
210	4.5/2.5	11.0	6.4	9.5	219	210

TABLE 4—*Detailed comparison of individual and averaged PDS analyses with an* in situ *analysis* [4].

| | | Load: 195 mW, Fuel: Oil Boiler O_2: East = 7.5%, West = 3.5% | | |
	Sample	PDS Dry NO_x, ppm	O_2, %	PDS NO_x, 3% O_2, dry
Point 1	A	173	8.2	243
	B	179	7.8	244
	C	174	7.7	246
Point 2	A	221	6.8	280
	B	219	8.0	303
	C	216	7.2	282
Point 3	A	172	7.8	234
	B	183	7.9	251
	C	188	6.8	238
				Avg PDS 258 ppm

NOTE—*In situ* NO_x reading at 3% O_2, dry; assuming 5% NO_x is NO_2 = 253 ppm.

In some boilers or under certain operating conditions or both, considerable stratification is observed. Table 4 details the individual PDS readings for each sample at each location. It is seen that a multipoint extractive analysis is necessary for optimum correlation. The boiler was operated at block load for the duration of the test so as to ensure minimum changes during the test period.

A more exhaustive comparison has been made, wherein a sampling system was constructed and installed through the roof of a flue duct directly above the *in situ* analyzer optical path. The optical path was 12 ft. Fourteen equally spaced sampling probes, each with their own flowmeter and controller were installed, and both a composite reading and the average of the individual points were recorded. Also, samples were extracted through the wall of the duct at three equally spaced points in the horizontal plane and 1 ft upstream of the *in situ* analyzer. The extracted samples were collected in 2-litre round-bottom flasks for PDS analysis, and then each point was read with a chemiluminescence analyzer set up and calibrated on the spot. Three series of tests were performed. The *in situ* and chemiluminescence analyzers were field calibrated, and the first tests were run. The test data are listed in Table 5. The *in situ* instrument then operated completely unattended for 22 days. A second test was now run in the exact same mode as the previous test. The chemiluminescence analyzer was field calibrated prior to the test. These test results are listed in Table 6. A calibration check was then performed on the *in situ* analyzer, and a second series of identical tests were performed the same day. These data are shown in Table 7.

TABLE 5—*Comparison of analytical techniques for boiler flue gas NO$_x$ measurements: accuracy directly after calibration of analyzers.*

	NO$_x$ (Stack Conditions) ppm as Given By			PDS Value, %	
	PDS	Chemi[a]	*In situ*	Chemi	*In situ*
A. Three-point horizontal traverse	227	...	221	...	97.4
B. Fourteen-point vertical composite	223	213	221	95.5	99.1
C. Fourteen individual points, averaged	226	219	221	96.9	97.8
D. Three-Point horizontal traverse	234	...	221	...	94.4

[a] Chemi = chemiluminescence.

TABLE 6—*Comparison of analytical techniques for boiler flue gas NO$_x$ measurements: accuracy 22 days after calibration of* in situ *analyzer* (*instrument completely unaltered during this period*).

	NO$_x$ (Stack Conditions) ppm as Given By			PDS Value, %	
	PDS	Chemi	*In situ*	Chemi	*In situ*
A. Three-point Horizontal traverse	193	213	196	110.4	101.5
B. Fourteen-point vertical composite	200	214	196	107.0	98.0
C. Fourteen individual points, averaged	195	220	196	112.8	100.5
D. Three-point horizontal traverse	182	208	196	114.3	107.7

TABLE 7—*Comparison of analytical techniques for boiler flue gas NO$_x$ measurements: accuracy after calibration of analyzer* (*same day as for Table 6*).

	NO$_x$ (Stack Conditions) ppm as Given By			PDS Value, %	
	PDS	Chemi	*In situ*	Chemi	*In situ*
A. Three-point horizontal traverse	182	204	196	112.1	107.7
B. Fourteen-point vertical composite	189	188	196	99.5	103.7
C. Fourteen individual points, averaged	193	217	196	112.4	101.6
D. Three-point horizontal traverse	185	209	196	113.0	105.9

Summary

Operating constraints of *in situ* analyzers have been explained, and a calibration technique has been tailored for these constraints. The calibration procedure has been designed to meet the following objectives:

1. Dynamic calibration of the entire system in the presence of the sample.
2. Provide accurate data.
3. Relative ease of performance.
4. Allow for automatic calibration.

Both laboratory and field comparison tests against other instrumental techniques and the EPA reference method shows that the accuracy can not only be within acceptable limits but also can be very high.

References

[1] Hanst, P. L. in *Advances in Environmental Science and Technology*, J. N. Pitts, Jr., and R. L. Metcalf, Ed., Wiley–Interscience, New York, 1971, pp. 91–213.
[2] Neulicht, R., *Stack Sampling News*, Vol. 2, No. 8, Feb. 1975, pp. 6–11.
[3] Burch, D. E. and Gryvnak, D. A. in *Analytical Methods Applied to Air Pollution Measurements*, R. K. Stevens and W. F. Herget, Eds., Ann Arbor Science, Ann Arbor, Mich., 1974, Chapter 10, pp. 183–231.
[4] Lord, H. C. in *Analytical Methods Applied to Air Pollution Measurements*, R. K. Stevens and W. F. Herget, Eds., Ann Arbor Science, Ann Arbor, Mich., 1974, Chapter 11, pp. 233–243.
[5] Homolya, J. B. in *Analytical Methods Applied to Air Pollution Measurements*, R. K. Stevens and W. F. Herget, Eds., Ann Arbor Science, Ann Arbor, Mich., 1974, Chapter 13, pp. 274–283.
[6] Gray, T. A. and Kuczynski, E. R. in *Environmental Pollution Instrumentation*, R. L. Chapman, Ed., Instrument Society of America, Pittsburgh, Pa., 1969, pp. 68–75.
[7] *Federal Register*, Vol. 36, No. 247, Environmental Protection Agency, 23 Dec. 1971, pp. 24891–24893.

J. B. Reeves[1]

Statistical Implications of the Environmental Protection Agency Procedure for Evaluating the Accuracy of Sulfur Dioxide and Nitrogen Oxide Monitors of Stationary Sources

REFERENCE: Reeves, J. B., "Statistical Implications of the Environmental Protection Agency Procedure for Evaluating the Accuracy of Sulfur Dioxide and Nitrogen Oxide Monitors of Stationary Sources," *Calibration in Air Monitoring, ASTM STP 598*, American Society for Testing and Materials, 1976, pp. 118–128.

ABSTRACT: The statistical parameter identified in the *Federal Register* for evaluating the accuracy of monitoring systems of sulfur dioxide (SO_2) and nitrogen oxide (NO_x) from stationary sources is the absolute value of the mean plus the 95 percent confidence interval for a set of test data. The test data are derived by differencing simultaneous measurements by the monitoring system and a reference method. The probability that a system will fail the evaluation is a function of the mean and standard deviation of the errors in the system, the mean and standard deviation of the errors in the reference method, the number of data points used in the evaluation, and the acceptance level. An equation defining the probability of rejection is derived, and curves are presented showing this probability when nine measurements are used in the evaluation. The influence of errors in the reference method on the probability of rejection are discussed. Data from the evaluation of SO_2 and NO_x monitors at a power plant are presented and discussed briefly.

KEY WORDS: calibration, monitors, evaluation, tests, standard deviation, electric power plants

The U.S. Environmental Protection Agency (EPA) has defined a procedure for evaluating nitrogen oxide (NO_x) and sulfur dioxide (SO_2) monitoring systems for stationary sources. The evaluation of monitoring system accuracy is based on a comparison of monitoring system measurements with simultaneous measurements by a reference method. How well this comparison defines the accuracy of the monitoring system, of course, depends upon how closely the reference method measures the true pollutant

---

[1] Research physicist, University of Dayton Research Institute, Dayton, Ohio 45469.

118

concentration. The ability to make a definitive decision to accept or reject the monitoring system based on its accuracy depends to some extent upon the repeatability of the reference method. The following paragraphs discuss the influence of these two aspects of a reference method (accuracy and repeatability) on the evaluation of NO_x and SO_2 monitoring systems. In the last section, results of the evaluation of NO_x and SO_2 monitoring systems at a power plant are presented and discussed.

Relationship Between Errors in the Reference Measurements and Errors in the Monitoring System Measurements

The EPA procedure defined in the *Federal Register*[2] for evaluating the accuracy of an SO_2 or NO_x monitoring system for a stationary source is based on a set of differences in simultaneous (or near simultaneous) measurements by a reference method and by the monitoring system. Both the reference measurement and the monitoring system may be in error from the true concentration at the time the measurements are taken. The measurements can be expressed as

$$X_{Mi} = X_{Ti} + e_{Mi}$$
$$X_{Ri} = X_{Ti} + e_{Ri}$$

where

$X_{Mi} = $ measurement made by the monitoring system at time t_i,
$X_{Ti} = $ true concentration of the pollutant at time t_i,
$X_{Ri} = $ measurement of the reference method at time t_i,
$e_{Mi} = $ error in the monitoring system measurement at time t_i, and
$e_{Ri} = $ error in the reference measurement at time t_i.

We will assume that the errors in the monitoring system and the reference method are distributed normally with means of μ_M and μ_R, respectively, and standard deviations of σ_M and σ_R, respectively. μ_M and μ_R can be either positive or negative and define the bias in the monitoring system and the reference method. σ_M and σ_R are positive quantities which define the degree of variation in the errors. If μ_M and μ_R were both zero, the monitoring system and the reference method would, on the average, yield the true pollutant concentration. If σ_M or σ_R were zero, the monitoring system or the reference method, respectively, would yield the same value each time a given concentration is measured. In other words, σ_M and σ_R are a measure of the repeatability of the measurement method when the true concentration does not change.

[2] *Federal Register*, Vol. 39, No. 177, Part 2, Washington, D. C., 11 Sept. 1974, pp. 32864–32869.

The difference in the monitoring system measurement and the reference measurement at some time t_i is

$$d_i = X_{Mi} - X_{Ri}$$
$$= X_{Ti} + e_{Mi} - (X_{Ti} + e_{Ri})$$
$$= e_{Mi} - e_{Ri}$$

The d_i's are distributed normally with a mean value, μ_D, defined by the equation

$$\mu_D = \mu_M - \mu_R \tag{1}$$

The standard deviation of the differences is defined by the equation

$$\sigma_D = (\sigma_M{}^2 + \sigma_R{}^2)^{1/2} \tag{2}$$

where the assumption has been made that the errors in the two measurement methods are independent. The quantities μ_D and σ_D can be estimated from n samples by the equations

$$\bar{d} = \frac{1}{n} \sum_{i=1}^{n} d_i \tag{3}$$

$$S_D = \left[\frac{n \sum\limits_{i=1}^{n} d_i{}^2 - \left(\sum\limits_{i=1}^{n} d_i \right)^2}{n(n-1)} \right]^{1/2} \tag{4}$$

where $\bar{d}$ is an estimate of μ_D and S_D is an estimate of σ_D. As n increases without bound, $\bar{d}$ approaches μ_D and S_D approaches σ_D. How close $\bar{d}$ is to μ_D is indicated by the confidence interval whose half width is defined as

$$CI_{1-\alpha} = t_{1-(\alpha/2),n-1} \frac{S_D}{\sqrt{n}} \tag{5}$$

where $t_{1-(\alpha/2),n-1}$ is the t-statistic associated with the $(1 - \alpha) \times 100$ percent confidence level and is a function of the degrees of freedom $(n - 1)$. For an α of 0.05, for example, one can be 95 percent confident that the true mean, μ_D, lies between $\bar{d} - CI_{0.95}$ and $\bar{d} + CI_{0.95}$. The confidence interval decreases as n increases.

The probability that a given monitoring system will pass the accuracy evaluation depends upon the errors in the reference method as well as on the errors in the monitoring system. In the next section, equations for evaluating these probabilities are derived. The influence of the errors in measurements by the reference method on these probabilities are then discussed.

Probability of Accepting or Rejecting a Monitoring System

According to the EPA procedure, a monitoring system's accuracy is considered acceptable if

$$|\bar{d}| + CI_{0.95} \leq K \qquad (6)$$

where K is the acceptance level. (For NO_x and SO_2 monitors, K is 20 percent of the mean of the reference measurements.) A monitoring system will fail the evaluation if

$$\bar{d} + CI_{0.95} > K$$

or if

$$\bar{d} - CI_{0.95} < -K$$

If a monitoring system meets the acceptance criteria, one can be 95 percent confident that the true difference in the monitoring system and the reference method is greater than $-K$ and less than $+K$.

The probability that a monitoring system will fail the evaluation is dependent upon both μ_D and σ_D. Figure 1 illustrates the situation when μ_D is positive. The solid, bell-shaped curve defines the frequency distribution of the population of differences in simultaneous measurements by the two methods. This distribution has a standard deviation of σ_D. The dashed, bell-shaped curve defines the distribution of estimates of the mean difference. This distribution has a standard deviation of $\sigma_D/\sqrt{n}$. Ninety-five percent of the estimates of μ_D will lie between $\mu_D - CI_{0.95}$ and $\mu_D + CI_{0.95}$.

As can be observed from Fig. 1, as μ_D increases, the probability that $\bar{d} + CI_{0.95}$ will be greater than K increases. Also (as long as μ_D is less than K) the probability that $\bar{d} + CI_{0.95}$ will be greater than K increases as σ_D increases.

The probability that a monitoring system will fail the evaluation can be calculated in the following manner. First, note that the probability that $\bar{d} + CI_{0.95} > K$ is the same as the probability that

$$\frac{(\bar{d} - \mu_D)\sqrt{n}}{S_D} > \frac{(K - \mu_D - CI_{0.95})\sqrt{n}}{S_D}$$

Upon substituting the expression in Eq 5 for $CI_{0.95}$, the above probability becomes

$$P\left\{ \frac{(\bar{d} - \mu_D)\sqrt{n}}{S_D} > \frac{[K - \mu_D - t_{0.975,n-1}(S_D/\sqrt{n})]\sqrt{n}}{S_D} \right\}$$

where $P\{\ \}$ denotes the probability that the statement within the brackets is true. The quantity $(\bar{d} - \mu_D)\sqrt{n}/S_D$ is distributed according to the well-

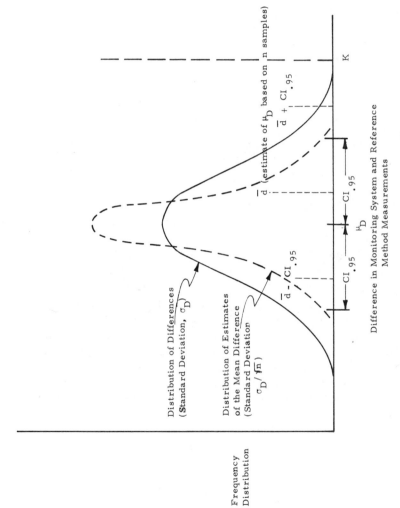

FIG. 1—*Graphical illustration of the relationships among* μ_D, σ_D, $\bar{d}$, $CI_{0.95}$, *and K.*

known student's t-distribution. Therefore, the probability statement can be written as

$$P\left\{t_{n-1} > \frac{[K - \mu_D - t_{0.975,n-1}(S_D/\sqrt{n})]\sqrt{n}}{S_D}\right\}$$

where the subscript $n - 1$ is the degrees of freedom associated with the problem. The probability that t_{n-1} will exceed any number can be calculated by numerically integrating the probability density function for t_{n-1}. A computer routine to perform this calculation is available in most statistical program packages. The t_{n-1} probability distribution is a bell-shaped curve centered at zero. The probability that t_{n-1} will exceed a number decreases as the number increases.

Following a similar line of development leads to the fact that the probability that $\bar{d} - CI_{0.95}$ will be less than $-K$ is the same as

$$P\left\{t_{n-1} < \frac{[-K - \mu_D + t_{0.975,n-1}(S_D/\sqrt{n})]\sqrt{n}}{S_D}\right\}$$

The probability (P_R) that a monitoring system will be rejected is the sum of the probability that $\bar{d} + CI_{0.95}$ will be greater than K and the probability that $\bar{d} - CI_{0.95}$ will be less than $-K$. That is

$$P_R = P_+ + P_- \tag{7}$$

where

$$P_+ = P\left\{t_{n-1} > \frac{[K - \mu_D - t_{0.975,n-1}(S_D/\sqrt{n})]\sqrt{n}}{S_D}\right\} \tag{8}$$

and

$$P_- = P\left\{t_{n-1} < \frac{[-K - \mu_D + t_{0.975,n-1}(S_D/\sqrt{n})]\sqrt{n}}{S_D}\right\} \tag{9}$$

If the sum of P_+ and P_- is greater than 1.0, the probability of rejecting the monitoring system is equal to 1.0. This occurs when the distribution of differences is so broad that the values of $\bar{d}$ which are small enough (or negative enough) to avoid failing the $\bar{d} + CI_{0.95} > K$ criteria are too small (or negative) to avoid failing the $\bar{d} - CI_{0.95} < K$ criteria. The probability that a monitoring system will be accepted is equal to $1 - P_R$. The above equations define P_R as a function of K, μ_D, S_D, and n. The estimated standard deviation (S_D) was used in computing P_R rather than the true standard deviation (σ_D) in order to simplify the calculation.

Probability of Rejecting NO$_x$ and SO$_2$ Monitoring Systems

According to the EPA procedure for evaluating the accuracy of NO$_x$ and SO$_2$ stationary source monitoring systems, nine differences are used in computing $\bar{d}$ and $CI_{0.95}$. The acceptance level (K) is equal to 20 percent

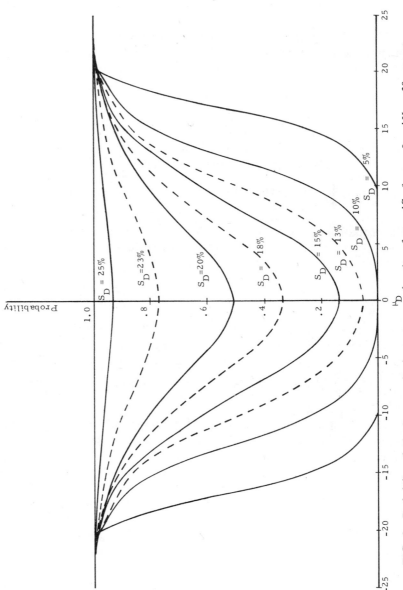

FIG. 2—*Probability of rejecting a monitoring system as a function of* μ_D *and* S_D *for* n = 9 *and* K = 20 *percent.*

of the mean value of the nine reference measurements $(\overline{X}_R)$. Figure 2 shows curves of the probability of rejecting a monitoring system (P_R) as a function of μ_D for various values of S_D when $n = 9$ and $K = 20$ percent. As can be seen from Fig. 2, P_R is highly dependent upon S_D. For an S_D of 5 percent of $\overline{X}_R$, a monitoring system with a true mean difference between -10 percent and $+10$ percent of $\overline{X}_R$ is extremely likely to pass the accuracy evaluation. If μ_D is $+15$ percent or -15 percent, the monitoring system has a 0.25 probability of being rejected. If μ_D is 20 or -20 percent, the system has a 0.975 probability of being rejected. For an S_D of 15 percent, a monitoring system with μ_D equal to zero would have a 0.13 probability of rejection. For an S_D of 20 percent, a monitoring system with μ_D equal to zero would have a probability of 0.51 of being rejected. If S_D were as large as 30 percent, no monitoring system could pass the accuracy evaluation.

The decision to accept or reject a monitoring system becomes more definitive as S_D becomes smaller. That is, for smaller S_D's, the curve of P_R rises more steeply from values of μ_D at which a system is very likely to be accepted, to μ_D's at which a system is very likely to be rejected. As S_D becomes larger, the slope of the curve in the transition range becomes less so that there is a broader band of μ_D's at which the decision to reject or accept a system could very well change if the evaluation were repeated.

Influence of Errors in the Reference Method on the Probability of Rejection

Equation 1 gives the relationship between μ_D and the mean error in the reference method (μ_R) as

$$\mu_D = \mu_M - \mu_R$$

According to this equation, μ_R can make μ_D larger or smaller than μ_M. If μ_R is of the opposite sign of μ_M, the magnitude of μ_D will be larger than the magnitude of μ_M, and the monitoring system will have a greater probability of being rejected than if μ_R were zero. Similarly, if μ_R is of the same sign as μ_M, the magnitude of μ_D will be smaller than the magnitude of μ_M, and the monitoring system will have a lesser probability of being rejected than if μ_R were zero. The larger the magnitude of μ_R, the greater the potential for an evaluator to make the wrong decision in accepting or rejecting a monitoring system. That is, there will be greater potential for the evaluator to accept a system which should be rejected (based on the value of μ_M) and to reject a system which should be accepted (again, based on the value of μ_M).

Equation 2 gives the relationship between σ_D and the repeatability of the reference method as characterized by σ_R as

$$\sigma_D = (\sigma_M{}^2 + \sigma_R{}^2)^{1/2}$$

When evaluating SO_2 monitors, σ_R is the standard deviation of the distribution of errors in EPA Method 6. When evaluating NO_x monitors, σ_R is the standard deviation of errors in reference values which are the average of three near simultaneous measurements by EPA Method 7. In this latter case, σ_R is equal to $\sigma_{R7}/\sqrt{3}$ where σ_{R7} is the standard deviation of the distribution of errors in EPA Method 7. According to the foregoing equation, as σ_R increases, σ_D increases and thus so do estimates (S_D) of σ_D. Any nonzero value of σ_R will tend to make the decision to accept or reject a system less definitive. The larger the value of σ_R, the more uncertain the evaluator will be in knowing whether or not his decision is correct. If σ_R is large, the value of σ_D will be large no matter how small σ_M is. In this case, the acceptance level K must be large, or no monitoring systems are likely to be accepted even if μ_M and σ_M are zero. For a K of 20 percent, a value of σ_R as high as 25 percent would mean that no system is likely to be accepted.

Results of the Evaluation of SO₂ and NOₓ Monitoring Systems at an Electric Power Station

EPA personnel conducted tests at the Duke Power Company Generating Station in Charlotte, North Carolina, during 1973 to evaluate a number of SO_2 and NO_x monitoring systems.[3,4] These data have been used to calculate values for $\bar{d}$, S_D, and $|\bar{d}| + CI_{0.95}$ based on nine pairs of measurements. The results are presented here to provide an indication of the magnitude of S_D that might be expected for such monitors. EPA Method 6 was used as a reference with SO_2 monitors, and Method 7 was used with NO_x monitors.

Table 1 shows the results for eight evaluations involving three SO_2 monitoring systems. As can be seen, System A passed the evaluation two out of three times, System B passed three out of three times, and System C failed two out of two times. The values of S_D ranged from 1.6 to 20.4 percent of the mean reference value, with several values occurring around 12 percent. If 12 percent is a typical value of S_D for SO_2 monitors, the EPA procedure for evaluating such monitors appears reasonable based on the curves in Fig. 1. The values of S_D in Table 1 suggest that the value of σ_R for Method 6 is less than 12 percent of $\bar{X}_R$ when $\bar{X}_R$ is near 500 ppm.

Table 2 shows the results of nine evaluations involving four NO_x monitors. The EPA procedure for NO_x monitors was not followed in these evaluations in that only one reference measurement was used in computing each d_i, rather than the average of three reference measurements. As can be seen from the table, none of the systems satisfied the condition $|\bar{d}| + CI_{0.95} \leq 20$ percent when this procedure was used. The values of S_D were all in the neighborhood of 45 percent of the mean reference value. How much of this is due to variability in the monitoring system and how much is due to variability in Method 7 is unknown. However, one experiment

[3] Homolaya, J. B., *Science of the Total Environment*, Vol. 3, 1975, pp. 349–362.

[4] A report on the NO_x data is in preparation by Michael Barnes of the Chemistry and Physics Laboratory, Research Triangle Park, N. C. 27711.

TABLE 1—*Accuracy of SO$_2$ monitoring systems using nine measurements.*

	$\dfrac{\bar{d},}{\bar{X}_R}, \%$	$\dfrac{S_D,}{\bar{X}_R}, \%$	$\dfrac{CI_{0.95},}{\bar{X}_R}, \%$	$\dfrac{\|\bar{d}\| + CI_{0.95},}{\bar{X}_R}, \%$	$\bar{X}_R,$ ppm
System A:					
Test 1	10.9	1.6	1.2	12.1	478.8
Test 2	25.4	20.4	15.7	41.1	498.4
Test 3	7.4	10.4	8.0	15.4	576.2
System B:					
Test 1	−8.2	2.5	1.9	10.1	475.7
Test 2	7.4	13.3	10.2	17.6	511.0
Test 3	−1.8	10.3	7.9	9.7	579.9
System C:					
Test 1	37.4	13.9	10.7	48.1	511.0
Test 2	24.1	12.7	9.8	33.9	579.9

indicated that the majority is due to variability in the reference method. Eleven reference measurements were taken in a 15 min period and their variability compared to the variability in three monitoring systems during the same period. The standard deviation for Method 7 was 22 percent of the mean reference value (381 ppm), while the standard deviations for the monitoring systems were near 1 percent. It is not likely that the NO$_x$ concentration in the stack gas changed much during the 15 min period. The fact that the eleven measurements were made in a short period of time

TABLE 2—*Accuracy of NO$_x$ monitoring systems using nine measurements.*[a]

	$\dfrac{\bar{d},}{\bar{X}_R}, \%$	$\dfrac{S_D,}{\bar{X}_R}, \%$	$\dfrac{CI_{0.95},}{\bar{X}_R}, \%$	$\dfrac{\|\bar{d}\| + CI_{0.95},}{\bar{X}_R}, \%$	$\bar{X}_R,$ ppm
System A:					
Test 1	−26.1	42.4	32.6	58.7	306.6
Test 2	2.1	46.1	35.4	37.5	194.9
System B:					
Test 1	−15.5	40.6	31.2	46.7	241.9
Test 2	−16.5	55.2	42.4	58.9	230.1
Test 3	21.8	45.8	35.2	57.0	275.4
System C:					
Test 1	−22.6	46.3	35.6	58.2	257.5
Test 2	−29.9	50.7	39.0	68.9	240.9
Test 3	13.1	45.8	35.2	48.3	275.3
System D:					
Test 1	−18.5	45.4	34.9	53.4	275.3

[a] Single measurements by Method 7 were used as a reference rather than the average of three measurements called for in the EPA procedure.

favors the continuous monitoring systems as far as a repeatability evaluation is concerned. If the measurements were made on the same concentration but with some variation in the concentration between measurements, the continuous systems might have shown more variability. A standard deviation of 22 percent in Method 7 suggests a standard deviation of 22 percent/$\sqrt{3}$ or 13 percent for the reference values used in the evaluation of NO_x monitoring systems when averages of three measurements are compared with the monitoring system readings. Judging from the values of S_D in Table 2, one might suspect that the variability in Method 7 is greater than 22 percent. If σ_R were 22 percent, the value of σ_M would have to have been 39 percent in order for σ_D to be 45 percent, as the estimates indicate.

Due to the potential for human error, manual reference methods such as Methods 6 and 7 may contribute more to the variability in the differences found in evaluating the accuracy of monitoring systems than do the systems themselves. Reducing this variability would reduce the uncertainty in the decision to accept or reject a system. The variability in Method 7 may be too large for this method to serve as a reference with reasonable probabilities of accepting "good" systems.

Acknowledgments

The author gratefully acknowledges the suggestions and assistance provided by Gerald Shaughnessy and Alan Berens of the University of Dayton Research Institute concerning the statistical aspects of this study.

Are Reference Methods Absolute?

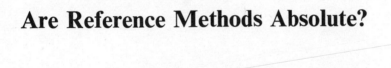

*W. B. DeMore,[1] J. C. Romanovsky,[2] Milton Feldstein,[3]
W. J. Hamming,[4] and P. K. Mueller[5]*

Interagency Comparison of Iodometric Methods for Ozone Determination

REFERENCE: DeMore, W. B., Romanovsky, J. C., Feldstein, Milton, Hamming, W. J., and Mueller, P. K., **"Interagency Comparison of Iodometric Methods for Ozone Determination,"** *Calibration in Air Monitoring, ASTM STP 598,* American Society for Testing and Materials, 1976, pp. 131–143.

ABSTRACT: In 1973 it was learned that measurements of oxidants by the Los Angeles Air Pollution Control District (LAAPCD) were about 30 percent lower than measurements by the California Air Resources Board (ARB) and that the discrepancy was due to differences in the calibration methods of the two agencies. To resolve this problem, the ARB appointed an Oxidant Calibration Committee for the purpose of evaluating the accuracy of the different agency calibration procedures.

The committee selected ultraviolet absorption photometry as the reference method for ozone measurement. Interagency comparisons of the various iodometric methods were conducted relative to the ultraviolet standard. The tests included versions of the iodometric methods as employed by ARB, LAAPCD, and the Environmental Protection Agency (EPA). An alternative candidate reference method for ozone measurement, gas phase titration, was also included in the test series.

Under the conditions of these tests, which were considered to be representative of procedures employed by the California agencies, the ARB method read high by 25 to 30 percent, and the LAAPCD method read low by about 4 percent. The EPA method, which is similar to the ARB method, also read high. The gas phase titration results were about 9 percent higher than the reference ultraviolet standard.

Based on the results of these tests and other considerations, the committee has recommended that future ozone calibration procedures in the State of California be referenced to an ultraviolet standard.

KEY WORDS: calibration, standards, monitors, air pollution, instruments, evaluation

[1] Supervisor, Environmental Chemistry and Physics Group, Jet Propulsion Laboratory, Pasadena, Calif. 91103.

[2] Senior science advisor, Environmental Sciences Research Laboratory, Environmental Protection Agency, Research Triangle Park, N. C., 27711.

[3] Deputy Air Pollution Control Officer, Bay Area Air Pollution Control District, San Francisco, Calif.

[4] Deceased, former Chief Air Pollution Analyst, Los Angeles County Air Pollution Control District, Los Angeles, Calif. 90013.

[5] Technical manager, Environmental Research and Technology, Inc., Westlake Village, Calif. 91360.

Both the California Air Resources Board (ARB) and the Los Angeles Air Pollution Control District (LAAPCD) have used continuous recording oxidant monitors for ozone measurements. However, the instruments were calibrated by slightly different iodometric procedures which were developed independently by each agency.

In 1973, it was learned that the iodometric methods used by the ARB and the APCD for calibration of ozone monitors were not equivalent. To resolve this problem, the ARB appointed an ad hoc Oxidant Measurement Committee and charged it with the responsibility to determine the accuracy of the various agency procedures, to recommend an accurate method for future use by all California agencies, and to provide for continuity of data by relating past methods to future methods.

After studying previous literature reports on the subject of ozone (O_3) analysis, it was determined by the committee that additional interagency comparisons with respect to an acceptable primary standard would be required. A series of tests was conducted at the ARB laboratories in El Monte, California, during the period 21 Oct. to 1 Nov. 1974. Participating agencies were the ARB, APCD, and the Environmental Protection Agency (EPA). Based on the results of the El Monte tests and other considerations, the committee submitted a final report of findings and recommendations to the ARB on 20 Feb. 1975 [1].[6]

The present paper is concerned with the question of the absolute accuracy of the agency calibration methods, based primarily on the results of the El Monte tests. Additional information and considerations used by the Oxidant Committee in evaluating the iodometric procedures can be found elsewhere [1].

Method

Absolute Calibration of the Ozone Stream

In order to define the absolute (correct) concentration of ozone against which to evaluate the various methods, a primary standard was required. The primary standard used in this work was ultraviolet (UV) absorption photometry. According to the photometric method, the O_3 concentration, c, is given by the equation

$$c(\text{ppm}) = \frac{10^6 T}{273 PKl} \log I_o/I_t$$

where

T = temperature, K;
P = total pressure, atm;

---

[6] The italic numbers in brackets refer to the list of references appended to this paper.

k = extinction coefficient of ozone, base 10, units cm^{-1} atm^{-1} standard temperature and pressure (STP);

l = path length, cm;

I_o = incident intensity;

I_t = transmitted intensity; and

ppm = parts per million.

The extinction coefficient used in this work, 135 cm^{-1} atm^{-1} at 2537 Å, is in agreement with results from the independent studies of Inn and Tanaka [2], Hearn [3], DeMore and Raper [4], Griggs [5], and most recently Becker, Schurath, and Seitz [6].

A one-meter photometric cell at the Jet Propulsion Laboratory (JPL) served as a primary photometric standard. As described next, this standard was certified by comparison with similar apparatus at the National Environmental Research Center, Las Vegas (NERC/LV).

For purposes of portability during the actual tests, an O_3 meter (Dasibi Model 1003-AH), which also is based on absorption photometry, was used as a secondary standard. The principle of operation of the Dasibi (DAS) instrument has been described by Behl [7] and by Bowman and Horak [8]. Evaluation of the instrument has been described by DeVera, Jeung, and Imada [9].

The ozone concentration as measured by the DAS O_3 meter is in principle given by the equation

$$c(\text{ppm}) = \frac{22.4T}{kP} \ln \frac{S}{S - R}$$

where

T = temperature, K;

S = span setting of instrument;

R = instrument reading;

k = extinction coefficient of ozone, base 10, units cm^{-1} atm^{-1} (STP); and

P = pressure, atm.

At low O_3 concentrations (R small compared to S), the foregoing expression can be simplified as follows

$$c(\text{ppm}) = \frac{22.4T}{kP} \times \frac{R}{S}$$

The quantity $22.4T/kP$ is the theoretical absolute span setting of the instrument. For the condition $S = 22.4T/kP$, the readout R should equal the true O_3 concentration, $c(\text{ppm})$. In practice, calibration against the primary laboratory photometer is required for maximum accuracy. For this purpose, the DAS instruments were first adjusted to the theoretical span setting for the ambient conditions of temperature and pressure. The temperature was taken as the measured temperature of the exit gas from the instrument.

The readings were then compared with measurements from the JPL one-meter photometric cell taken from a common stream of ozonized air. The air was ambient room air which was passed through a charcoal filter but not dried.

The data, Table 1, were taken on three separate days. The data are plotted in Fig. 1. The linear regression equation is

$$(O_3)\text{abs UV} = 1.054(O_3)\text{DAS} + 0.028$$

Thus, for test ozone concentrations measured by this instrument, the corresponding absolute O_3 concentrations as measured by the laboratory photometer could be obtained from the foregoing expression.

To corroborate the JPL calibration and to verify portability of the instrument calibration, the same O_3 meter was transported to the NERC/LV. Through the generous cooperation of that agency, the in-

TABLE 1—*DAS calibration data: comparison of DAS with JPL photometer.*

DAS Reading, ppm	Photometer Reading, ppm
12 Oct. 1974	
0.434	0.485
0.435	0.485
0.843	0.899
0.844	0.895
0.845	0.941
0.850	0.913
0.850	0.900
0.848	0.908
0.841	0.908
20 Oct. 1974	
0.841	0.915
0.835	0.906
0.836	0.940
0.835	0.915
0.256	0.305
0.257	0.294
26 Oct. 1974	
0.221	0.261
0.221	0.256
0.225	0.263
0.223	0.259
0.579	0.649
0.578	0.647
0.849	0.946

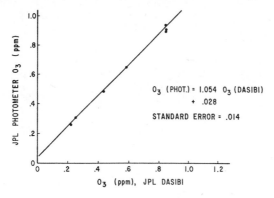

FIG. 1—*DAS calibration data.*

strument was compared there with ozone measurements made by the NERC/LV photometric apparatus. The latter is similar in principle to the JPL equipment but differs somewhat in detail. The results of this comparison are shown in Table 2 and Fig. 2. The excellent agreement obtained supports the basic accuracy of the photometric calibration and serves to demonstrate that the DAS instrument can be transported from one laboratory to another without loss of calibration.

Ozone Measurements by Gas Phase Titration

At the request of the EPA, an alternative candidate procedure for absolute O_3 measurement, called gas phase titration (GPT) [10], was also employed in the El Monte tests. Since this method is considered by the committee to be less well-established than UV photometry, the latter was selected as the preferred primary standard.

Experimental Arrangements in the El Monte Tests

The study protocol is presented in Table 3. O_3 was generated and supplied at various concentrations to a common glass manifold from which the

TABLE 2—*Calibrated JPL DAS compared to NERC/LV photometer (15 Oct. 1974).*

Calibrated DAS (JPL), ppm	Photometer (NERC/LV), ppm
1.175	1.215 ± 0.018
1.010	0.983 ± 0.031
0.848	0.851 ± 0.021
0.695	0.672 ± 0.02
0.691	0.684 ± 0.02
0.530	0.531 ± 0.017
0.374	0.364 ± 0.018
0.222	0.210 ± 0.02

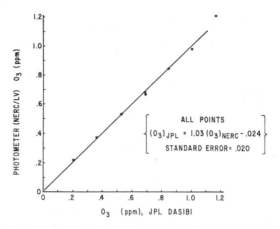

FIG. 2—*Comparison of calibrated DAS (JPL) with NERC/LV photometer.*

three agency teams could sample identical concentrations. Each agency provided experienced personnel to conduct its own standard procedure. Simultaneously with the agency measurements, the O_3 stream was sampled with the DAS O_3 monitor to determine the absolute levels.

During the experiment, purified air (Liquid Carbonic 1-A cylinder) was supplied through a humidifier to a modified calibrator (Monitor Labs 8500) which generated O_3. Humidification was employed because the normal ARB and LAAPCD methods employ air of ambient humidity, and it was considered important to duplicate the normal procedures in every reasonable detail. As later revealed [1], humidity is in fact an important variable in the iodometric method, although not in the UV method. The O_3 stream then entered a glass manifold containing eight sampling ports and an exhaust port. The system is illustrated in Fig. 3. A 3000-ml round-bottom flask was used as the humidifier. The relative humidity used was 40 to 60 percent. All connections between system components were made with Teflon tubing. The manifold contained eight equally spaced sampling ports, each facing in the downstream direction of the flow. Additional tests of air purity which were conducted are described elsewhere [1].

The essential features of the respective agency procedures are summarized next. Detailed descriptions are available [1].

ARB Procedure—The ARB reference procedure for ozone uses a 2 percent neutral buffered potassium iodide (KI) reagent. The air sample to be analyzed is drawn through the reagent in a midget impinger, and O_3 present in the sample air liberates iodine (I_2) from the iodide reagent. The quantity of I_2 liberated is determined using a spectrophotometer which has been calibrated by I_2 reagent standardized with sodium thiosulfate

TABLE 3—*Study protocol matrix.*[a]

Test No.	LAAPCD	ARB	EPA
1	A-10	B-10	C-10
2	A-40	B-40	C-40
3	A-00	B-00	C-00
4	A-60	B-60	C-60
5	A-20	B-20	C-20
6	A-80	B-80	C-80
7	A-40	B-40	C-40
8	A-80	B-80	C-80
9	A-20	B-20	C-20
10	A-00	B-00	C-00
11	A-60	B-60	C-60
12	A-10	B-10	C-10
13	A-00	B-00	C-00
14	A-10	B-10	C-10
15	A-40	B-40	C-40
16	A-60	B-60	C-60
17	A-20	B-20	C-20
18	A-80	B-80	C-80

[a] Protocol Notes:

1. Capital letters designate the agency-operated procedure to be used in the comparison study.

   A = LAAPCD procedure.
   B = ARB procedure.
   C = EPA procedure.

2. Numbers represent the nominal concentrations, in parts per hundred million, of O_3 in air to be simultaneously sampled from a common manifold.

$(Na_2S_2O_3)$ solution which, in turn, has been standardized against primary grade potassium biiodate (KI_2O_3).

EPA Procedure—The EPA reference procedure for O_3 is similar to the ARB procedure except that the EPA procedure uses a 1 percent neutral buffered KI reagent and the I_2 solution is standardized with primary standard grade arsenious oxide.

APCD Procedure—The APCD reference procedure for O_3 uses a 2 percent unbuffered KI reagent. The air sample to be analyzed is drawn through the reagent in an impinger of APCD design, and O_3 present in the sample air liberates I_2 from the iodide reagent. The quantity of I_2 liberated is determined by titrating the reagent with $Na_2S_2O_3$ solution. The $Na_2S_2O_3$ used in the titration is standardized with potassium dichromate $(K_2Cr_2O_7)$ solution. The procedure utilized by the APCD was modified in January 1974 to include the use of dry ice in the standardization of the dilute $Na_2S_2O_3$ in order to improve the precision of the titrations.

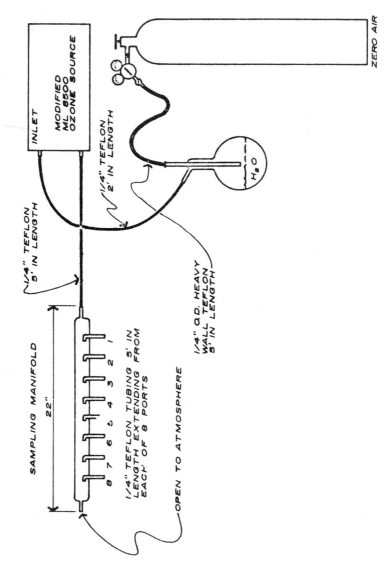

FIG. 3—*Diagram of experimental arrangements for El Monte tests.*

TABLE 4—*Summary of interagency comparisons: O_3 concentrations in parts per million.*

Test No.	UV Monitor	ARB	LAAPCD	EPA
1	0.117	0.147	0.053	0.120
2	0.411	0.510	0.360	0.475
3	0.000	0.001	0.000	0.000
4	0.614	0.761	0.543	0.728
5	0.219	0.276	0.246	0.244
6	0.771	0.962	0.715	0.936
7	0.337	0.433	0.290	0.386
8	0.654	0.862	0.609	0.779
9	0.181	0.230	0.147	0.194
10	0.507	0.634	0.429	0.603
11	0.102	0.127	0.062	0.098
12	0.000	0.002	0.000	0.011
13	0.000	0.002	0.000	0.002
14	0.106	0.138	0.069	0.094
15	0.345	0.459	0.277	0.355
16	0.507	0.650	0.450	0.580
17	0.179	0.217	0.135	0.190
18	0.659	0.898	0.606	0.780

Results

O_3 measurements obtained by the various agency procedures are shown in Table 4, along with the absolute measurements as obtained with the calibrated DAS instrument.

The EPA GPT procedure yielded results which were higher than the DAS measurements. Figure 4 shows a plot of these data. The linear regression equation is

$$(O_3)GPT = 1.09(O_3)abs\ UV - 0.003$$

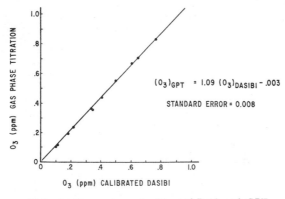

FIG. 4—*Comparison of calibrated DAS with GPT.*

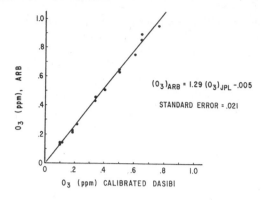

FIG. 5—*Comparison of calibrated DAS with ARB KI results.*

The data obtained by the various agency procedures are plotted in Figs. 5, 6, and 7. The linear regression equations are

$$(O_3)ARB = 1.29(O_3)abs\ UV - 0.005$$

$$(O_3)EPA = 1.24(O_3)abs\ UV - 0.035$$

$$(O_3)APCD = 0.96(O_3)abs\ UV - 0.032$$

Discussion

The principal objective of this study has been to determine the accuracy of O_3 calibration procedures used by the ARB and the LAAPCD. The EPA procedure was included because it is similar to the ARB procedure and provides a useful point of comparison. There was no intention to make a general evaluation of the iodometric method, but rather to compare the actual versions of the methods used by the respective agencies with an

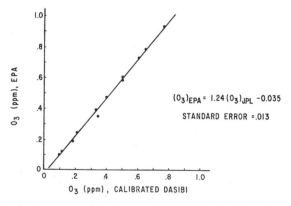

FIG. 6—*Comparison of calibrated DAS (JPL) with EPA KI results.*

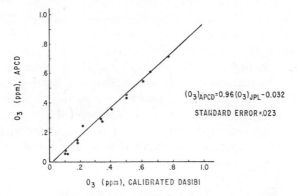

FIG. 7—*Comparison of calibrated DAS with APCD results.*

absolute standard. The procedures were conducted by representatives of the individual agencies, using their own apparatus and chemical reagents.

A major difference between the methods is that the ARB and EPA procedures employ neutral buffered KI solutions, whereas the LAAPCD solutions are unbuffered. The results obtained indicate that under the conditions of this test the neutral buffered versions (ARB and EPA) read about 25 to 30 percent high with respect to the primary standard. This implies that the I_2 released is greater than the stoichiometric amount given by the equation

$$O_3 + 2I^- + H_2O \rightarrow I_2 + O_2 + 20H^-$$

Excess I_2 release in the neutral buffered analysis, relative to UV photometric measurements, has been previously reported [11], as have discordant results between the EPA KI procedure and UV photometry [12].

The unbuffered KI method used by the LAAPCD appears to show approximately 1:1 stoichiometry, at least at relatively high O_3 concentrations. Both the LAAPCD and EPA results showed a negative intercept relative to the UV standard. The reason for this is not known with certainty but may be due to an impurity in the KI solutions which consumes O_3 with no concurrent I_2 release.

The negative intercept caused the LAAPCD calibration method to read low at low O_3 levels. The EPA readings, being intrinsically high, were brought more nearly into agreement with the UV readings at low O_3 levels because of the negative intercept.

It is known that all the iodometric methods are sensitive to relatively minor changes in technique [1,12]. Thus, the foregoing results cannot be expected to hold in a quantitative sense for all applications of iodometric O_3 analysis. For example, the negative intercepts observed in some cases are not necessarily intrinsic properties of those methods. Also, the presence of humidity is now known to be a significant factor [1].

The accuracy of the present evaluation depends on the reliability of the photometric method which was used as the standard of reference. The general principle of absorption photometry is well established, and the specific application to O_3 analysis should be straightforward, provided that the O_3 extinction coefficient is known accurately at the wavelength of analysis, 254 nm. Five separate measurements of this quantity [2–6] have agreed to within better than 2 percent. In three of these measurements [2,5,6] the O_3 concentrations were determined manometrically. In the other two [3,4] the concentration measurement was based on the stoichiometry of O_3 decomposition

$$O_3 \rightarrow 3/2O_2$$

The consistency of results obtained by these two independent methods, each used by more than one investigator, provides compelling evidence that the ozone extinction coefficient is accurately known.

The measurements of Becker et al [6] are particularly significant in connection with the reliability of the extinction coefficient, because the O_3 concentration was in the parts per million range and was about 10^3 times lower than that used in the other measurements. The good agreement obtained tends to indicate that there is no dependence of the extinction coefficient on concentration.

As discussed previously in the Methods section, the actual test measurements of O_3 concentration were made with a secondary standard, the calibrated DAS instrument. The assumption that the secondary standard was correctly calibrated was tested, as previously discussed, by comparison with the NERC/LV photometer (Fig. 2), and later by comparison with an independent photometric apparatus at the Statewide Air Pollution Research Center, University of California, Riverside. In both cases the agreement was excellent. The DAS calibration was also rechecked against the JPL photometer immediately following the El Monte tests. In no case was evidence obtained for loss of calibration upon transportation of the DAS instrument. A number of tests have shown that the DAS readings are not humidity dependent.

As shown in Fig. 4, the GPT results were consistently 9 percent higher than those obtained from the DAS instrument. This discrepancy is greater than the known error of either method, and the source is not known at the present time.

The essential conclusions of this study have been that the neutral buffered version of the KI analysis as used by the ARB reads about 29 percent high compared to the UV photometric determination, and that the unbuffered version as used by the LAAPCD is more nearly correct. None of the methods tested showed good accuracy over the range of O_3 concentrations relevant to air pollution monitoring. For these and other reasons the Committee recommended that oxidant analyzers in California should be calibrated by the UV photometric method rather than the iodometric method. At the May 1975 meeting of the ARB this recommendation was accepted.

Acknowledgments

The authors are grateful for assistance rendered by the following groups and agencies: the Statewide Air Pollution Research Center, University of California, Riverside; the Environmental Protection Agency National Environmental Research Centers at Las Vegas, Nevada, and at Research Triangle Park, North Carolina.

Staff of the Air Resources Board and the Los Angeles County Air Pollution Control District cooperated extensively with the Committee in all of its tests and evaluations. Particular assistance was rendered by Janet Dickinson of the LAAPCD and Jerome Wendt of the ARB.

This paper presents the results of one phase of research carried out at the Jet Propulsion Laboratory, California Institute of Technology, under Contract NAS7-100, sponsored by the National Aeronautics and Space Administration.

References

[1] "Comparison of Oxidant Calibration Procedures," report of the Ad Hoc Oxidant Measurement Committee of the California Air Resources Board, 20 Feb. 1974.
[2] Inn, E. C, Y. and Tanaka, Y., *Journal of the Optical Society of America*, Vol. 43, 1953, p. 870.
[3] Hearn, A. G., *Proceedings*, Physiological Society, London, Vol. 78, 1961, p. 932.
[4] DeMore, W. B. and Raper, O., *Journal of Physical Chemistry*, Vol. 68, 1964, p. 412.
[5] Griggs, M., *Journal of Chemistry and Physics*, Vol. 49, 1968, p. 857.
[6] Becker, K. H., Schurath, U., and Seitz, H., *International Journal of Chemical Kinetics*, Vol. VI, 1974, p. 725.
[7] Behl, B. A., "Absolute Continuous Atmospheric Determination by Differential UV Absorption," paper presented at the 65th Meeting, Air Pollution Control Association, June 1972.
[8] Bowman, L. D. and Horak, R. F., "A Continuous Ultraviolet Absorption Ozone Photometer," AID 724430, Instrument Society of America, 1972, pp. 103–108.
[9] deVera, E. R., Jeung, E., and Imada, M., "Equivalency Determination and Calibration Procedure for a UV Absorption Ozone Monitor," AIHL Report No. 160, California Department of Health, Berkeley, Calif., May 1974.
[10] Hodgeson, J. A., Baumgardner, R. E., Martin, B. E., and Rehme, K. A., *Analytical Chemistry*, Vol. 43, 1971, p. 1123.
[11] Boyd, A. W., Willis, C., and Cyr, R., *Analytical Chemistry*, Vol. 42, 1970, p. 670.
[12] "Summary Report: Workshop on Ozone Measurement by the Potassium Iodide Method," EPA-650/4-75-007, National Environmental Protection Agency, Research Triangle Park, N. C., Feb. 1975.

J. H. Margeson,[1] *R. G. Fuerst,*[1] *P. C. Constant,*[2] *M. C. Sharp,*[2] *and G. W. Scheil*[2]

Evaluation and Collaborative Testing of a Continuous Colorimetric Method for Measurement of Nitrogen Dioxide in Ambient Air

REFERENCE: Margeson, J. H., Fuerst, R. G., Constant, P. C., Sharp, M. C., and Scheil, G. W., "**Evaluation and Collaborative Testing of a Continuous Colorimetric Method for Measurement of Nitrogen Dioxide in Ambient Air,**" *Calibration in Air Monitoring, ASTM STP 598*, American Society for Testing and Materials, 1976, pp. 144–155.

ABSTRACT: A continuous colorimetric method for measurement of nitrogen dioxide (NO_2) in ambient air, which uses Saltzman type absorbing solutions, was evaluated and then subjected to a collaborative test.

The evaluation shows that dynamic calibration is required to obtain reliable results. Static calibration is not reliable. The method write-up specifies dynamic calibration.

The collaborative test was carried out by having ten collaborators sample ambient air and the same ambient air spiked with a reliable source of NO_2 for four days at a common site in Kansas City, Missouri; NO_2 concentrations of 50 to 370 $\mu g/m^3$ were sampled.

The results show that, based on 1-h avg concentrations, the within-laboratory standard deviation is 6 percent of the concentration over the range 90 to 370-μg NO_2/m^3, and the between-laboratory standard deviation is 14 percent of the concentration over the same range. The results also show that the method has a significant positive bias. This bias cannot be accurately quantitated because different collaborators give widely different biases, that is, the bias is collaborator dependent. The "average" bias ranges from +3 to +15 percent of the NO_2 concentration over the just mentioned range.

The lower detectable limit of the method is 19 $\mu g/m^3$.

KEY WORDS: calibration, colorimetric analysis, nitrogen dioxide tests, precision, bias, evaluation, standards

[1] Chief and chemist, respectively, Ambient Air Methods Section, Quality Assurance Branch, Environmental Monitoring and Support Laboratory, Environmental Protection Agency, Research Triangle Park, N. C. 27711.

[2] Head, Environmental Measurement Section, senior statistician, and associate chemist, respectively, Midwest Research Institute, Kansas City, Mo. 64110.

On 14 July 1972, the U.S. Environmental Protection Agency (EPA) withdrew the EPA promulgated [1][3] reference method for measuring atmospheric concentrations of nitrogen dioxide (NO_2) because of demonstrated inadequacies in the procedure [2,3]. After the withdrawal, EPA selected five candidate procedures to replace the original method: a continuous colorimetric (Saltzman) procedure, a continuous chemiluminescence procedure, a manual arsenite procedure, a manual triethanolamine-quaiacol-sulfite procedure, and a manual triethanolamine procedure.

This work describes an evaluation of the continuous colorimetric method to determine its reliability.

The first phase of the work was a laboratory investigation to develop specifications and procedures for the use of the method and the corporation of these results in a detailed method write-up describing the proper use of the method. This method was then subjected to a collaborative test to determine its bias and precision in the hands of a group of typical users.

Experimental Procedure

Laboratory Evaluation

Two air monitors (Technicon IV)[4] were used. The plumbing (air and solution flow rates) of one was modified to allow use of the Saltzman absorbing solution. The other instrument was not modified and was used with the Lyshkow absorbing solution, for which the Technicon IV was designed. The Saltzman absorbing solution contains 0.5 percent sulfanilic acid, 5.0 percent acetic acid, and 0.005 percent N-(1-Naphthyl)-ethylenediamine dihydrochloride (NEDA). The Lyshkow absorbing solution contains 0.15 percent sulfanilamide, 1.5 percent tartaric acid, 0.005 percent NEDA, and 0.005 percent 2-naphthol-3,6-disulfonic acid disodium salt.

The operating procedures recommended by the manufacturer were followed in using the instruments.

Dynamic instrument calibration was accomplished using atmospheres generated from a National Bureau of Standards (NBS) permeation device (prototype of Standard Reference Material 1629) and known amounts of clean dilution air. Static calibration was carried out using sodium nitrite ($NaNO_2$) solutions and a stoichiometric factor of 0.72-mol NO_2^-/mol NO_2 [4].

Collaborative Test

This was carried out at a common site in rural Kansas City, Missouri, using the sampling system shown in Fig. 1. Incoming ambient air was split into a spiked and unspiked line with a sampling manifold at the end of

---

[3] The italic numbers in brackets refer to the list of references appended to this paper.

[4] Mention of commercial trade names does not imply endorsement by the Environmental Protection Agency.

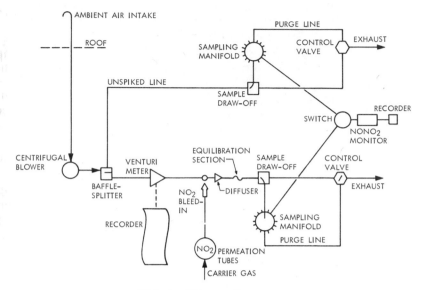

FIG. 1—*NO₂ sampling system.*

each line. The spike was generated by adding known amounts of NO_2 at a constant rate over a 24-h period from permeation devices (same as just mentioned) maintained at 25.1 ± 0.1°C. Since the spike concentration of NO_2 was used as the standard against which bias was determined, its integrity had to be established. Teflon parts were used downstream from the injection of the spike, to minimize loss of NO_2 to the walls, and a high-constant flow rate, 60 litre/min of ambient air, was maintained through the spiked line. The high flow rate and consequent short NO_2 residence time minimizes loss of NO_2 by reaction with water vapor and allows an ample excess of sample over that being taken by the collaborators.

The integrity of the spike was checked before and during the test by monitoring the NO_2 concentration in the spiked and unspiked manifold with a NO_2 chemiluminescent monitor (Bendix), as shown in Fig. 1. The difference in NO_2 concentration between the spiked and unspiked manifolds was within 5 $\mu g/m^3$ (limit of instrument sensitivity) of that predicted by the gravimetric permeation rate and the air volume. Therefore, the latter data were used to determine the spike values.

Additional details on the laboratory evaluation [5] and the collaborative test [6] can be found in the referenced reports.

Discussion

Laboratory Evaluation

Continuous colorimetric methods for measuring NO_2 are based on absorption of NO_2 from the air into an acid solution containing a diazonium salt precursor and a coupling agent. A dye is produced, and the color intensity, which is directly proportional to the NO_2 concentration, is measured in a colorimeter. The resulting electrical signal is then transmitted to a recorder where the concentration is determined from the recorder chart and the calibration curve.

Users of continuous colorimetric methodology for NO_2 measurements indicate that both the modified Saltzman [7] and Lyshkow [8,9] absorbing solutions are being used. Accordingly, both were included in this evaluation.

Because it would have been prohibitive from a time-cost standpoint to evaluate all of the available continuous colorimetric instruments with the two absorbing solutions, we used one rather popular instrument, the Technicon IV. An accurate calibration of any method is, of course, extremely important. Dynamic procedures are preferred generally over static ones, because the former simulates actual use conditions, whereas, the latter does not. Both procedures are in use, however, with continuous colorimetric methods for NO_2. Because Technicon recommends static calibration [10], it was decided to compare static calibration with an accurate dynamic procedure as a reference.

A reliable NO_2 permeation device was used as the basis for dynamic calibration, against which the results of the static calibration were compared. The experiments involved calibrating an instrument by both dynamic and static procedures, as described in the experimental procedure. Both modified Saltzman and Lyshkow absorbing solutions were used. The millivolt response was plotted against NO_2 concentration for the dynamic and static procedures, and the data were fitted to a straight line by the method of least squares. A typical result is shown in Fig. 2 for the Lyshkow absorbing solution.

The results show that, with both absorbing solutions, the slopes of the static calibration curves were significantly different from those obtained by dynamic calibration. The dynamic slope in Fig. 2 is 15 percent less than the static slope. A repeat of this experiment using a different Technicon IV instrument showed a slope difference of twice the first value (-31 percent).

In the experiments with the modified Saltzman absorbing solution, where yet another Technicon IV instrument was used, the dynamic slope was 17 percent greater than the static slope. Thus, the foregoing relationship of the slopes has been reversed.

All of these results suggest that differences in dynamic and static calibrations can depend on individual instrument design. Accordingly, dynamic calibration using a reliable NO_2 source was specified as the calibration procedure in the method write-up.

No laboratory experiments were carried out to determine chemical interferences in this method, because considerable work had already been done. The main interferent is ozone (O_3). Baumgardner et al [11] quantitated the O_3 interference and found it to depend on the O_3/NO_2 ratio.

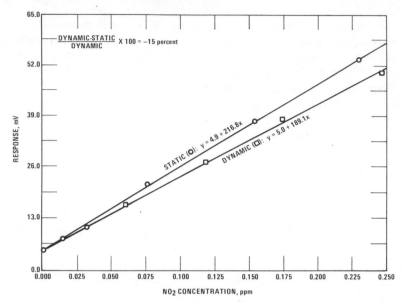

FIG. 2—*Comparison of dynamic and static calibration using Lyshkow absorbing solution.*

The method write-up developed as a result of this work was then subjected to a collaborative test.

Collaborative Test

Collaborative testing has long been recognized as an effective way of determining the statistical limits of error inherent in an analytical method [*12*]. To provide useful information on the performance of a method, an adequate number of test participants who are representative of the average user community using the method, should be selected. Ten volunteer collaborators from nine[5] organizations were selected to participate in the test. The selection was based primarily on past experience in use of the method, ability to furnish equipment necessary to perform the test in accordance with the method, and type of organization. Nine of the collaborators selected were from state and local organizations, and one was from an industrial laboratory. The collaborators and their affiliations are listed in the Acknowledgment section; they are referred to subsequently as collaborators A through J to maintain anonymity.

The test involved sampling ambient air and the same air spiked with NO_2 for four days at the common site. Spikes of approximately 50, 100, 200, and 300-μg NO_2/m^3 were added (one level per day) over a 24-h period

---

[5] One organization provided two collaborators, each of whom had his own equipment and worked independently of the other.

to obtain typical ambient NO_2 concentrations. The ambient NO_2 concentration varied from 10 to 50 $\mu g/m^3$ over a 24-h period. Although these values were somewhat low, compared to typical ambient NO_2 levels, the concentration did exhibit the normal variability typical of ambient conditions. Thus, the collaborators were sampling an atmosphere that contained a known recoverable amount of NO_2, and the concentration was changing with time.

The collaborators were provided with a copy of the method and instructed to follow it in detail.

All collaborators made a dynamic calibration and established a static span point at their home laboratories prior to the test for reference at the site. They used a static calibration check during the test period. Each collaborator also supplied his own chemicals and prepared his own absorbing solution. Each collaborator recorded all pertinent sampling data on his recorder chart. The calculations of the NO_2 levels from the recorder chart readings were made after returning to their home laboratories.

These procedures were used to minimize biasing the results.

Experimental Design

It was desired to determine estimates of both precision and bias of the method. Precision was determined by having all ten collaborators monitor the spiked line at each level. Bias was determined at each level, over a shorter time period, by having half the collaborators monitor the spiked line and the other half the ambient line. All data were reported as 1-h avg concentrations.

Since some spiked readings were being taken throughout the test, but ambient readings were only sometimes obtained, there were two experimental designs used.

One statistical model applies to all the spiked readings but does not incorporate any ambient observations. In this analysis, then, all ten collaborators are used to estimate precisions.

This analysis of variance model is

$$X_{ijkl} = \mu C_i + t_j + L_k + e_{l(ijk)} \tag{1}$$

where

μ = overall mean,
C_i = i^{th} collaborator, $i = 1, \ldots, 10$,
t_j = j^{th} hour, $j = 1, \ldots, 20$,
L_k = K^{th} NO_2 level, $K = 1, \ldots, 4$,
$e_{l(ijk)}$ = measurement error in l^{th} reading in ijk^{th} cell, and
$l = 1$ for every ijk.

Since the NO_2 level may change from hour to hour, there are no replicates in this framework ($l = 1$ always). Also, some cells are missing altogether (because a collaborator was sometimes on the ambient line and did not get a spiked reading). Each collaborator measured the spiked line only (a maximum of) 17 out of the 20 experimental hours. So all effects have to be adjusted for this sample imbalance.

Therefore, a general analysis of variance was performed. Four such analyses were performed (one per level), because it turned out that the precision of the method depended on the NO_2 level.

The second experimental design model describes the data set of 6 h/run, when both ambient and spiked readings were taken. Since the hourly variation in ambient NO_2 is significant, a "true" value was constructed for each of the 6 h (per level). That is, for each hour, the true value was estimated as the spiked NO_2 amount plus the average ambient reading in that hour. An individual response is a bias; that is, the collaborator's reading on the spiked line minus the true value. Thus, the data framework becomes three responses per collaborator per level. Thus, the bias estimates are based on five collaborators on the spiked line and the other five collaborators on ambient. Since these groups of five may be separated in their means, a potential error is introduced into the bias determination. The effect of this bias was minimized by having the collaborators switch to the ambient or spiked line after 3 h.

The experimental design model for this data set is

$$X_{ijk} = \mu + C_i + L_j + CL_{ij} + e_{k(ij)} \tag{2}$$

where

μ = overall mean,
C_i = ith collaborator, $i = 1, \ldots, 9$[6]
L_j = jth NO_2 level, $i = 1, \ldots, 4$,
CL_{ij} = collaborator-level interaction,
$e_{k(ij)}$ = kth measurement error in ijth cell, $k = 1, \ldots, 3$ for every ij, and
X_{ijk} = ijkth bias (collaborator reading-true value).

Collaborators' Data

Table 1 shows one of the four data sets obtained in the test. Run A gives the data obtained when all ten collaborators were sampling the spiked line. Runs B and C give the data when the collaborators were divided between the spiked and ambient lines. These four data sets were analyzed statistically to determine precision and bias.

Precision

The analysis of variance on the spiked values was carried out at each level because the variances within a collaborator were not homogeneous

---

[6] Collaborator G is not included since he produced less than one half the designed set of observations.

TABLE 1—Collaborators data; spike value 102 µg/m³.

Run	Date	Time	A	B	C	D	E	F	Gᵃ	H	I	J
							Collaborator					
A	29-7-74	1800 to 1900ᵇ	113ᵇ	...	...	119	128	132	201	184	116	115
	29-7-74	1900 to 2000	116	...	175	123	133	132	154	184	120	124
	29-7-74	2000 to 2100	133	...	186	152	152	141	160	196	133	139
	29-7-74	2100 to 2200	178	197	235	200	195	188	220	230	169	143
	29-7-74	2200 to 2300	184	205	237	206	199	197	226	247	177	147
	29-7-74	2300 to 2400	188	210	250	207	203	207	226	256	178	152
	30-7-74	2400 to 0100	190	212	259	214	210	207	226	266	184	158
	30-7-74	0100 to 0200	178	197	250	206	197	197	192	259	175	143
	30-7-74	0200 to 0300	160	178	231	196	178	188	154	240	156	...
	30-7-74	0300 to 0400	154	173	220	188	167	169	135	237	147	...
	30-7-74	0400 to 0500	148	169	212	186	164	169	122	240	143	...
	30-7-74	0500 to 0600	137	160	194	176	158	160	98	230	135	...
	30-7-74	0600 to 0700	162	182	218	202	175	179	109	249	150	...
	30-7-74	0700 to 0800	128	178	216	190	169	179	84	254	143	...
B	30-7-74	0930 to 1000ᵇ	2ᶜ	...	...	20ᵈ	...	...	150	116	122	141
	30-7-74	1000 to 1100	0ᶜ	9ᵈ	26ᵈ	10ᵈ	...	132	141	97	118	137
	30-7-74	1100 to 1200	0ᶜ	9ᵈ	15ᵈ	5ᵈ	...	132	141	94	113	132
	30-7-74	1200 to 1300	0ᶜ	9ᵈ	13ᵈ	5ᵈ	4ᵈ	122	132	97	111	135
C	30-7-74	1300 to 1400	109	132	...	102	122	9ᵈ	47ᵈ	14ᵈ	11ᵈ	4ᵈ
	30-7-74	1400 to 1500	126	165	158	108	132	19ᵈ	141ᵈ	19ᵈ	17ᵈ	21ᵈ
	30-7-74	1500 to 1600	113	132	154	101	122	9ᵈ	66ᵈ	2ᵈ	11ᵈ	8ᵈ
	30-7-74	1600 to 1630ᵇ	113	132	154	99	120	9ᵈ	9ᵈ	2ᵈ	11ᵈ	8ᵈ

ᵃ Data from Collaborator G is an outlier.
ᵇ Indicates reading is for ≤ ½ h.
ᶜ,ᵈ From unspiked samples—all other results are spiked samples.

over the four levels. An F-test was performed to determine the significance of the time and collaborator variances. The F-values for time and collaborators were significant at all four NO_2 levels. This means that the NO_2 concentration varied significantly with time, which is to be expected since ambient air is involved in the measurements, and that different collaborators have significantly different average NO_2 concentrations at all four levels. A detailed statistical analysis of the four data sets [6] shows that a significant collaborator-level interaction exists.

The individual components of variance are shown in Table 2, at all four levels, along with the within- and between-laboratory relative standard deviations. The levels are the average of the collaborators' values, which is an approximation to the exact NO_2 concentration existing in the spiked line. The standard deviation within a collaborator (laboratory) is given by σ_e, and the standard deviation between laboratories is given by $\sqrt{\sigma_e^2 + \sigma_c^2}$. The values in Table 2 show that the between-laboratory relative standard deviation is higher than the within-laboratory relative standard deviation, as expected. Both values are essentially constant at three of the four levels. The within-laboratory values range from 5 to 11 percent (avg 6 percent), and the between-laboratory values range from 11 to 18 percent (avg 14 percent).

Bias

The biases from the four data sets were subjected to an analysis of variance using the model just given, and an F-test was performed on the variances. All of the F-values were significant. Therefore, the bias does differ between collaborators, and does depend on the NO_2 level, and there is a significant collaborator-level interaction. Table 3 gives the four average true NO_2 levels for the different 6-h test periods, along with the individual collaborators' average bias at the different levels.

The significance of the collaborator-level interaction can be seen best in Fig. 3, where the percent bias is plotted against the true NO_2 level for nine collaborators (collaborator G omitted as an outlier). Collaborator curves

TABLE 2—*Components of variance, spiked readings,* $\mu g/m^3$.

	Level			
Source	90	154	212	371
σ_e	5.7	17.0	9.5	18.0
σ_e, %	6.3	11.0	4.5	4.8
σ_c	7.8	21.2	27.0	48.0
$\sqrt{\sigma_e^2 + \sigma_c^2}$	9.6	27.2	28.6	51.2
$\sqrt{\sigma_e^2 + \sigma_c^2}$, %	10.7	17.7	13.5	13.8

TABLE 3—*Collaborator (average biases ($\mu g/m^3$) versus level.*

Collaborator	Average True Level			
	(112)	(302)	(198)	(60)
D	−12	−5	1	1
A	3	−10	−8	−3
C	37	84	36	27
F	13	10	0	2
B	27	−1	−21	−2
J	22	76	43	11
H	−17	−2	5	−7
I	2	244	2	3
E	9	−2	1	3
Average	9(8%)	44(15%)	7(3%)	4(6%)
Overall average: +10%				

are, in general, significantly nonparallel. This means that the bias is collaborator dependent.

On the average (Table 3), the bias is greatest, +15 percent, at the highest NO_2 level, 300 $\mu g/m^3$, and least, +3 percent, at 200 $\mu g/m^3$. The overall average bias is +10 percent. These average results are not sufficiently descriptive of the bias situation, however. Only four of the collaborators (D, A, F, and E) exhibited fairly consistent biases over the four levels; the remaining five collaborators show variations of from 10 to 30 percent, with one variation of 80 percent.

Lower Detectable Limit

The lower detectable limit (LDL) was estimated in two ways, from the collaborators ambient readings and from their calibration curve data [6]. The two values were 15 and 19 $\mu g/m^3$. Thus, the smallest NO_2 concentration that can be detected as significantly different from zero, when comparing results from different laboratories, is approximately 19 $\mu g/m^3$ (0.01 ppm).

Conclusions

The continuous colorimetric method, when used with dynamic calibration, exhibits relatively stable and not excessively large precision errors over the range 90 to 370-μg NO_2/m^3. However, the bias is not stable over a similar range of NO_2 concentrations and cannot be accurately quantitated.

The method has an acceptable LDL for ambient monitoring. However, until the source of bias is identified, and either removed from the method

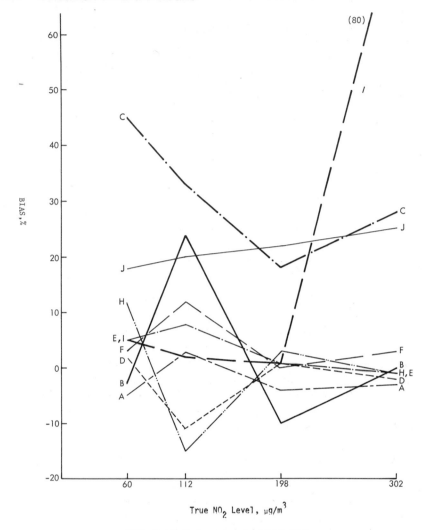

FIG. 3—*Collaborator-level interaction.*

or accurately quantitated, data obtained with this method may be significantly erroneous.

Acknowledgment

The authors wish to acknowledge the assistance and cooperation of the participating laboratories, and express sincere appreciation for the voluntary efforts of the staff members who represented each organization. The representatives and organizations participating in the test are:

Michigan Department of
   Natural Resources
Lansing, Michigan 48926
(Ken Smith)

Kennecott Copper Corporation
Salt Lake City, Utah 84111
(Lynn Hutchinson)

Air Pollution Control District of
   Jefferson County
Louisville, Kentucky 40208
(Harold Davis)
(Cole McKinney)

Kansas City Air Pollution
   Control Laboratory
Kansas City, Missouri 64116
(Glenn Smith)

Air Pollution Control District
County of Los Angeles
Los Angeles, California 90013
(John Higuchi)

New Jersey Department of
   Environmental Protection
Division of Environmental Quality
Trenton, New Jersey 08625
(Norman J. Lewis)

Nassau County Department of Health
Hemstead, New York 11550
(Cleveland Dodge)

State of Utah
Department of Social Services
Salt Lake City, Utah 84113
(Rolf E. Doebbeling)

Wayne County Department of Health
Air Pollution Control Division
Detroit, Michigan 48207
(Larry Saad)

References

[1] Federal Register, No. 36, 25 Nov. 1971, pp. 22396–22397.
[2] Hauser, T. R. and Shy, C. M., Environmental Science and Technology, Vol. 6, 1972, pp. 890–894.
[3] Merryman, E. L. et al, Environmental Science and Technology, Vol. 7, 1973, pp. 1056–1059.
[4] Saltzman, B. E., Analytical Chemistry, Vol. 26, 1954, pp. 1949–1955.
[5] Margeson, J. H. and Fuerst, R. G., Report No. 650/4-75-022, Environmental Protection Agency, Research Triangle Park, N. C., April 1975.
[6] Constant, P. C., Jr., Sharp, M. C., and Scheil, G. W., Report No. 650/4-75-011, Environmental Protection Agency, Research Triangle Park, N. C., Feb. 1975.
[7] Saltzman, B. E., Analytical Chemistry, Vol. 32, 1960, pp. 135–136.
[8] Lyshkow, N. A., Journal of the Air Pollution Control Association, Vol. 15, 1965, pp. 481–484.
[9] U.S. Patent 3,375,079.
[10] Technicon Auto Analyzer Methodology Air Monitor IV, Industrial Method #136-71AP, preliminary data released Dec. 1972.
[11] Baumgardner, R. E., Clark, T. A., Hodgeson, J. A., and Stevens, R. K., Analytical Chemistry, Vol. 47, 1975, pp. 515–521.
[12] Manual for Conducting an Interlaboratory Study of a Test Method, ASTM STP 335, American Society for Testing and Materials, 1963.

J. K. Taylor[1]

Evaluation of Data Obtained by Reference Methods

REFERENCE: Taylor, J. K., **"Evaluation of Data Obtained by Reference Methods,"** *Calibration in Air Monitoring, ASTM STP 598*, American Society for Testing and Materials, 1976, pp. 156–163.

ABSTRACT: The key role of reference methods for measurement of air pollutants in regulatory matters demands that the data obtained in their use be precise and accurate, but no procedures have been established for evaluating its reliability and validity for the intended use. This paper discusses the general principles of reliable analytical measurements and presents guidelines by which the quality of data obtained by reference methods or other procedures may be evaluated.

KEY WORDS: air pollution, standards, quality control, calibration, intercalibration, evaluation

Reference methods for air pollution measurement are assuming a role of increasing importance. Not only are they specified for use in questions of compliance with air quality and emissions standards but also for the evaluation of the measurements made by other methods for establishing equivalency of methodology [1].[2] Accordingly, reference method data should meet high standards for accuracy, and procedures need to be established to assure their reliability and validity. This paper discusses the general principles of reliable measurement and presents guidelines by which analytical data obtained by reference methods or other measurement procedures can be evaluated.

Nomenclature

The hierarchy of analytical measurement nomenclature is given in Table 1, together with examples and the way in which each type is validated. The analytical usefulness of techniques, based on general scientific principles, is established by the research of many scientists. Methods,

---

[1] Chief, Air and Water Pollution Analysis Section, Analytical Chemistry Division, National Bureau of Standards, Washington, D. C. 20234.

[2] The italic numbers in brackets refer to the list of references appended to this paper.

TABLE 1—*Analytical nomenclature.*

Name	Example	Validation
Technique	spectrophotometry	scientific community
Method	pararosaniline	individual research
Procedure	ASTM D 2914-70T	collaborative testing
Application	concentration of SO_2	SRM

involving steps required to apply the technique to a specific measurement problem are developed by individual research. A procedure or protocol consists of detailed instructions for use of a method. It may result from the research of an individual or by group action such as the consensus of a committee, for example. The adequacy of the written word is all important in this situation, and this is best validated by collaborative testing [2].

Analytical methods may be classified as indicated in Table 2, according to the *type* of information furnished, the operational *mode* of the measurement, and the *purpose* of the data. The information may be interpreted on the basis of fundamental principles and hence should be independent of the method by which it is obtained; or it may be empirical and hence of practical use in limited situations. Methods of the latter type are ordinarily closely dependent on detailed procedures; hence, standardization is a prerequisite for concordant data. Absolute methods are generally considered to be those in which the constituent of interest is isolated from the sample and measured with reference to a physical standard. Gravimetry, classical Orsat gas analysis, and coulometry are examples. The reliability of such methods depends upon that of the physical calibrations, the precision and accuracy of the physical measurements, and the efficiency of separation of the constituent of interest. Comparative methods depend on comparison of the sample with a chemical (compositional) standard using an appropriate sensor, with or without the prior separation of the constituent of interest. Their reliability is critically dependent on the quality of the reference

TABLE 2—*Classification of analytical methods.*

Type:
Fundamental
Empirical

Mode:
Absolute
Comparative

Purpose:
Reference
Routine
Special

standards, but less sensitive to physical calibrations and separation efficiency, provided the reference sample and the unknown are comparable and measured under similar conditions [3].

The end use of the data is a method-defining characteristic. Reference methods are those used to obtain reference data on specific substances, to establish the composition of reference materials, or to provide referee data for regulatory purposes. Routine methods are used to provide data for the basic regular or customary courses of action and may or may not require dependability equal to or greater than reference methods. Special purpose methods may be used as occasion demands, in research situations, for example. In each case, the end use ordinarily defines the requisite maximum tolerances of precision and accuracy. Standard methods, more properly called standard procedures, may be any of the previously mentioned that obtain the endorsement of a standards-making body which has the responsibility to specify the qualifications under which it is endorsed.

Chemical Measurement Process

Compositional measurements are ordinarily made to answer such specific questions as the following: "Does the material meet a given specification?," or "Is a given substance present at toxic levels?," or "Has an air quality violation occurred?" Analytical data must be of sufficient accuracy to provide a basis for decision. The importance of minimization of error (or uncertainty) is illustrated by Fig. 1. When the result is plotted with respect to the possible error, the area of indecision is emphasized. In the case of a product just meeting a specification, half of the tests made will rate it as unsatisfactory [4]. On the other hand, the larger the uncertainty in measurement, the greater the excess quality necessary to assure acceptance, as indicated by the dotted triangle in the figure. Similarly, only gross violations of air quality can be attested to when large measurement uncertainties exist.

The validity of analytical measurements (including an assignment of uncertainty) can only be estimated when made by a reliable measurement system. The elements of such a system are illustrated in Fig. 2. In principle, the variances of each element are additive, and, when significantly different, the result will be influenced most by that of major magnitude.

Obviously, the sample is of major concern and must have adequate homogeneity, stability, and a well-defined relation to the population from which it is derived. The method used for measurement must have adequate sensitivity, selectivity, and reproducibility. All required calibrations need to be made with requisite reliability and frequency. The frequency requirements will vary, depending on the expertise of the laboratory and the precision requirement of the given situation. Quality control measures to assure that stability of the system need to be established for each step in the

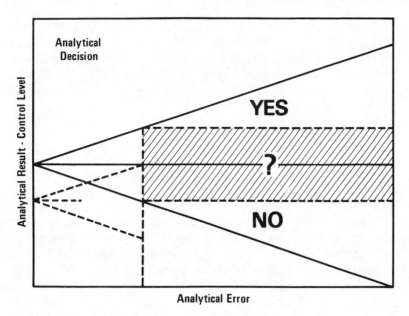

FIG. 1—*Consequences of analytical error.*

measuring process and for the overall process as well. All of the above activities are the responsibility of the measurement laboratory, and, when quantitatively established, serve not only to minimize effort, but also permit it to state its confidence in a given measurement and its relation to any similar measurement on a time basis, which is the minimum requirement for consideration of the data. If only internal actions are concerned, measurements so made may be of requisite reliability for decisions.

When measurements are made for external action, a further requirement is that of interrelatability to other measurement systems. This can be best

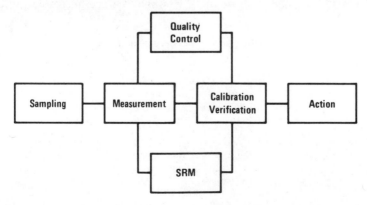

FIG. 2—*Chemical measurement process.*

accomplished by the use of readily available reference standards, such as the National Bureau of Standards (NBS) standard reference materials (SRM) [5]. The experience gained by measurement of such materials can verify freedom from systematic error (or bias) or indicate whether corrective measures need to be taken to ensure compatibility of data with that of other measurement systems.

Minimization of Analytical Error

Analytical errors result principally from intrinsic errors in methodology, ambiguous or poorly defined procedures, faulty or improper usage (often ascribable to inadequately trained measurement personnel), and deficiencies in calibration. The intrinsic errors in a given method must be relatively insignificant, or the method should be abandoned in favor of more reliable ones as they become available. The ruggedness test suggested by Youden [6] is helpful in identifying the pitfalls of a candidate method. While these are identified best by an individual researcher during method development, limited round-robin studies, if properly designed and controlled, are also useful for this purpose. However, the principal objective of a round robin is to evaluate procedures, the detailed instructions for carrying out a specific analytical measurement [7]. It would appear that many round robins lose sight of this and feel that their prime objective is to evaluate the precision and accuracy of a candidate procedure. Outliers are often considered to be problems for rejection rather than providing valuable insight into potential ambiguities of a procedure.

The minimum performance parameters that need specification in a procedure are listed in Table 3. The tolerances for each procedural step need to be stated to provide a given overall precision level. Copious notes and precautions are always in order. Each participant in a round robin should do sufficient preliminary work to gain a full understanding of the procedure and should demonstrate quality control before his results should be

TABLE 3—*Performance parameters.*

Type of sample
Forms determined
Range of applicability
Limit of detection
Biases
Interferences
Special requirements
Calibration limitations
Other limitations
Critical steps and tolerances
Time and skills requirement
Precision

considered. Unless the reasons for all outlying results are fully understood and evaluated for possible procedural corrections, the procedure should not advance to the status of a standard.

The scientists of laboratories using standard methods should recognize that evaluated procedures may be a necessary but not sufficient requirement for good measurements. They must realize that a foolproof procedure does not exist, and that they must thoroughly understand the measurements performed and the sources of variance and their magnitude.

Deficiencies in calibration are becoming a prime source of analytical error, particularly in the case of comparative measurements. Many laboratories do not have the capability to prepare their own calibration standards, such as span gases, for example, and so they must obtain them from others. Accordingly, the data of the laboratory can be markedly influenced by factors beyond its control. It is interesting to note that some recent collaborative studies have proved to be as much of an evaluation of calibration gases as of the method under test [8,9].

Intercalibration

Intercalibration may be defined as the process to validate measurements made by different laboratories (or measurement stations within a laboratory) to assure compatibility of data. The means for effecting intercalibration can be provided best by an unbiased party, and the role of a SRM for this purpose has already been mentioned. Unless its identity can be disguised, the SRM can be used only as a calibrant, since the prior knowledge of its composition prejudices its use for quality control purposes.

For intercalibration of stations in a measurement network, double blind samples are to be preferred when possible. Ideally, the sample should be indistinguishable from the normal work load so that both its composition and its presence in the measurement system are unknown.

Round-robin tests to maintain a periodic test on the performance of a group of laboratories are a valuable means toward quality assurance of analytical data [6].

The use of a single test sample by a laboratory with demonstrated quality control can indicate the reliability of measurement of a sample of that kind and level, within the uncertainty of sample composition. Two samples at the same compositional level can minimize errors due to sample variability but shed little light on the nature of measurement error over the range of interest.

A series of samples (for example, five) spanning the compositional range of interest can provide valuable information on the reliability of measurements and can identify the nature of analytical errors, whether additive or multiplicative, which is essential for instituting corrective measures. The use of several samples also lessens the requirements for sample homogeneity, provided compositional levels are distributed randomly among all the samples of each level.

Youden has described how round robins of this kind can be used to rank the performance of a group of laboratories [6]. However, this is not necessarily the prime objective of such an exercise. The ultimate objective should be to identify measurement problems, and it is clear that the participating laboratories should have demonstrated quality control so that any problems identified are believed to be real and recurring in nature. As round robins are used for diagnostic and corrective purposes, they provide an invaluable service to the improvement of analytical reliability.

Conclusion

Analytical data can never be accepted at face value. It is the responsibility of the measurement laboratory to assign limits of uncertainty to its reported values. This is a minimum requirement for consideration, and, further, it should be prepared to furnish information in support of its claims. The acceptor must establish reasonable criteria for evaluation for acceptance and release to potential users. Procedures such as those described by Brewers et al [10] should be useful to minimize errors of reporting, detect redundancies, detect and validate anomalies, and improve analytical and sampling techniques.

The production of analytical data for environmental, as well as other purposes, is a difficult and important activity that can only be reliably accomplished by laboratories of demonstrated capability, using reliable methodology. Some form of certification of the ability of a laboratory to provide data for regulatory purposes would appear to be inevitable. The criteria for certification would have to be established after careful consideration. In this respect, the words of the late W. J. Youden would appear to be especially applicable. "It is interesting that in other activities, such as passing a college examination, a standard is set that a large majority of the students can meet successfully. No one is disturbed that some fail for lack of application or equipment. In a very real sense, the situation is closely parallel to the performance of the laboratories with a test procedure. Assign a large standard deviation, and all the laboratories get in. But an examination that everybody can pass does not do justice to the course, nor does it reveal its actual merit [11]."

References

[1] Hauser, T. R. and Shearer, S. D., *Environmental Science and Technology*, Vol. 9, 1975, p. 539.
[2] Youden, W. J., *Materials Research and Standards*, Jan. 1963.
[3] Taylor, J. K., *Analytical Chemistry*, Vol. 19, 1947, p. 368.
[4] Youden, W. J., *Industrial Quality Control*, Vol. XV, No. 11, May 1959.

[5] Cali, J. P., et al, "NBS Monograph 148," National Bureau of Standards, Jan. 1975.
[6] Youden, W. J., "Standard Techniques for Collaborative Tests," The Association of Official Analytical Chemistry, Washington, D.C., 1967.
[7] Youden, W. J., *Journal of the Association of Official Agricultural Chemists*, Vol. 46, 1963, pp. 55–62.
[8] McKee, H. C. and Childers, R. E., "Collaborative Study of Reference Method for the Continuous Measurement of Carbon Monoxide in the Atmosphere (Non-Dispersive Infrared Spectrometry)," PB 211–265, Office of Measurement Standardization, Environmental Protection Agency.
[9] Constant, P. C., Jr., Scheil, G., and Sharp, M. C., "Collaborative Study of Method 10–Reference Method for Determination of Carbon Monoxide Emissions from Stationary Sources–Report of Testing," EPA-650/4-75-001, Environmental Protection Agency, 1975.
[10] Brewers, J. M., Macaulay, I. D. Sundby, B., and Buckley, D. E. in *Water Quality Parameters*, *ASTM STP 573*, American Society for Testing and Materials, 1975, pp. 550–565.
[11] Youden, W. J., *Materials Research and Standards*, Nov. 1961.

R. N. Dietz[1] *and J. D. Smith*[1]

Calibration of Permeation and Diffusion Devices by an Absolute Pressure Method

REFERENCE: Dietz, R. N. and Smith, J. D., **"Calibration of Permeation and Diffusion Devices by an Absolute Pressure Method,"** *Calibration in Air Monitoring, ASTM STP 598*, American Society for Testing and Materials, 1976, pp. 164–179.

ABSTRACT: By following the change in absolute pressure above a permeation device, calibration of such sources can be performed in substantially less than one hundredth the time required using conventional gravimetric procedures. The sensitivity of the Brookhaven calibration procedure is achieved by combining high resolution pressure and temperature measuring instruments with newly designed permeation wafer devices giving low total volume when connected to the pressure measuring device. Using Brookhaven low (<20 nl/min at 30°C) and ultra-low (<1 nl/min) calibrated permeation devices, the inaccuracies and expense associated with the use of exponential dilution flasks and large quantities of diluent "zero" gas for providing part-per-billion calibration gases are reduced markedly. In addition, controlled flow rates of noncondensable gases such as carbon monoxide and methane can be provided at microlitre-per-minute rates using Brookhaven porous glass diffusion devices.

KEY WORDS: permeability, diffusion, porous glass, calibration, ratings, devices, volume

Accurate, low-level sources for calibration of monitors for air pollution studies are extremely important. Methods of producing standard sources that are reliable and provide for reproducible results from one laboratory to another are needed if correlation of air pollution measurements from different regions of the country are to be attempted. Two types of sources are in typical use—permeation devices and prepared gas mixture cylinders.

The first such permeation devices, permeation tubes, provide rates which are typically two or more orders of magnitude too high for convenient calibration of air monitors at ambient levels. Lower rate permeation wafer devices are also available, but calibration by standard gravimetric procedures usually requires several months or longer [1].[2] Gas mixtures can be

---

[1] Chemical engineer and technical assistant, respectively, Department of Applied Science, Brookhaven National Laboratory, Upton, N. Y. 11973.

[2] The italic numbers in brackets refer to the list of references appended to this paper.

accurately prepared by careful pressure dilution techniques, but many mixtures change in concentration with time because of adsorption or reaction with the container walls [2]. Once the mixture has been prepared, the concentration cannot be readily determined by an absolute procedure.

This paper describes a method for calibration of low-rate permeation devices based on measuring small pressure changes in an enclosed volume connected to the device. High sensitivity permits precise calibration in one hundredth the time using conventional gravimetric [3,4] and volumetric [5,6] procedures. Calibration of Brookhaven diffusion devices for non-condensable gases such as carbon monoxide (CO) is also demonstrated.

Experimental

Calibration Equipment

The calibration apparatus shown schematically in Fig. 1 had a section for supplying a calibrated flow rate of diluent gas and a section for permeation and diffusion rate determinations. The flow section, which consisted of conventional pressure gages and mass flowmeters, was connected to the permeation calibration section through needle valve, V8. The calibration section consisted primarily of the oven for the device, a four-way switching valve (Whitey No. 43YF52-316), V14, a quartz bourdon tube pressure gage (P5), and a vacuum pump (VPI) and gage (VGI) for maintaining and monitoring the reference side of the quartz gage at less than 0.005 mm Hg.

Pressure was determined with a quartz pressure gage (Texas Instruments Model 141) connected to a digital voltmeter (Electronic Research Company (ERC) Model 3010B) having a resolution of 0.1 mV which corresponded to a pressure resolution of 0.002 mm Hg. Temperature was measured at four

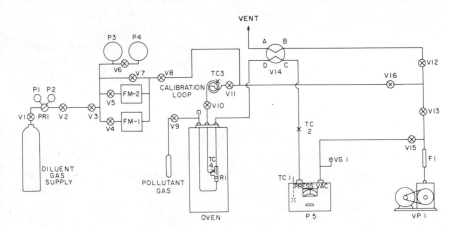

FIG. 1—*Calibration system.*

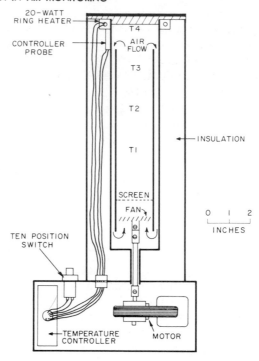

FIG. 2—*Brookhaven concentric tube permeation oven.*

locations—the quartz gage (TC 1), the interconnecting ⅛-in. stainless steel line (TC 2), the calibration loop (TC 3), and the permeation device oven (TC 4)—using silicon semiconductor probes and a digital thermometer (ERC Model 9300C) having a resolution of 0.01°C. Absolute accuracy of the four probes was adjusted to within better than 0.1°C using 50-Ω trim pots.

The pressure, as millivoltage, and four temperatures were sampled periodically and recorded using an ERC digital recording system which included a 24-h clock and a digital printer (Systron-Donner Model 5103B). The print command was initiated automatically at one of eight switch-selectable time intervals of from 1 min to 20 h.

A special oven, shown in Fig. 2, was designed and built at Brookhaven when tests showed that several commercial permeation ovens had very poor vertical temperature profiles—exceeding 0.6°/in. at 30°C and 2.5°/in. at 60°C. The Brookhaven oven had a 20-W ring heater located at the top of the forced air recirculation oven controlled by a power-proportional temperature controller (Model 70, RFL Industries). Temperature was held constant to within ±0.02°C, and the vertical profile was 0.1°/in. at 30°C and 0.2°/in. at 60°C.

To minimize ambient temperature effects, the calibration laboratory was maintained to within ±0.2°C using a power proportional heater in the winter and, in the summer, by an air conditioner controlled by a Lab Monitor (Pope Scientific, Inc.) having a resolution of 0.1°C.

Permeation and Diffusion Devices

Conventional permeation tubes and permeation wafer devices were calibrated in the Brookhaven system by using a 35-cm³ glass vessel in the oven. To increase the resolution of the calibration system, permeation and diffusion devices were designed such that the total volume within the oven would be less than 1 cm³.

The Brookhaven permeation wafer device, fabricated essentially using a ⅛-in. compression tee, is shown in an assembly view in Fig. 3. The ¹⁄₁₆-in. fill tube was welded to the ⅛-in. U-tube, and the ferrules were

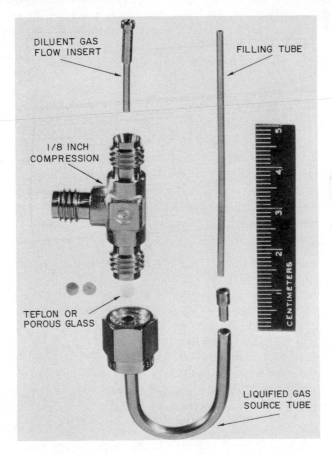

FIG. 3—*Assembly view of Brookhaven permeation wafer device.*

preswaged to the U-tube, using shim spacers, to provide 30 percent compression on the Teflon wafer. After installation of the wafer, which was cut from sheet stock with the sharpened end of a compression fitting, the entire assembly was leak checked with sulfur hexafluoride (SF_6) by electron capture chromatography (sensitivity of 0.001 nl/min at 1 atm differential). The permeate (for example, nitrogen dioxide (NO_2)) was condensed into the U-tube from a stainless steel volumetric filling system, the atmosphere above the condensate was charged to 700 mm Hg nitrogen (N_2), and the $\frac{1}{16}$-in. tube was flattened and electric-discharge welded.

Diffusion devices were made in a similar fashion by using a wafer cut from a rod of porous glass in place of the Teflon piece. The glass (Corning Glass Works, 40 Å average pore diameter) was cut into wafers 10 to 100 mils thick by a precision saw (Macrotome 2). Flat rings of polyvinyl chloride (PVC), cut from $\frac{3}{32}$-in. inside diameter by $\frac{5}{32}$-in. outside diameter Tygon tubing, were used to make a leak tight seal on each side of the glass wafer. The compression for providing the seal was made with a preswaged $\frac{1}{16}$ to $\frac{1}{8}$-in. reducer which provided the inlet connection for the gas to be calibrated (carbon monoxide (CO), methane (CH_4), etc.). For both devices, the diluent gas flow insert provided positive sweeping action of flow across the wafer.

Procedure

Quartz Gage Calibration—The quartz gage had a rated accuracy, traceable to the National Bureau of Standards (NBS), of 0.015 percent of full scale with a repeatability of 1 part in 100 000. For small pressure changes, the photocell output was nearly linearly related to the differential gage readings. With a vacuum on both sides of the quartz bourdon tube, the dial readings were changed manually and the output voltage recorded. A program on a 9100A Hewlett-Packard calculator was used to correlate the calibration curve.

System Volume Determinations—The calibration loop volume (Fig. 1) was predetermined by weighing when filled with water. During permeation rate determinations, the system volume consists of that from valve V10, the device and lines in the oven, the line from the oven—through V14—to the quartz gage P5, and the gage itself. The tubing volume (V_t), external to the oven, was calculated from the dimensions of the tubing. Substituting a union in place of the permeation oven assembly, the gage volume (V_g) was determined by pressure-volume techniques using the known calibration loop volume (V_L). Finally, with the oven chamber assembly reinstalled, the volume of the device in the chamber (V_c) was similarly determined.

Device Calibration—With V14 rotated 90 deg from the position shown in Fig. 1, a low flow of N_2 (~5 cm³/min) from V8, through the device, and out the vent was used while the oven chamber equilibrated at temperature—

about 1 h. At the same time, the quartz gage was evacuated for zeroing and calibration (if necessary) and to remove traces of permeate from previous runs. V14 was returned to the original position, the N_2 pressure in the system was adjusted to 760 mm Hg, V10 was closed, and the permeation or diffusion rate calibration commenced.

Temperatures and pressure readings were recorded at intervals of about every 10 to 20 mV, which corresponded to pressure increments of 0.3 to 0.6 mm Hg. The total volume in the system was computed, with the aid of the programmable calculator, from the individual volumes in the system— tubing, gage, and oven chamber—corrected for pressure and individual temperatures. The program also computed the permeation rate and the 95 percent confidence interval (two standard deviations) by least-mean-square fit of a straight line through the incremental volume increases versus time. For NO_2 permeation devices, appropriate corrections for association to dinitrogen tetroxide (N_2O_4) were made [7].

Results

Calibration System

The quartz gage incremental readings were plotted versus the output voltage as shown in Fig. 4. By empirical means it was found that the slope $\Delta Q/V$, correlated well by

$$\frac{\Delta Q}{V} = d\,\frac{e^{b|V+m|} - 1}{|V + m|} + c$$

where ΔQ was the change in pressure reading, millimetres of mercury, from the starting (null) value (Q^*) and V was the voltage output, millivolts. For the data shown in Fig. 4, the values determined for the constants were: c, 0.01552 ± 0.00003; d, 0.01550 ± 0.00011; b, 0.02246 ± 0.00002; and m, 15.7 ± 0.1. The overall relative standard deviation of the correlation was 1.2 percent.

From the calibration loop volume ($V_L = 1.065$ cm³) and the calculated volume for the tubing ($V_T = 1.252$ cm³), the volume of the gage ($V_g = 0.893$ cm³) and the device ($V_c = 0.625$ cm³) were determined. Since the total calibration system volume was 2.770 cm³, and the temperature and pressure resolutions were 0.01°C and 0.002 mm Hg, respectively, a volume change of as little as 100 nl could be resolved. When diffusion rates exceeded 10 μl/min, the system volume was increased to 80.166 cm³ to keep the rate of pressure increase in reasonable bound.

Permeation Devices

Commercially available low rate permeation devices for sulfur dioxide (SO_2) and hydrogen sulfide (H_2S) (Metronics Associates, Inc.) were cali-

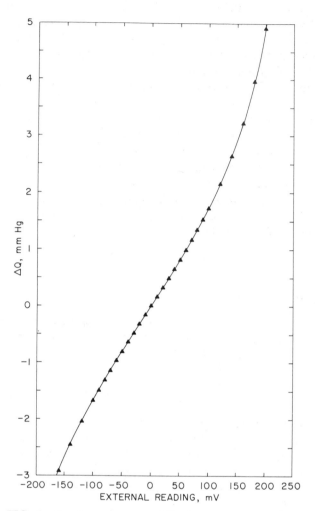

FIG. 4—*Quartz pressure gage deflection versus output voltage.*

brated by weighing the devices to within 0.1 mg for a period of three months. A calibration curve for the H_2S device is shown in Fig. 5. Using a 35-cm³ glass vessel, the Metronics devices were calibrated in the Brookhaven apparatus in about two to three days (see Fig. 6 for the H_2S source).

A permeation wafer device of the Brookhaven design, containing a ¼-in. outside diameter by 30-mil-thick tetrafluoroethylene (TFE) Teflon wafer, was filled with NO_2 and calibrated from 30 to 70°C as shown in Fig. 7. An activation energy of 10.19 ± 0.08 kcal/mol was determined.

Another NO_2 permeation wafer device, but with a ⅛-in. outside diameter by 30-mil fluorinated ethylene propylene (FEP) Teflon wafer, was filled

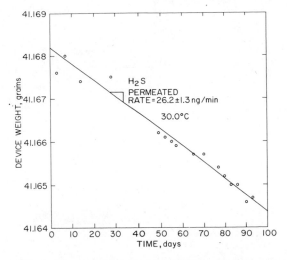

FIG. 5—*Gravimetric calibration of Metronics H₂S device.*

with 0.2 g of liquefied NO_2 (enough to last for 20 to 30 years), and 19 calibration runs were performed between 30 and 60°C (four are shown in Fig. 8). The rates for this device were about an order of magnitude less than those for the ¼-in. device. The activation energy was calculated at 11.74 ± 0.06 kcal/mol (solid line in Fig. 9).

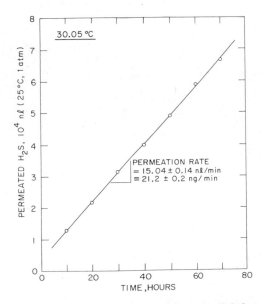

FIG. 6—*Pressure calibration of Metronics H₂S device.*

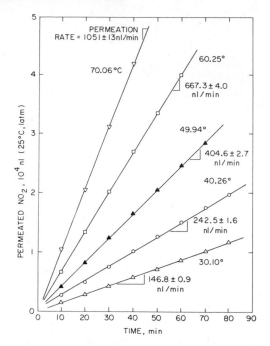

FIG. 7—*Permeation of ¼-in. NO₂ waver device.*

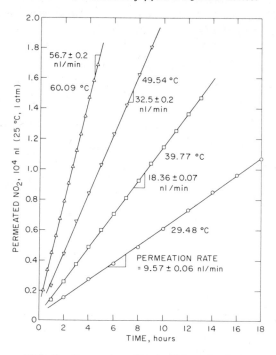

FIG. 8—*Permeation of ⅛-in. NO₂ wafer device.*

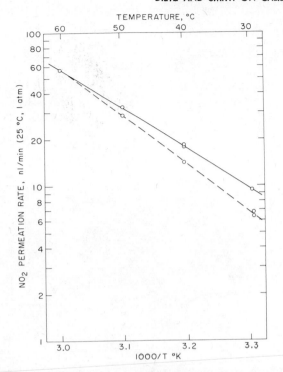

FIG. 9—*NO₂ permeation rate versus reciprocal temperature.*

A third NO_2 device, fabricated with a 90-mil-thick FEP Teflon wafer and having about one third the exposed surface area of the device above, was calibrated at 29.90°C (0.534 ± 0.008 nl/min), 50.39°C (1.600 ± 0.035 nl/min), and 70.05°C (5.86 ± 0.07 nl/min). An activation energy of 12.3 ± 1.2 kcal/mol was calculated.

Liquefied ammonia (NH_3) was used to fill another device with a ⅛-in. by 30-mil FEP Teflon wafer. A permeation rate of 1.19 ± 0.01 nl/min at 25.9°C was determined in just 42 h.

Diffusion Device

A diffusion device, containing about a ⅛-in. outside diameter by 30-mil-thick porous glass wafer, was connected to a 100 cm³ buffer volume supplied with CO at pressure from 5 to 30 ± 0.05 psig and from 30 to 200 ± 0.5 psig. The buffer volume eliminated error from pressure fluctuation due to regulator creep. Twenty seven runs were performed at a temperature of about 27°C, six of which are shown in Fig. 10. Each run was completed in less than 10 min with a precision of about 1 percent. All 27 runs were fitted by least-mean-square analysis to the straight line shown in Fig. 11. The points represent the rate for the six runs of Fig. 10.

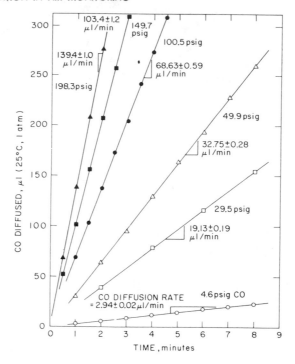

FIG. 10—*Diffusion of CO through porous glass wafer device.*

Discussion

Calibration System

The quartz gage photocell output was found to be sensitive to room temperature changes in the linear region of about −2.5 percent/°C. By placing a 2000-Ω shunt resistor across the output, temperature sensitivity was reduced to −1.9 percent/°C, and the linear pressure region was doubled. Since the gage temperature, which was controlled only by the room temperature, usually varied by less than 0.2°C during the course of a permeation or diffusion calibration, error related to photocell temperature sensitivity was safely less than 0.4 percent.

A second calibration system, which was constructed but not used to date, has a lower total system volume (about 0.7 cm³) for increased resolution. About 80 percent of the new system volume is in the new quartz gage instrument (Texas Instruments Model 145-02). Since this gage has a self-contained temperature control unit with a deviation of less than ±0.05°C (at the conditions in our laboratory), errors related to photocell temperature sensitivity are eliminated. In addition, the gage has a greater linear range.

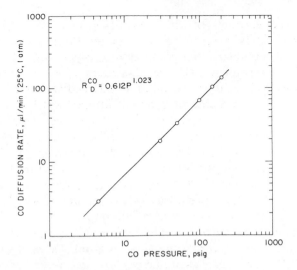

FIG. 11—*CO diffusion rate versus pressure.*

Since the diffusion devices were calibrated at pressures up to 200 psig, provision was made to protect the 25-psig proof pressure quartz gage. For data obtained with the CO diffusion device, a relief valve was included in the interconnecting line. Slight expansion of the valve during calibration runs gave diffusion rate determinations which were low by 3 to 7 percent. A new safety concept, based on a voltsensor detecting the approach to over pressure condition, using the output of the quartz gage, operates a solenoid relief valve on the diffusion gas supply.

Permeation Devices

The results obtained with the low rate SO_2 and H_2S Metronics devices are compared to the manufacturer's estimated rates as shown in Table 1. The agreement is reasonably good for the H_2S device, but the gravimetric determination for the SO_2 device appears to be too high. Calibration by the gravimetric procedure required considerably longer time.

TABLE 1—*Calibration of Metronics low permeation devices.*

| | Rate at 30.0°C, ng/min | | Approximate |
Method	H_2S	SO_2	Calibration Time
Stated value	32.6 ± 3.3	30.0 ± 3.0	estimated by Metronics
Gravimetric	26.2 ± 1.3	45.3 ± 0.8	92 days
Brookhaven	21.2 ± 0.2	24.8 ± 0.5	30 to 70 h
	(15.04 ± 0.14	(9.24 ± 0.19	
	nl/min)	nl/min)	

Problems were encountered with controlling the degree of compression on the Teflon wafers using Swagelok tees for the body of the devices. Examination of the wafers after compression showed that, in most cases, the extent of compression was 80 percent or more, when only 30 percent was the desired goal. Temperature cycling up to 50 to 60°C caused the wafers to leak at the seal. By switching to Gyrolok fittings, which have a positive stop on the front ferrule, the problem was eliminated completely. A test wafer was cycled every few days between 70°C at 100-psig N_2 and room temperature and checked for leaks using the SF_6 technique. For a three month test period, at 100-psig SF_6, the leak rate was less than 0.003 nl/min. Another specimen tested at 80°C was leak-tight for two weeks but, by the fourth week, had developed a leak rate of about 0.75 nl/min. Presently, a temperature of 60°C appears to be a safe upper limit.

To determine the extent of possible correction for back diffusion of the diluent nitrogen during calibration, the permeation of several gases through the 30-mil FEP Teflon wafer (nominally ⅛ in.) was measured as shown in Table 2. From the last column in the table, it is evident that the choice of N_2 as the diluent was quite fortuitous. The back diffusion of N_2 is just 1.9 percent of the NO_2 permeation rate at 30°C and only 1.1 percent at 60°C. Since N_2 is being added to the NO_2 at the time of fabrication of the wafer devices, errors due to back diffusion of N_2 should be less than 0.5 percent (in the case of NO_2 wafer devices) and will be neglected.

The rate of permeation of N_2 obtained for the wafer device at 30°C (0.19 nl/min) can be used to obtain a permeability coefficient of 0.7×10^{-10} cm^3-cm/cm^2s/cm Hg. Huang and Kanitz [7] determined a value of 3.0×10^{-10} using much larger surface areas and thinner films, and Rogers et al [9] reported a value of 2.1×10^{-10}. Apparent activation energies were in closer agreement—8.5 kcal/mol (Huang and Kanitz), 8.0 (this work), and 7.3 (Rogers et al).

TABLE 2—*Permeation rate of several gases—FEP teflon wafer (0.076 cm thick; 0.044 cm² area) with N_2 diluent gas.*

Permeate Gas	Temperature, °C	Measured Rate,[a] nl/min	Corrected Rate,[b] nl/min	Percent of NO_2 Rate
NO_2	30		10	. . .
	60		57	. . .
O_2	60.1	2.71	1.67	2.9
A	60.0	1.57	1.10	1.9
N_2	30.0	0.19	0.19	1.9
	60.1	0.63	0.63	1.1

[a] Measured at 2 atm abs of permeate with 1 atm abs of diluent.
[b] Corrected for back diffusion of N_2 and adjusted to 1 atm differential pressure of permeate (except for NO_2 which was at its corresponding vapor pressure).

In the temperature range of 30 to 60°C, the NO_2 permeation rate from the $\frac{1}{8}$-in. device could be duplicated with about 2 percent repeatability but only after first heating to 60°C. The equilibrated rates at 30, 40, and 50°C were lower (initial activation energy of 14.1 ± 0.1 kcal/mol as shown by dashed line in Fig. 9) for the calibration runs on the first temperature scan. Subsequent temperature scans, up and down, followed the lower activation energy value (11.74). The original activation energy for the $\frac{1}{4}$-in. NO_2 wafer device was 14.3 ± 0.5 kcal/mol [1]—very close to the initial value for the $\frac{1}{8}$-in. device—and subsequently dropped to 10.19. Similar temperature effects were noted by experimenters at NBS [2,10]. The exact nature of this change, which cannot be related to short term equilibration (a new, constant rate was attained in just 1 to 2 h for a temperature change of 10 to 20°C), may be clarified when similar permeation wafer devices for H_2S and SO_2 have been studied as well as NO_2 devices varied over smaller temperature ranges.

Preliminary work has also been started on fabrication of high-pressure permeation sources. SF_6, having a vapor pressure of about 300 psig at room temperature, is used as a tracer gas for following the movement of air masses (for example, power plant plumes) over great distances [8]. For calibration of electron capture gas chromatographs, a SF_6 source in the range of 0.1 to 1 nl/min is desirable. A $\frac{1}{4}$-in. long by 0.045-in. outside diameter plug of silicone rubber was inserted in a $\frac{1}{16}$-in. outside diameter stainless steel tube, and the tubing outside diameter was reduced to about 0.040 in. using a swaging-drawing machine. With the resultant 50 percent compression on the silicone rubber plug, the device was proof tested at 500 psig and permeated SF_6 at 1 nl/min at room temperature.

Diffusion Device

The CO diffusion rate is almost a linear (power of 1.023) function of the differential pressure (Fig. 11). The deviation from unit power may be attributable to a gradually increasing cross-sectional area of the exposed porous glass due to outward expansion of the flat PVC ring on the CO side as the pressure was increased.

A problem was encountered with the PVC flat rings when the temperature of the device was raised to 50 to 60°C. Apparently the plasticizer compounds in the Tygon material irreversibly plugged the 40 Å pores of the diffusion glass. No noticeable plugging has occurred at 25°C. Future devices will be evaluated with sealing rings cut from silicone and Viton rubber tubing. Temperature annealing from 700 to 1200°C, which gives controlled shrinkage of the porous glass, will be examined as a method to further reduce diffusion rates.

A diffusion device for nitrous oxide (N_2O) was very recently calibrated at pressure differentials from 40 to 800 mm Hg and was used to calibrate a chromatographic procedure for the determination of atmospheric N_2O [*11*]. It was immediately obvious that a problem of back diffusion of diluent gas had been overlooked. With 1 atm abs of air on the diluent side of the porous glass and the same pressure of N_2O on the other side, N_2O diffused at a rate proportional to the partial pressure driving force—not the total pressure differential which was zero.

To eliminate the problems associated with back diffusion of the diluent gas, which was related to the adsorption of diluent gas on the diluent side of the porous glass, future devices will contain a 10-mil inside diameter capillary tube on the diluent side. Thus both sides of the porous glass will be exposed just to the diffusing gas, dilution will take place after the short length of capillary tubing (about ⅜ in. long), and the porous glass will act solely as a pressure restriction device.

Conclusions

The Brookhaven calibration procedure is an extremely rapid and precise method for the calibration of all types of permeation devices. Problems encountered with sensitive gravimetric procedures, for example, effects of humidity [9], are eliminated completely. Porous glass diffusion wafers provide an important alternative approach to the dynamic preparation of gas mixtures containing parts per million amount of noncondensable gases.

Acknowledgments

Appreciation is expressed to Allan Auskern for his suggestion of using porous glass and help with precision cutting of the material, to V. P. Aneja for gravimetric calibration of the Metronics devices, and to J. B. Clements and A. E. O'Keeffe (U.S. Environmental Protection Agency) for financial support of this work.

References

[1] Dietz, R. N., *Analytical Chemistry*, Vol. 46, No. 2, Feb. 1974, pp. 315–318.
[2] Hughes, E. E., "Development of Standard Reference Materials for Air Quality Measurement," ISA Reprint 74–704, Instrument Society of America, New York, Oct. 1974.
[3] Scaringelli, F. P., O'Keeffe, A. E., Rosenberg, E., and Bell, J. P., *Analytical Chemistry*, Vol. 42, No. 8, July 1970, pp. 871–876.
[4] Scaringelli, F. P., Rosenberg, E., and Rehme, K. A., *Environmental Science and Technology*, Vol. 4, No. 11, Nov. 1970, pp. 924–929.
[5] Saltzman, B. E., Feldmann, C. R., and O'Keeffe, A. E., *Environmental Science and Technology*, Vol. 3, No. 12, Dec. 1969, pp. 1275–1279.
[6] Saltzman, B. E., Burg, W. R., and Ramaswamy, G., *Environmental Science and Technology*, Vol. 5, No. 11, Nov. 1971, pp. 1121–1128.
[7] Huang, R. Y. M. and Kanitz, P. J. F. in *Permselective Membranes*, C. E. Rogers, Ed., Marcel Dekker, New York, 1971, pp. 71–88.

[8] Dietz, R. N. and Cote, E. A., *Environmental Science and Technology*, Vol. 7, No. 4, April 1973, pp. 338–342.

[9] Rogers, C. E., Fels, M., and Li, N. N. in *Recent Developments in Separation Science*, N. N. Li, Ed., Chemical Rubber Co. Press, Cleveland, Ohio, 1972, pp. 107–155.

[10] Rook, H. L., Hughes, E. E., Fuerst, R. S., and Margeson, J. H., "Operation Characteristics of NO_2 Permeation Devices," American Chemical Society Division of Environmental Chemistry Preprints, Vol. 14, No. 1, April 1974, pp. 321–328.

[11] Dietz, R. N. and Cote, E. A., "Determination of Atmospheric Nitrous Oxide by Helium Ionization Gas Chromatography," to be published.

Discussion of Specific Techniques

D. L. Williams[1]

Permeation Tube Equilibration Times and Long-Term Stability

REFERENCE: Williams, D. L., **"Permeation Tube Equilibration Times and Long-Term Stability,"** *Calibration in Air Monitoring, ASTM STP 598*, American Society for Testing and Materials, 1976, pp. 183–197.

ABSTRACT: The time required to reach permeation rate equilibrium after a temperature change, and the long-term rate stability were investigated for fluorinated ethylene propylene (FEP) and tetrafluoroethylene (TFE) Teflon permeation tubes filled with sulfur dioxide, hydrogen sulfide, methyl mercaptan, and dimethyl sulfide. The effect of repeated temperature changes on the repeatability of permeation rates was determined for permeation tubes filled with ammonia, nitrogen dioxide, and sulfur compounds. A two-stage process to equilibrium was observed for tubes made of FEP Teflon. Permeation through TFE Teflon requires one fifth the time to reach equilibrium and does not exhibit the same two-stage equilibration process. Long-term stability was good for both FEP and TFE membranes. Permeation rates were reproducible after repeated temperature cycles.

KEY WORDS: permeability, calibration, sulfur dioxide, methyl mercaptan, hydrogen sulfide, dimethyl sulfide, nitrogen dioxide, ammonia, tetrafluoroethylene resins, equilibrium times, rate stability, air pollution, analyzers

Permeation tubes have gained wide use as a means of generating known span gas concentrations for calibrating air pollution analyzers. At a fixed temperature, permeation tubes release microgram quantities of pure gas at a constant rate. Introducing this gas into a known flow of carrier gas provides a simple, reliable way to generate part-per-million and part-per-billion concentrations for dynamic calibration [1,2].[2]

In the specification of procedures for permeation tube use, several important questions have arisen concerning proper techniques, that is, what length of time is required to bring the permeation tube to rate equilibrium, should permeation devices be refrigerated to prolong useful life, can permeation rates be repeated after temperature cycling, and how stable are the permeation rates over the useful life of the device [3–9].

[1] Environmental analyst, Metronics Associates, Inc., Palo Alto, Calif. 94304.
[2] The italic numbers in brackets refer to the list of references appended to this paper.

To answer these questions, for the purpose of establishing better guide-lines in the calibration of air monitors, permeation rates were measured for devices having various types of Teflon, wall membrane thicknesses, types of gases, and temperature conditioning history.

Procedure

Equipment

Standard rate permeation tubes were constructed of fluorinated ethylene propylene (FEP) Teflon tubing having 0.187 in. outside diameter and 0.030 in. wall thickness. High emission permeation tubes made of tetra-fluoroethylene (TFE) Teflon tubing with 0.312 in. outside diameter and 0.030 in. wall thickness were used. Low-emission tubes were constructed of drilled FEP Teflon rod to give a 0.090 in. wall thickness. Gases used to fill the permeation tubes were of the best quality, furnished by commercial suppliers with stated purities of 99.5 percent or better.

Method

Permeation rates were determined gravimetrically over periods of weeks to months by weighing periodically on a semimicro balance (Mettler). Permeation tubes were maintained, between weighings, in a glass chamber immersed in a constant temperature oil bath with 0.1°C control, and were purged continuously with a flow of dry nitrogen (N_2).

Short-term permeation rate changes, occurring over a period of minutes to several days, were determined for the sulfur containing gases by record-ing the output from a flame photometric detector. A metered carrier flow of air, scrubbed through activated charcoal, was passed into a constant temperature chamber containing the permeation tube and into a mixing chamber, using Teflon and glass materials which would be in contact with the test gas stream. The probe to the total sulfur analyzer (Bendix) drew sample air from the mixing chamber, and the analog output was recorded on strip charts.   .

Experimental Work

Time to Rate Equilibrium

Permeation tubes, made of FEP and TFE Teflon, filled with sulfur dioxide (SO_2), hydrogen sulfide (H_2S), methyl mercaptan (CH_3SH), and dimethyl sulfide (($CH_3)_2S$) each, were conditioned at various temperatures for periods of time exceeding one week. Initial temperatures were selected on the basis of how permeation tubes are typically stored, that is, freezer temperature ($-15°C$), room temperature (22°C), and 30°C. After conditioning, the tubes were placed immediately into a constant temperature system preset at 30 or 43°C, and the permeation rate changes were monitored on the sulfur analyzer.

Permeation rate equilibrium was achieved in two stages for tubes made of FEP Teflon. SO_2, permeating through an 0.030-in. FEP wall, achieved equilibrium at 43°C approximately 10 h after starting at freezer temperature and at 30°C (Fig. 1). In both cases, the rates rose to an initial level in the first 20 min and leveled off at 80 to 90 percent of final value through the second hour. A slight decrease of 1 to 2 percent was noted during the first stage, prior to the start of the second stage increase to the final level. The second stage was achieved between the second and tenth hours. The final values, which were observed at the end of both runs, agreed within 1 percent.

The time to reach equilibrium at 30°C from an initial freezer storage condition was 20 to 25 h or was twice that required to reach equilibrium at 43°C (Fig. 2). For the smaller temperature change from 22 to 30°C, the permeation rate plateaued at a high level (96 percent) within the first ½ h, but still indicated a two-stage process which was completed during the fifth through tenth hours. Due to earlier problems with fluctuations of 2 percent in the carrier flow, this experiment was repeated using a mass flowmeter and recorder to verify the significance and accuracy of the last 4 percent change.

To achieve lower permeation rates, a thicker wall tube is often used. However, the thicker wall was found to increase greatly the time to reach

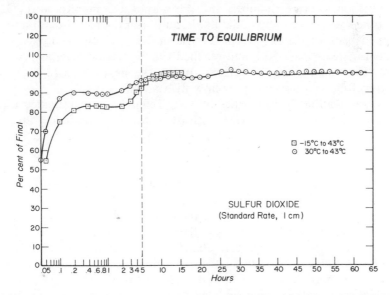

FIG. 1—*Time to equilibrium: SO_2 permeation tubes made of 0.030-in. wall FEP Teflon raised to 43°C from freezer temperature and 30°C.*

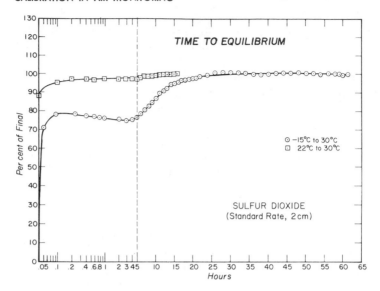

FIG. 2—*Time to equilibrium: SO₂ permeation tubes made of 0.030-in. wall FEP Teflon raised to 30°C from freezer temperature and room temperature.*

equilibrium. The trace in Fig. 3 represents the permeation rate from a 0.090-in.-thick walled FEP permeation tube which was equilibrated at room temperature (approximately 22°C). The tube was then placed in a 43°C constant temperature chamber, and the output was monitored for 320 h. The tube rate peaked above the final equilibrium value in 0.2 h and then dropped back to the 82 percent level after 2 h. The tube output began a gradual increase after 30 h and reached the 98 percent level at 100 h (4.2 days). Fluctuations of ±2 percent during the next 200 h (8 days) were noted to follow observed carrier-flow fluctuations.

The permeation characteristics of TFE Teflon were investigated using a stainless steel permeation device, with the permeation occurring through a 0.030-in.-thick TFE wafer in the end cap. A new permeation device was placed in the 43°C constant temperature chamber 1 h after initial filling, and the output monitored. The trace immediately went off scale (Fig. 4), due to residual SO₂ on the external surface of the steel capsule, and then dropped to zero within 30 min. After 2.3 h total elapsed time from initial filling, the device began permeating through the membrane and reached a level value after 8 h. The device was then conditioned at 30°C for 32 h and replaced in the 43°C temperature chamber to check the repeatability of the equilibrium value. The analyzer trace reached the 95 percent level within 30 min, remained level for 1 h, and then rose to the final level after 3 h. The final value of the second run was 3 percent higher than the run to 43°C after initial filling.

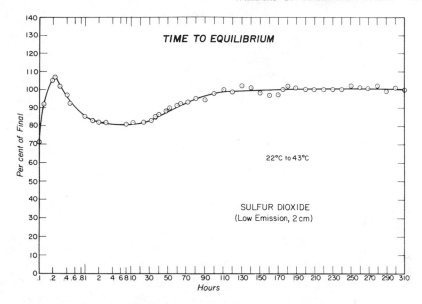

FIG. 3—*Time to equilibrium: SO₂ permeation tube made of 0.090-in. wall FEP Teflon raised to 43°C from room temperature.*

H₂S, permeating through 0.030-in. FEP Teflon tubing, demonstrated a definite two-stage equilibration process and required 10 to 13 h to reach final equilibrium at 43°C (Fig. 5). The analyzer trace reached 59 percent of final value within 5 min and remained level for 1 h. No initial peak was observed, as was noted with SO₂-filled FEP tubes. From the 60 percent level at 1 h, the H₂S rate increased to the 98 percent level after 9 h.

CH₃SH, permeating through 0.030-in. FEP tubing, again demonstrated a two-stage equilibration process which required approximately 30 h to reach a final level at 43°C, after starting at −15°C (Fig. 6). The tube output rose to a peak of 117 percent of final within 12 min and declined slowly for the next 5 h. The permeation rate then increased, reaching the 98 percent level after 26 h. The CH₃SH tube then was equilibrated at 30° with a N₂ purge flow for one week, and another equilibrium run to 43°C was made. Within 10 min, the permeation rate reached the 90 percent level. When the CH₃SH traces are compared, it is noted that, when the tube was conditioned at 30°C with a purge flow, there was no initial peak in the rate. It is concluded that the initial peak on the −15 to 43°C run was due to outgassing of a surface buildup of CH₃SH during the cold storage without purge flow.

(CH₃)₂S, permeating through 0.030-in. wall TFE tubing, was found to reach rate equilibrium within 30 min after a temperature change, but required a conditioning period, after initial filling, of greater than 60 h.

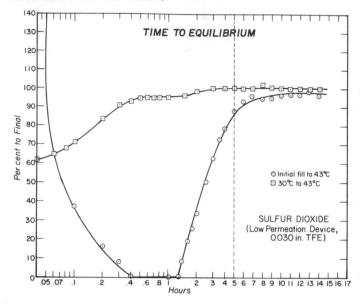

FIG. 4—*Time to equilibrium: SO₂ permeation device with 0.030-in. TFE Teflon membrane raised to 43°C from time of initial fill and 30°C.*

A new 0.030-in. wall TFE permeation tube was filled with $(CH_3)_2S$ and placed directly in the 43°C constant temperature chamber (Fig. 7). Outgassing of surface material took the analyzer trace off scale initially, then returned to zero within 1.5 h. Permeation through the wall started after 18 h. It was noted that the trace had not stabilized after 63 h. The tube was then removed, conditioned at 30°C with a N_2 purge for an additional 32 h, and rerun to 43°C equilibrium (Fig. 8). On the second 43°C equilibrium run, the trace rose to 98 percent of the equilibrium value within 20 min and remained at the equilibrium value after the first hour. Using the equilibrium value obtained on this second run as a reference, the permeation rate recorded on the first run had reached the 94 percent level.

Due to its higher molecular weight and the lower vapor pressure, dimethyl disulfide $((CH_3)_2S_2)$ has a permeation rate approximately one tenth that of $(CH_3)_2S$. It was expected, therefore, to have a longer time to equilibrium after a given temperature change. However, a 0.030-in. wall TFE $(CH_3)_2S_2$ permeation tube, which had been conditioned for several weeks at 30°C, also reached an equilibrium value within 20 min after the temperature was changed to 43°C. The equilibrium level was maintained for 14 h.

Long-Term Stability

During the investigation of times to rate equilibrium ranging between 15 and 60 h, a level would be established at which small percentage changes

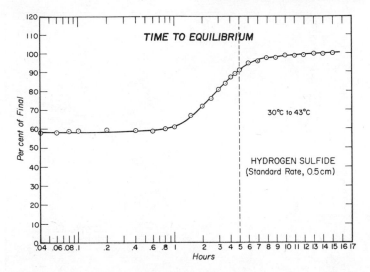

FIG. 5—*Time to equilibrium: H₂S permeation tube made of 0.030-in. wall FEP Teflon raised to 43 from 30°C.*

occurred, but the cause of the change was difficult to identify. The tube permeation rate could be changing at a slow rate, or, more likely, the drift was due to electronic drift in the analyzer or carrier flow changes. To determine the longer term changes, permeation rates were determined gravimetrically, using the least squares fit of the weight loss data for two or more consecutive periods.

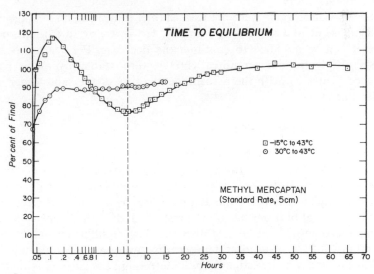

FIG. 6—*Time to equilibrium: CH₃SH permeation tube made of 0.030-in. wall FEP Teflon raised to 43°C from freezer temperature and 30°C.*

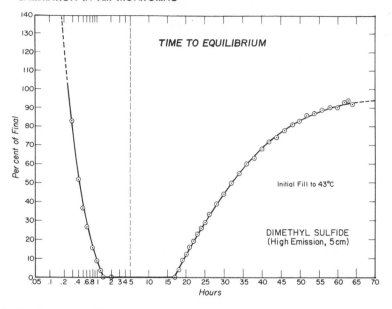

FIG. 7—*Time to equilibrium: (CH₃)₂S permeation tube made of 0.030-in. wall TFE Teflon raised to 43°C from initial filling.*

SO₂ tubes, made from TFE and FEP Teflon tubing, indicated permeation rates to be stable within 1 percent over the period of time measured (Table 1). The 0.090-in. wall FEP tube maintained a stable rate for six months within ±0.5 percent.

H₂S permeation rates were the least stable, indicating an average 3 percent decrease in 20 days (Tables 2 and 3). However, more data are needed before it can be assumed to continue the decrease. Permeation rates for CH₃SH, (CH₃)₂S, and ammonia (NH₃) were stable over the periods measured (Table 2), with the percentage changes of the same order as the standard error.

Effect of Temperature Cycling

Permeation tubes can be used at various temperatures to achieve a relatively wide range of permeation rates. For example, raising the tube temperature from 30 to 40°C approximately doubles the permeation rate. The feasibility of changing the temperature back and forth to achieve multiple point calibrations has been questioned, due to the lack of information on the time it takes to establish the new equilibrium value and the repeatability of the rate after temperature cycling. The repeatability of permeation rates was investigated by determining the rates gravimetrically at 30°C, then 40°C, and again at 30°C. Each tube was maintained at a given temperature for a period of time sufficient to establish the permeation

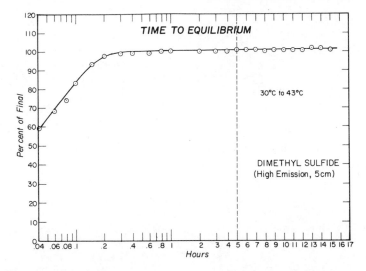

FIG. 8—*Time to equilibrium:* $(CH_3)_2S$ *permeation tube made of 0.030-in. wall TFE Teflon raised to 43 from 30°C.*

TABLE 1—*Stability of SO_2 permeation rates through FEP and TFE Teflon at constant temperature (tube wall thickness is 0.030 in. with exception noted).*

Tube Type	Temperature, °C	Time, days	Data Points	Permeation Rate, ng/min/cm	Standard Error, %	Percentage Change
SO_2 (FEP 1)	30	11	3	474.0	0.38	
	30	11	5	471.6	0.25	−0.51
SO_2 (FEP 2)	30	13	4	476.3	0.10	
	30	9	4	471.8	0.66	−0.95
SO_2 (FEP 3)	30	13	4	480.0	0.02	
	30	9	4	480.2	0.04	+0.04
SO_2 (FEP 4)	30	13	4	474.7	0.14	
	30	9	4	474.7	0.07	0.00
SO_2 (FEP 5) with 0.090-in. wall	43	36	5	586.5	0.70	
	43	44	4	589.5	0.06	+0.51
	43	75	4	591.0	0.20	+0.25
	43	22	4	589.0	0.40	−0.34
SO_2 (FEP 6) with 0.090-in. wall	43	24	8	496.0	0.30	
	43	41	6	498.5	0.10	+0.50
	43	12	6	493.0	1.30	−1.10
SO_2 (TFE 1)	30	11	4	2923	0.26	
	30	11	3	2912	0.10	−0.38
SO_2 (TFE 2)	30	11	4	2864	0.25	
	30	11	3	2854	0.11	−0.35

TABLE 2—*Stability of permeation rates at a constant temperature for H_2S, CH_3SH, $(CH_3)_2S$, and NH_3 (tube wall thickness is 0.030 in.).*

Tube Type	Tempera-ture, °C	Time, days	Data Points	Permeation Rate, ng/min/cm	Standard Error, %	Percentage Change
H_2S (FEP 1)	30	8	7	481.0	0.44	
	30	10	5	461.4	0.85	−4.2
H_2S (FEP 2)	30	11	5	519.0	0.22	
	30	11	4	511.0	0.51	−1.6
CH_3SH (FEP 1)	30	11	3	42.9	...	
	30	7	4	43.8	...	+2.1
CH_3SH (FEP 2)	30	7	3	42.7	...	
	30	7	4	42.2	...	−1.2
CH_3SH (TFE 1)	30	11	5	313.0	0.35	
	30	11	3	311.2	0.40	−0.58
CH_3SH (TFE 2)	30	11	5	316.5	0.27	
	30	11	3	314.2	0.36	−0.73
$(CH_3)_2S$ (TFE 1)	30	17	4	68.6	1.9	
	30	7	4	67.4	2.8	−1.8
NH_3 (FEP 1)	30	13	4	339.8	0.17	
	30	10	3	335.9	0.13	−1.2
NH_3 (FEP 2)	30	13	4	335.8	0.24	
	30	10	3	334.0	0.30	−0.54

TABLE 3—*Average change of permeation rates at a constant temperature.*

Tube Type	Tempera-ture, °C	Time, days	Number of Tubes	Average Percentage Change
SO_2 (FEP)	30	22	4	−0.36
SO_2 (thick FEP)	43	177	1	+0.43
SO_2 (TFE)	30	22	2	−0.36
H_2S (FEP)	30	22	2	−2.9
CH_3SH (FEP)	30	18	2	+0.45
CH_3SH (TFE)	30	22	2	−0.66
$(CH_3)_2S$ (TFE)	30	24	1	−1.8
NH_3 (FEP)	30	23	2	−0.87

rate to an accuracy of 1 percent (one to three weeks) and a sufficient number of data points to assure that the tube was at an equilibrium value.

SO_2 permeation rates at 30°C through TFE and FEP Teflon tubing increased by 2 to 5 percent after running at 40°C. Table 4 shows that the increase for FEP tubes ranged from 4.8 to 5.2 percent, and for TFE tubes, the increase was 1.9 to 4.9 percent after one temperature cycle. Repeating

TABLE 4—*Repeatability of SO_2 permeation rates through FEP and TFE Teflon with temperature cycling (tubes wall thickness is 0.030 in.).*

Tube Type	Tempera- ture, °C	Time, days	Data Points	Permeation Rate, ng/min/cm	Standard Error, %	Ratio to Initial
SO_2 (FEP 1)	30	12	8	458	0.22	1.000
	40	7	6	1000	0.51	2.183
	30	7	10	481	0.29	1.050
	40	12	7	1004	0.08	2.192
	30	15	7	482	0.12	1.052
SO_2 (FEP 2)	30	12	8	457	0.37	1.000
	40	7	6	1005	0.38	2.199
	30	7	10	481	0.33	1.052
	40	12	7	1007	0.08	2.203
	30	15	7	482	0.17	1.055
SO_2 (FEP 3)	30	12	8	454	0.20	1.000
	40	7	6	981	0.99	2.161
	30	7	10	477	0.10	1.051
	40	12	7	999	0.16	2.200
	30	15	7	479	0.19	1.055
SO_2 (FEP 4)	30	12	8	460	0.24	1.000
	40	7	6	1012	0.22	2.200
	30	7	10	482	0.39	1.048
	40	12	7	1012	0.09	2.200
	30	15	7	484	0.10	1.052
SO_2 (TFE 1)	30	7	9	2816	1.15	1.000
	40	6	7	5538	0.16	1.966
	30	15	5	2870	0.95	1.019
	40	7	3	5606	0.34	1.991
	30	22	7	2918	0.08	1.036
SO_2 (TFE) 2)	30	7	9	2710	0.95	1.000
	40	6	7	5420	0.16	2.000
	30	15	5	2844	0.81	1.049
	40	7	3	5432	0.16	2.004
	30	22	7	2860	0.08	1.055

the temperature cycle to 30°C indicated an average additional rate increase for TFE of 1.1 percent, and FEP tubes increased 0.2 percent (Table 5). Thick-walled FEP tubes filled with SO_2 indicated a larger increase after a cycle to 43°C from 30°C with an average increase of 9.4 percent (Tables 5 and 6).

CH₃SH permeation rates repeated better with TFE tubing than with FEP. This is attributed to the longer times to equilibrium required for FEP tubes and the low permeation rates which gave a higher standard error (Table 7). Longer testing would be required for both CH_3SH and $(CH_3)_2S$ to establish confidence in the percentage changes observed. NH_3 permeation through FEP tubes repeated very well through one temperature cycle, with a 0.3 percent decrease and 0.9 percent increase observed (Table 7).

TABLE 5—*Average change of permeation rates with temperature cycling.*

Tube Type	Number of Tubes	Average Percentage Change		
		First 30-deg Cycle, %	First 40-deg Cycle, %	Second 30-deg Cycle, %
SO_2 (FEP)	4	+5.0	+0.6	+0.2
SO_2 (TFE)	2	+3.4	+0.7	+1.1
SO_2 (thick FEP)	2	+9.4	...	...
CH_3SH (FEP)	2	+16	...	...
CH_3SH (TFE)	2	+0.4	...	...
$(CH_3)_2S$	1	−3.9	...	...
NH_3	2	+0.3	...	...

TABLE 6—*Repeatability of SO_2 permeation rates through thick-walled FEP Teflon permeation tubes with temperature cycling (tube wall thickness is 0.090 in.).*

Tube Type	Temperature, °C	Time, days	Data Points	Permeation Rate, ng/min/cm	Standard Error, %	Ratio to Initial
SO_2 (thick FEP 1)	30	34	10	193	0.52	1.000
	43	20	7	522	0.67	2.705
	30	27	6	211	0.92	1.093
SO_2 (thick FEP 2)	30	34	10	157	0.48	1.000
	43	20	7	426	0.61	2.713
	30	27	6	172	1.30	1.095

Repeatability of nitrogen dioxide (NO_2) permeation rates, as shown in Table 8, is seen to be dependent on type of Teflon used, wall thickness, and age of the permeation device. The results tabulated for the one temperature cycle in Table 8 represent the total life of the NO_2 tubes. The second permeation rate determination at 30°C for NO_2 tubes, when performed with less than 10 percent liquid fill remaining, indicated a 13 percent decrease. The rate decrease is attributed to the probable presence of trace moisture in the NO_2, which has a significant effect as the tube nears exhaustion. The two tubes designated NO_2 (FEP 3 and 4) indicated that permeation rates increased slightly after temperature cycling when the last rate determination was made prior to reaching 10 percent remaining liquid fill. NO_2 permeation rates at 30°C through 0.090-in. FEP increased 17 to 20 percent after cycling to 40°C (Table 8). Best repeatability of NO_2 permeation rates was observed using TFE Teflon tubing, with an average decrease of 2.8 percent over the tube life (Table 9).

Conclusions

Permeation tubes made of FEP Teflon (0.030-in. wall) achieve permeation rate equilibrium in two stages after a temperature change. The permeation

TABLE 7—*Repeatability of CH_3SH, $(CH_3)_2S$, and NH_3 permeation rates with temperature cycling (tube wall thickness is 0.030 in.).*

Tube Type	Temperature, °C	Time, days	Data Points	Permeation Rate, ng/min/cm	Standard Error, %	Ratio to Initial
CH_3SH (FEP 1)	30	12	7	35.3	1.47	1.000
	40	24	9	87.1	0.46	2.467
	30	22	8	46.5	0.15	1.317
CH_3SH (FEP 2)	30	12	7	45.9	0.96	1.000
	40	24	9	93.4	0.54	2.035
	30	22	8	46.2	0.13	1.006
CH_3SH (TFE 1)	30	12	8	309	0.30	1.000
	40	32	8	614	0.08	1.987
	30	22	7	311	0.23	1.006
CH_3SH (TFE 2)	30	12	8	314	4.11	1.000
	40	32	8	617	0.11	1.965
	30	22	7	315	0.26	1.003
$(CH_3)_2S$ (TFE)	30	20	5	70.7	0.77	1.000
	40	20	7	138	2.40	1.952
	30	24	7	68.0	1.06	0.962
NH_3 (FEP 1)	30	13	9	340	2.97	1.000
	40	20	7	688	0.25	2.024
	30	24	6	339	0.03	0.997
NH_3 (FEP 2)	30	13	9	332	0.42	1.000
	40	20	7	673	0.31	2.027
	30	24	6	335	0.12	1.009

reaches a plateau at 60 to 90 percent of the final equilibrium value during the first 1 to 4 h, then climbs slowly to the final equilibrium value in 10 to 30 h. Higher temperatures required the shorter times to equilibrium. Thick-walled FEP Teflon permeation tubes also exhibited a two-stage equilibration, but required over four days to reach final equilibrium. Permeation through TFE Teflon requires approximately one fifth the time to reach equilibrium, as opposed to FEP Teflon, and does not exhibit the characteristic two-stage equilibration.

Long-term permeation rate stability is good for both FEP and TFE Teflon membranes. Rates at a constant temperature were stable within 1 percent for SO_2, CH_3SH, and NH_3. H_2S permeation rates were less stable and should be determined every two to four weeks to maintain a known accuracy of 2 percent.

Permeation rates can be reproduced within 1 percent with repeated temperature changes for SO_2 tubes made of FEP and TFE Teflon after the first temperature cycle. However, during the first cycle to a 10 deg higher temperature, permeation rates through FEP Teflon were 5 to 18 percent higher when returned to the initial temperature. Permeation tubes made of TFE also indicated better repeatability of permeation rates with

TABLE 8—*Repeatability of NO_2 permeation rates with temperature cycling (wall thickness is 0.030 in. except where noted).*

Tube Type	Tempera- ture, °C	Time, days	Data Points	Permeation Rate, ng/min/cm	Standard Error, %	Ratio to Initial
NO_2 (FEP 1)[a]	30	12	9	1766	0.89	1.000
	40	10	6	3896	1.43	2.206
	30	4	4	1549	2.34	0.877
NO_2 (FEP 2)[a]	30	12	8	1758	0.94	1.000
	40	10	6	3770	1.72	2.144
	30	4	4	1523	1.93	0.866
NO_2 (FEP 3)[b]	30	9	6	1853	0.73	1.000
	40	8	6	4425	0.44	2.388
	30	10	6	1894	1.14	1.022
NO_2 (FEP 4)[b]	30	9	6	1838	0.76	1.000
	40	8	6	4354	0.54	2.369
	30	10	6	1855	1.30	1.009
NO_2 (0.090 in. FEP 1)	30	8	6	665	0.05	1.000
	40	21	7	1680	0.80	2.526
	30	29	8	795	0.04	1.195
NO_2 (0.090 in. FEP 2)	30	9	7	710	0.07	1.000
	40	21	7	1760	0.91	2.479
	30	29	8	830	0.05	1.169
NO_2 (TFE 1)[c]	30	7	9	13250	0.60	1.000
	40	3	6	24650	0.44	1.860
	30	13	8	13040	0.68	0.984
NO_2 (TFE 2)[c]	30	7	9	13960	0.56	1.000
	40	3	6	26100	0.96	1.870
	30	13	8	13410	1.47	0.961

[a] Second run at 30°C was performed when liquid fill was less than 10 percent. One drop of liquid remained at last weighing.

[b] Second run at 30°C was terminated when liquid fill dropped to 10 percent.

[c] Rate dropped rapidly last three days before tube was exhausted.

TABLE 9—*Average change of NO_2 permeation rates with temperature cycling from 30 to 40 and back to 30°C.*

Tube Type	Number of Tubes	Average Percentage Change
NO_2 (FEP)	2	+1.6[a]
NO_2 (FEP)	2	−12.8[b]
NO_2 (thick FEP)	2	+18.2
NO_2 (TFE)	2	−2.8

[a] Approximately 10 percent liquid fill at end of second 30°C rate measurement.

[b] Second 30°C rate measurement started with 10 percent liquid fill remaining.

temperature cycling. Results of temperature cycling of NO_2 permeation tubes indicate that the repeatability of rates is dependent on the liquid fill remaining in the tube, the type of Teflon used, and the wall thickness. Further investigation will be required before NO_2 permeation rates can be predicted accurately after a temperature change.

References

[1] O'Keeffe, A. E. and Ortman, G. C., *Analytical Chemistry*, Vol. 38, May 1966, pp. 760–763.

[2] Scaringelli, F. P., O'Keeffe, A. E., Rosenberg, E., and Bell, J. P., *Analytical Chemistry*, Vol. 42, No. 8, July 1970, pp. 871–876.

[3] Cedergren, A., Wikby, A., and Bergner, K., *Analytical Chemistry*, Vol. 47, 1974, pp. 100–106.

[4] Blacker, J. H. and Brief, R. S., *American Industrial Hygiene Association Journal*, Vol. 9, 1971, pp. 668–672.

[5] DeMaio, L., *Instrumentation Technology*, Vol. 19, No. 5, 1972, pp. 37–41.

[6] Lucero, D. P., *Analytical Chemistry*, Vol. 43, 1971, pp. 1744–1749.

[7] Saltzman, B. E., Burg, W. R., and Ramaswany, G., *Environmental Science and Technology*, Vol. 5, 1971, pp. 1121–1128.

[8] Saltzman, B. E., Feldman, C. R., and O'Keeffe, A. E., *Environmental Science and Technology*, Vol. 3, No. 12, 1969, pp. 1275–1279.

[9] Scaringelli, F. P., Rosenberg, E., and Rehme, K. A., *Environmental Science and Technology*, Vol. 4, No. 11, Nov. 1970, pp. 924–928.

K. A. Rehme[1]

Application of Gas Phase Titration in the Calibration of Nitric Oxide, Nitrogen Dioxide, and Ozone Analyzers

REFERENCE: Rehme, K. A., "Application of Gas Phase Titration in the Calibration of Nitric Oxide, Nitrogen Dioxide, and Ozone Analyzers," *Calibration in Air Monitoring, ASTM STP 598*, American Society for Testing and Materials, 1976, pp. 198–209.

ABSTRACT: A detailed procedural description of a technique developed and applied within the U. S. Environmental Protection Agency for the dynamic calibration of ambient air monitors for nitric oxide, nitrogen dioxide, and ozone is presented. A gas phase titration technique, utilizing the rapid gas phase reaction between nitric oxide and ozone, is used in such a manner that, with the concentration of one of the three gases known, the concentrations of the other two can be determined. A working cylinder of nitric oxide in nitrogen is standardized using one of three possible primary standards. Cylinder nitric oxide is then used as a secondary standard for routine calibrations. Ozone is added to excess nitric oxide in a dynamic calibration system, and a calibrated chemiluminescence nitric oxide analyzer is used as an indicator of changes in concentration. The decrease observed on the calibrated nitric oxide analyzer upon addition of ozone is equivalent to the concentration of nitric oxide consumed, the concentration of ozone added, and the nitrogen dioxide concentration produced. Once the concentration of the three gases has been determined, rapid and routine calibrations of ozone, nitric oxide, and nitrogen dioxide monitors may be performed at a common manifold. Experimental results showing the interrelationships that exist among the three gases are also presented.

KEY WORDS: gas phase titration, calibration, ozone, nitric oxide, nitrogen dioxide, monitors, gases

Gas phase titration (GPT) refers to a technique for the dynamic calibration of ambient air monitors for nitric oxide (NO), nitrogen dioxide (NO_2), total oxides of nitrogen (NO_x), and ozone (O_3). The technique utilizes the rapid gas phase reaction between NO and O_3 to produce a stoichiometric quantity of NO_2 in accordance with the following equation [1,2][2]

$$NO + O_3 \rightarrow NO_2 + O_2 \qquad k = 1.0 \times 10^7 \text{ 1 mol}^{-1}\text{s}^{-1} \qquad (1)$$

---

[1] Chemist, Environmental Monitoring and Support Laboratory, Environmental Monitoring Center, U. S. Environmental Protection Agency, Research Triangle Park, N. C. 27711.

[2] The italic numbers in brackets refer to the list of references appended to this paper.

The quantitative nature of the reaction is used in such a manner that, with the concentration of one of the three basic components known, the concentrations of the other two are defined. Generally, a high-pressure cylinder containing known amounts of NO in nitrogen (N_2) is used as a working standard to either verify the output of an O_3 generator or to produce known concentrations of NO_2 by GPT. The NO cylinder must be referenced to some acceptable standard reference material. The GPT technique was used by Hodgeson et al [1] to confirm the stoichiometry in the neutral iodometric procedure for O_3. The application of the GPT technique to the calibration of ambient air monitors was an outgrowth of Hodgeson's work and is now used routinely by the U. S. Environmental Protection Agency (EPA) [3].

GPT Dynamic Calibration System

Apparatus

Figure 1, a schematic of a typical GPT dynamic calibration system, shows the placement of most of the components listed next. All connections between components in the calibration system downstream of the O_3 generator must be glass or Teflon.

Air Flow Controller—A device capable of maintaining constant air flow within ±2 percent.

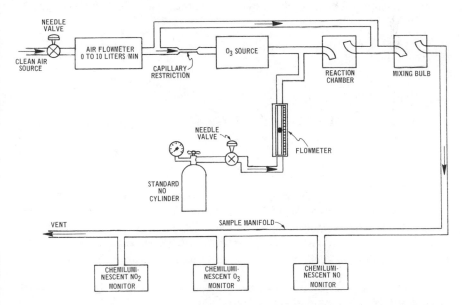

FIG. 1—*Flow scheme for calibration of NO, NO₂, NOₓ, and O₃ monitors by GPT.*

Air Flowmeter—A properly calibrated flowmeter capable of measuring and monitoring air flows within ±2 percent.

NO Flow Controller—A device capable of maintaining constant NO flow within ±2 percent. (Component parts in contact with NO must be of a nonreactive material.)

NO Flowmeter—A properly calibrated flowmeter capable of measuring and monitoring NO flows within ±2 percent.

Capillary Restriction—Glass or stainless steel capillary of sufficient length and internal diameter to allow approximately one tenth of the total air flow to pass through the O_3 generator. Alternately, a separate zero air supply, flow controller, and flowmeter can be used with the O_3 generator.

Ozone Generator—A device capable of generating sufficient and stable levels of O_3 for reaction with NO.

Reaction Chamber—A glass mixing chamber of sufficient volume to allow for the quantitative reaction of O_3 and NO.

Mixing Chamber—A glass chamber of proper design to provide thorough mixing of the pollutant gas stream and diluent air.

Sample Manifold—A multiport properly vented all-glass manifold.

Reagents

NO Cylinder—High-pressure cylinder containing 100 ppm NO in N_2 with less than 1 ppm NO_2.

Zero Air—Cylinder air or purified air containing no more than 0.002 ppm of NO, NO_2, and O_3.

NO Cylinder Calibration

Analysis of the NO cylinder to be used as a working standard is recommended because the nominal NO concentration of cylinders supplied by some vendors has been found to be inaccurate. Three techniques commonly used to analyze the NO content are:

Comparison With an NBS NO in N_2 Standard Reference Material[3]—A chemiluminescence NO analyzer is calibrated by accurate dilution of NO from the National Bureau of Standards standard cylinder. The NO in the working standard is then diluted accurately, and its response measured on the NO analyzer. If the NO flows and dilution air flow are measured

---

[3] "Standard Reference Gases for Automotive Emissions Analysis," *SRM 1684—Nitric Oxide in Nitrogen, 100 ppm*, National Bureau of Standards Standard Reference Materials, U. S. Department of Commerce, 16 Dec. 1974.

accurately, the NO concentration in the working standard can be determined.

Comparison of NO_2 Generated by GPT With an NBS NO_2 Standard Reference Material[4]—A chemiluminescence NO/NO_2 analyzer is calibrated with NO_2 generated from an NBS NO_2 permeation device. Using the GPT system, an NO concentration is generated by dilution of the NO working standard. The response is measured on the chemiluminescence NO analyzer, and O_3 from the uncalibrated generator is added to the NO stream. The resultant NO_2 response and the corresponding decrease in NO response are measured. The amount of NO consumed is equivalent to the amount of NO_2 generated. If the NO flow and dilution air flow are measured accurately, the NO concentration in the working standard can be determined.

GPT of NO With Known O_3 Concentrations—The O_3 generator in the GPT system is calibrated using the 1 percent neutral buffered potassium iodide (NBKI) procedure [4]. An NO concentration is generated by dilution of the NO working standard. The NO response on the chemiluminescence NO analyzer is measured. Known quantities of O_3 are added in increments from the calibrated O_3 generator and the resultant NO responses measured. A plot is made of NO response (y-axis) versus O_3 concentration added (x-axis). A straight line is drawn from the y-axis through the linear portion of the curve and extrapolated to the x-axis (equivalence point). The O_3 concentration at the equivalence point is the O_3 concentration equivalent to the initial diluted NO concentration. The NO concentration in the working standard is calculated from

$$C_{NO} = \frac{F_0 \times C_0'}{F_{NO}} \tag{2}$$

where

C_{NO} = cylinder NO concentration, ppm;
F_{NO} = NO flow, cm^3/min;
C_0' = equivalence point O_3 concentration, ppm; and
F_0 = total air flow, cm^3/min.

A typical titration curve is shown in Fig. 2.

Calibration of Ambient Air Monitors by GPT

This technique has been designed primarily for the calibration of chemiluminescence analyzers for NO, NO_2, NO_x, and the calibration of O_3 generators used for calibrating O_3 analyzers. Any detector that has a rapid

---

[4] "Nitrogen Dioxide Permeation Device (Individually Calibrated)," *SRM 1629*, National Bureau of Standards Standard Reference Materials, U. S. Department of Commerce, 14 Jan. 1975.

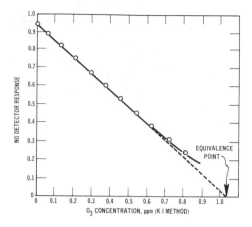

FIG. 2—*GPT of NO with O₃.*

and linear response to NO could be used as the indicator in the GPT step. Only those types of NO_2 analyzers that do not respond to NO may be calibrated, since the NO_2 calibration samples will contain varying amounts of excess NO. Once an O_3 generator has been calibrated by GPT, it can be used for the calibration of any type of O_3 analyzer.

NO, NO_2, and NO_x Analyzers

NO analyzers are calibrated by dynamic flow dilution of a working cylinder containing a known concentration of NO in N_2. The analyzer under calibration is allowed to sample zero air, and the proper zero adjustments are made. An NO concentration of approximately 80 percent of the desired full-scale range is generated by flow dilution. The exact NO concentration is calculated from

$$[NO] = \frac{F_{NO} \times C_{NO}}{F_{NO} + F_O} \tag{3}$$

where

    [NO] = diluted NO concentration, ppm;
    F_{NO} = NO flow, cm³/min;
    C_{NO} = cylinder NO concentration, ppm; and
    F_O = total air flow, cm³/min.

After the analyzer response has stabilized, the span adjustments are made for the desired output range. Several other NO concentrations are generated by decreasing the NO flow or increasing the air flow. The exact NO concentrations generated are calculated using Eq 3, and the corresponding analyzer responses are measured. The analyzer response versus NO concentration is plotted, and the NO calibration curve is drawn.

NO_2 analyzers are calibrated by GPT of excess NO with O_3. The analyzer under calibration is allowed to sample zero air, and the proper zero adjustments are made. A NO concentration is generated by flow dilution and the response of the calibrated NO analyzer recorded. Ozone is added to the NO stream and the resultant NO response recorded. Record the O_3 generator setting if subsequent O_3 analyzer calibrations are anticipated. The decrease in NO concentration is equivalent to the NO_2 concentration generated and the O_3 concentration added

$$[NO_2]_i = [O_3]_i = [NO]_o - [NO]_i \qquad (4)$$

where

$[NO_2]_i$ = NO_2 concentration generated, ppm;
$[O_3]_i$ = O_3 concentration added, ppm;
$[NO]_o$ = initial NO concentration, ppm; and
$[NO]_i$ = NO concentration after O_3 addition, ppm.

A NO_2 concentration of approximately 80 percent of the desired full-scale range is generated by GPT, and the NO_2 span control is adjusted to give the desired analyzer response. A multipoint calibration is obtained by decreasing the amount of O_3 added in stepwise fashion, calculating the exact NO_2 concentrations generated using Eq 4, and measuring the corresponding analyzer responses. Record the O_3 generator setting for each stepwise addition of O_3. A plot of analyzer response versus NO_2 concentration generated results in the NO_2 calibration curve.

O_3 Analyzers

O_3 analyzers are calibrated using an O_3 generator calibrated by GPT. The calibration of the O_3 generator is obtained by observation of the decreases in NO concentration on the calibrated NO analyzer as a function of generator setting. The output of the O_3 generator at each setting is calculated from Eq 4. The output of the O_3 generator, corrected for dilution of O_3 by the NO flow, is given by

$$[O_3]_i' = [O_3]_i \times \frac{F_{NO} + F_O}{F_O} \qquad (5)$$

where

$[O_3]_i'$ = output of O_3 generator (corrected for dilution by the NO flow), ppm;
$[O_3]_i$ = output of O_3 generator (uncorrected for dilution by the NO flow), ppm;
F_{NO} = NO flow, cm^3/min; and
F_O = total air flow, cm^3/min.

A plot of corrected O_3 concentration versus O_3 generator setting results in the O_3 generator calibration curve. The generator should be recalibrated on a regular basis because the output will decrease due to the decay in the ultraviolet (UV) lamp intensity. The output of the generator should also be verified any time the generator is moved to a new location or ambient temperature or pressure changes occur.

O_3 analyzers are calibrated by generating a series of O_3 concentrations over the desired range using the calibrated O_3 generator. A plot of analyzer response versus O_3 concentration results in the O_3 calibration curve.

Calibration of O_3 Analyzers by Reverse GPT

An alternate technique for the calibration of O_3 analyzers is based on the gas phase reaction of NO with excess O_3. This technique is recommended only if a NO analyzer is not available. Flow conditions in the dynamic calibration system are optimized to ensure the quantitative reaction of NO with O_3 and to minimize the effect of the slower competing reaction of NO_2 with O_3

$$NO_2 + O_3 \rightarrow NO_3 + O_2 \quad k = 4.3 \times 10^4 \text{ l mol}^{-1}\text{s}^{-1} \quad (6)$$

An O_3 concentration of unknown magnitude is generated, and sufficient NO of known concentration is added to decrease the O_3 concentration by 90 to 95 percent of its original value, as measured on an uncalibrated O_3 analyzer. If the exact NO concentration is known, the concentration of O_3 can be determined and can then be used to calibrate the O_3 analyzer.

The O_3 analyzer under calibration is allowed to sample zero air, and the proper zero adjustments are made. The O_3 generator setting is adjusted to provide an O_3 concentration of approximately 80 percent of the desired full-scale range. The analyzer response, I_o, is recorded. The NO flow is adjusted until the O_3 analyzer response has been decreased by 90 to 95 percent of its original value and the analyzer response, I, is recorded. The exact NO concentration is calculated from

$$[NO] = \frac{F_{NO} \times C_{NO}}{F_{NO} + F_o} \quad (7)$$

where

$[NO]$ = NO concentration, ppm;
F_{NO} = NO flow, cm^3/min;
C_{NO} = cylinder NO concentration, ppm; and
F_O = total air flow, cm^3/min.

The O_3 concentration is calculated from

$$[O_3] = \frac{I_o}{\left(I_o \times \dfrac{F_O}{F_{NO} + F_o}\right) - I} \times [NO] \quad (8)$$

$$\simeq \frac{I_o}{I_o - I} \times [NO] \quad (9)$$

(The correction for flow dilution in Eq 8 is usually small and may be ignored.)

When the NO flow is removed, the O_3 analyzer response should return to its original value, I_o. The span control is then adjusted to the desired full-scale range using the exact O_3 concentration calculated in Eq 9. A multipoint calibration can be obtained by repeating this procedure at several O_3 concentrations over the desired range or by accurate dilution of the O_3 concentration just determined. A plot of analyzer response versus O_3 concentration results in the O_3 calibration curve.

The reverse GPT technique described for the calibration of O_3 analyzers was verified by comparison of calibration data obtained by the reverse GPT and the normal GPT techniques. The span control on each analyzer was left unadjusted over the course of the two-week comparison. Calibration curves for each instrument and each technique were obtained, and the least squares slopes and intercepts were determined. The results are shown in Table 1. Excellent agreement was obtained between the two techniques.

Verification of GPT Technique and Comparison with Other Calibration Techniques

During the development of the GPT technique, the Saltzman procedure for NO_2 [5] was used to verify the NO_2 concentrations generated. A chemiluminescence NO analyzer was calibrated by flow dilution of a standard NO cylinder. The NO cylinder was prepared by a volumetric dilution technique and standardized by comparison with two commercial standard NO cylinders. These two cylinders were calibrated by infrared absorption analysis by the manufacturer. Various concentrations of NO_2 were generated by GPT and verified using the manual Saltzman procedure. The NO_2 concentrations by GPT were calculated from the decrease in NO concentration on addition of O_3 using Eq 4. A plot of NO_2 (Saltzman) versus NO_2 (GPT) is shown in Fig. 3.

A visible absorption technique was also used to verify NO_2 concentrations generated by GPT. A spectrophotometer consisting of a light source, a monochromator, a multiple-pass white cell, an amplifier, and a recorder was used to measure NO_2 concentrations in the 0 to 10 ppm range by visible absorption at a wavelength of 4358 Å. The path length used was 2000 cm. Zero air was passed through the white cell, and the light intensity, I_o, was measured. NO_2 was generated by GPT and passed through the cell. The attenuated light intensity, I, was measured, and the NO_2 concentration was calculated from

$$
\begin{aligned}
[NO_2] &= \frac{(10^6)(P_o)(T)}{(a)(b)(P)(T_o)} \log \frac{I_o}{I} \\
&= \frac{(10^6)(760)(T)}{(6.86)(2000)(P)(273)} \log \frac{I_o}{I} \qquad (10) \\
&= \frac{202.9T}{P} \log \frac{I_o}{I}
\end{aligned}
$$

TABLE 1—Calibration data using reverse and normal GPT.

| | Bendix O₃ (I) | | | | Bendix O₃ (II) | | | |
| | Reverse GPT | | Normal GPT | | Reverse GPT | | Normal GPT | |
Date	Slope, % chart/ppm	Intercept,[a] % chart	Slope, % chart/ppm	Intercept,[a] % chart	Slope, % chart/ppm	Intercept,[a] % chart	Slope, % chart/ppm	Intercept,[a] % chart
23/4/75	211.7	4.6	208.0	5.5	231.2	4.6	225.5	5.6
24/4/75	206.2	4.8	...	...	227.7	4.6	...	...
30/4/75	...	...	...	...	(228.7)[b]	(4.9)[b]	...	...
7/5/75	...	...	208.0	4.6	...	...	225.1	4.6
8/5/75	...	...	214.5	5.0	...	...	233.6	5.2
9/5/75	214.1	5.0	214.9	4.9	233.8	5.0	234.2	4.8

[a] Recorder zero offset of 5 percent.
[b] Obtained by a one-point determination and flow dilution.

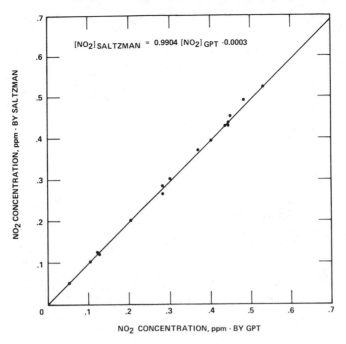

FIG. 3—*Comparison of NO₂ by GPT and Saltzman colorimetric.*

where

$[NO_2]$ = NO₂ concentration, ppm;
10^6 = conversion factor, ppm/atm;
P_o = pressure at standard conditions = 760 mm Hg;
T = temperature of measurement, K;
a = NO₂ absorptivity at 4358 Å = 6.86 atm⁻¹cm⁻¹;
b = path length = 2000 cm;
P = pressure of measurement, mm Hg;
T_o = temperature at standard conditions = 273 K;
I_o = incident light intensity; and
I = attenuated light intensity.

The NO₂ concentrations by GPT were calculated from the decrease in NO concentration on addition of O₃ using Eq 4. A plot of NO₂ (visible absorption) versus NO₂ (GPT) is shown in Fig. 4.

Chemiluminescence NO, NO₂, and NOₓ analyzers are calibrated routinely by EPA personnel using the GPT technique to generate NO₂. Comparison of NO₂ calibration data using the GPT technique with calibration data obtained using NO₂ permeation devices shows agreement within ±5 percent.

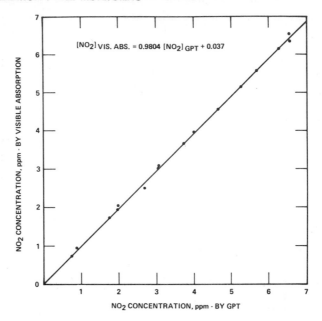

$$[NO_2]_{VIS. ABS.} = 0.9804 \ [NO_2]_{GPT} + 0.037$$

FIG. 4—*Comparison of NO₂ by GPT and visible absorption.*

Attempts to show the interrelationships between NO consumed, O_3 added, and NO_2 produced in the GPT technique have not always been successful. For example, when O_3, determined iodometrically using the 1 percent NBKI procedure, is used to generate NO_2 by GPT, ratios of O_3 consumed to NO_2 produced as high as 1.10 have often been observed. It is suspected that this discrepancy is due to variability or bias in the 1 percent NBKI procedure. Current investigations are in progress at EPA to evaluate and improve the 1 percent NBKI procedure for O_3 and should result in a better understanding of why the foregoing discrepancy exists. Agreement between O_3 concentrations determined by UV photometry and by GPT have been reported [6]. The O_3 concentrations were determined by GPT using an NBS NO in N_2 standard reference material.

The 1 percent NBKI procedure and GPT have been used by the author to measure the output of several NO_2 permeation devices. A NO cylinder was assayed by GPT using O_3 concentrations determined iodometrically. A prototype chemiluminescence NO analyzer was calibrated by flow dilution of cylinder NO. Several NO_2 permeation devices were used to generate NO_2 concentrations over a 0 to 0.5 ppm range. The NO_2 was passed through an external carbon converter and measured as NO with the chemiluminescence NO analyzer. The converter efficiency was determined experimentally using a GPT technique. The permeation rate of each NO_2 device was then calculated from the experimental data and compared with the gravimetrically determined permeation rate. The results are

TABLE 2—*Comparison of gravimetric and measured NO_2 permeation rates.*

Tube No.	No. of Data Points	Gravimetric Rate, $\mu g/min$	Measured Rate, $\mu g/min$	Difference, %
7-15	11	1.215 ± 0.015	1.197	-1.5
7-33	10	2.045 ± 0.027	2.055	$+0.5$
7-29	9	1.779 ± 0.027	1.851	$+2.9$
7-12	15	1.873	1.854	-1.0
RX-3	10	1.155	1.186	$+2.7$

shown in Table 2. Agreement between the experimentally determined rates and the gravimetric rates was within ± 3 percent. The results of this experiment indicated that a 1:1 agreement exists between O_3 added (based on 1 percent NBKI) and NO_2 produced.

Conclusions

The GPT technique offers a convenient means of dynamically calibrating NO, NO_2, NO_x, and O_3 analyzers at a common manifold. NO_2 concentrations generated by GPT have been verified by both chemical (Saltzman method) and physical (visible absorption) analyses and shown to be equivalent to NO_2 generated by permeation devices. The technique can be traceable to one or more of three primary standards. The GPT calibration technique is used routinely within EPA, and calibration systems utilizing GPT are now commercially available.

References

[1] Hodgeson, J. A., Baumgardner, R. E., Martin, B. E., and Rehme, K. A., *Analytical Chemistry*, Vol. 43, No. 8, July 1971, pp. 1123–1126.
[2] Rehme, K. A., Martin, B. E., and Hodgeson, J. A., "The Application of Gas-Phase Titration in the Simultaneous Calibration of NO, NO_2, NO_x, and O_3 Atmospheric Monitors," presented at the 164th American Chemical Society National Meeting, Office of Research and Monitoring, U. S. Environmental Protection Agency, New York, Sept. 1972.
[3] Rehme, K. A., Martin, B. E., and Hodgeson, J. A., "Tentative Method for the Calibration of Nitric Oxide, Nitrogen Dioxide, and Ozone Analyzers by Gas Phase Titration," EPA Publication No. EPA-R2-73-246, U. S. Environmental Protection Agency, Research Triangle Park, N. C., March 1974.
[4] "Reference Method for the Measurement of Photochemical Oxidants Corrected for Interferences due to Nitrogen Oxides and Sulfur Dioxide," National Primary and Secondary Ambient Air Quality Standards, Appendix D, *Federal Register*, Vol. 36, 30 April 1971, pp. 8195–8197, 8199–8200.
[5] Saltzman, B. E., "Selected Methods for the Measurement of Air Pollutants," Publication No. 999-AP-11, Public Health Service, 1965, p. C–1.
[6] DeMore, W., California Institute of Technology, private communication.

W. G. Lee[1] *and J. A. Paine*[2]

Stability of Nitric Oxide Calibration Gas Mixtures in Compressed Gas Cylinders

REFERENCE: Lee, W. G. and Paine, J. A., "Stability of Nitric Oxide Calibration Gas Mixtures in Compressed Gas Cylinders," *Calibration in Air Monitoring, ASTM STP 598*, American Society for Testing and Materials, 1976, pp. 210–219.

ABSTRACT: A preliminary experimental study has been made to determine the factor affecting the stability of reactive calibrations gas mixtures. The model system selected for study was nitric oxide (NO), at various concentrations in nitrogen, argon, and helium as the inert diluting gas. Quantitative data have been obtained which indicate that cylinder conditioning and concentration of the mixture are major factors affecting shelf life. Total mixture pressure and temperature cycling appear to play a minor role in stability, except at low parts-per-million concentrations. No major differences were found in comparing mixture stability in stainless versus chrome-molybdenum steel.

It was observed that the chemiluminescence detecting principle for determining NO appears sensitive to the inert matrix gas used in mixtures. The measured concentration of NO in the mixture varies with the molecular weight of the inert gas.

KEY WORDS: calibration, gases, nitric oxide, gas cylinders, chemiluminescence, air pollution, evaluation

The United States has proclaimed a national commitment to reduce and control pollution of the total natural environment, which includes air, water, and land. One of the major efforts in this program is the control of air pollution. Air pollution may occur from many sources, such as automotive emissions, industrial manufacturing, and residential dwellings. In order to monitor, control, and regulate these emissions, precise calibration gas mixtures of pollutants, such as sulfur dioxide (SO_2), hydrocarbons (HC), oxides of nitrogen (NO_x), carbon monoxide (CO), etc., must be used and must also be reliable with respect to the stability of the concentration of the pollutant in the mixture. Because of the physical state of the pollutants, economic considerations, and quantities necessary for pollution analysis, the packaging of calibration standards has been restricted mainly to high pressure steel or aluminum cylinders.

[1] Marketing and technical specialist, Liquid Carbonic Corporation, Chicago, Ill. 60603.
[2] Laboratory manager, Liquid Carbonic Corporation, San Carlos, Calif. 94070.

Although containers of this type would appear to be suited ideally for this service, the long-term reliability of this type of calibration standard has become highly questionable and controversial in the past one to two years. The major problem with standards of this type is that the pollution component, for example, nitric oxide (NO), is highly reactive with the walls of the containers and also with trace impurities which may be present in the matrix gas.

The problem is compounded further by the fact that most standards are in the low parts-per-million range, and, therefore, extreme care must be used in preparing the container. Also, rigid control of matrix gas impurities and precise mixture preparation techniques must be employed to ensure the long-term, constant residence of the pollutant in the final homogeneous calibration mixture. Other factors, such as final total mixture pressure, varying total pressure with use, and exposure of the container to extremes of temperature cycling, have been postulated as affecting the reliability of long-term stability of pollution calibration standards. The literature to date is sparse with respect to definitive quantitative data on the effect of various parameters on shelf life. Since accurate and reliable calibration mixtures are essential to any meaningful monitoring and regulation program of sources, an experimental study was designed to assess the effect of various selected parameters on reactive gas mixture stability.

For the purpose of quantification, NO was selected as a model reactive gas compound for study in mixtures with various inert gases. The effect on shelf life of the following parameters were selected for evaluation: (1) concentration of NO in mixture; (2) total cylinder pressure; (3) matrix gas— nitrogen, argon, helium; (4) cylinder conditioning; (5) temperature cycling; and (6) cylinder construction material—conventional high pressure steel cylinders (chrome-molybdenum or manganese and stainless steel—Type 304).

Experimental Section

Equipment and Materials

The equipment and materials used were: (1) Harrisburg steel cylinders, Department of Transportation (DOT) 3AA-2265 (chrome-molybdenum), 43 268 cm^3 internal volume and Whitey (Marison Company) stainless steel Type 304 cylinders, 500 cm^3 internal volume, DOT 3E-1800; (2) Superior stainless steel Type 316 shut-off valve, viton-o-ring and Kel-F seat; (3) single-stage Type 316 stainless steel regulator (Veriflow), Kel-F and Teflon seat; (4) 50-in. manometer, mercury filled; (5) Panametrics Model 1000 hygrometer for moisture determination; (6) Thermox oxygen analyzer; (7) Beckman Model #951, NO/NO_x analyzer with chemiluminescence method of detection; (8) National Bureau of Standards

(NBS) standard reference material—94.0-ppm NO in nitrogen (N_2) (span gas); (9) NO—99.0 percent; (10) nitrogen— 99.998 percent with <1-ppm oxygen (O_2), <1-ppm water (H_2O); (11) helium—99.995 percent, <1-ppm O_2, <1-ppm H_2O; (12) argon—99.999 percent, <1-ppm O_2, <1-ppm H_2O; (13) NO/N_2 dilution blends—9.676 percent and 1.017 percent NO; and (14) 0 to 3000 psi mirror faced gages—10 psi divisions with ± 1 percent accuracy.

Cylinder Preparation and Conditioning

All cylinders used in this study were new and were never in any other gas service. Prior to filling, all cylinders were inspected visually for foreign material, and solvent cleaning was found to be unnecessary. After inspection, the cylinders were valved with the appropriate valve.

Cylinder conditioning of the chrome-molybdenum cylinders was accomplished generally by preparing NO/N_2 mixtures in the cylinders at the following concentrations: 5, 20, 50, 100, 250, 500, 1000, and 4000-ppm NO. The same procedure was used for argon and helium matrix gas mixtures. Final fill pressures were approximately 2000 psig. The cylinders were allowed to stand for 30 days and then blown down and evacuated to less than 100 μm. A typical example would be the following procedure used for a 100-ppm NO in nitrogen blend. An evacuated cylinder (as described previously) was connected to a mercury manometer manifold. A vacuum was then pulled on the manifold system containing the cylinder, with the valve to the cylinder now open. Manometer and temperature readings were recorded and the necessary corrections applied before NO was added to the cylinder from a previously prepared 1.05 percent NO in nitrogen standard. After the NO addition, the cylinder was filled to 2000 psig at 21°C with the appropriate matrix gas. The cylinder was then placed on an automatic cylinder roller and mixed for 30 min before being placed in inventory and allowed to stand for 30 days at ambient temperature. At the end of this period of time, the cylinder was blown down and evacuated to less than 100 μm, prior to preparation of an actual test calibration mixture. The important point to be noted in this procedure is that the conditioning is always made with a mixture concentration equal to the calibration test mixture which would be finally prepared in the cylinder. Experiments with stainless steel cylinders were run without conditioning. Pre-preparation of this container consisted only of evacuation to less than 100 μm.

One special cylinder was prepared by coating the interior lining of the cylinder with silicon dioxide (SiO_2) by filling the cylinder with a mixture of 5 percent silane (SiH_4) in N_2 pressurized to 2000 psi. This cylinder was allowed to stand for 30 days at ambient temperature before being blown down, purged with nitrogen, and evacuated to less than 100 μm prior to preparing the NO mixture.

Preparation of Test Mixtures

All chrome-molybdenum steel cylinders were filled at the preconditioned concentrations, using the NO dilution blends with a ±5 percent preparative tolerance. Pure NO was used for the 4000 ppm blend. The NO was added to the cylinders, using a mercury manometer on the filling manifold, as previously described. After filling to a final pressure of approximately 2000 psig and ensuring adequate mixing on a cylinder roller, the mixtures were allowed to stand for 24 h prior to the initial analysis. The stainless steel cylinders were transfilled from the steel cylinder mixture blends with selected NO mixtures from 5 to 4000 ppm.

Method of Analysis

All gas mixtures were analyzed on a NO/NO_x analyzer (Beckman Model #951) which utilizes the chemiluminescent method of detection for NO. This instrument converts NO to nitrogen dioxide (NO_2) by the gas-phase oxidation with molecular ozone, which is produced in the instrument from an external supply of oxygen.[3] All values tabulated are expressed as total NO_x and are relative to the reference NBS standard.

The following is a sample procedure for the analysis of an NO mixture. The analyzer was allowed to warm up for at least 2 h prior to analysis. The converter efficiency was checked,[3] and the ozone regulator was adjusted to read 20 psig. The pressure regulator on the NBS span gas and NO test mixture was adjusted to 10 psig. The sample pressure regulator on the instrument was adjusted to 4 psig for test mixtures in the range of 5 to 1000 ppm, and 3.5 psig for the 4000-ppm mixtures. The bypass flowmeter was adjusted to read 2 litre/min. The instrument was zeroed, with the adjusted span to read span gas value on the NO_x mode, and switched to sample mode to read and record concentrations of test mixtures.[3] The linearity of the analyzer is ±1 percent of full scale, and the precision is ±0.5 percent of full scale. The NBS span gas, which was used throughout the measurement of test mixtures, never changed more than 0.3 percent, as measured against an in-house standard, prepared to evaluate the stability of the NBS span gas which underwent a pressure change from 1800 to 400 psig during the experimental study.

Temperature Cycling

This procedure consisted of placing test mixtures outdoors in direct sunlight for 8 h periodically (average outside temperature 27 to 32°C). This was followed by placing the cylinders in the laboratory for temperature equilibration with ambient laboratory temperature before analysis.

---

[3] Beckman Model #951, NO/NO_x analyzer, Beckman Instruments, Inc., Fullerton, Calif. 92634, March 1973.

Results and Discussion

Generally, it may be assumed from chemical and theoretical considerations that the instability of NO mixtures in compressed gas cylinders will arise from homogeneous reactions of the NO molecule with impurities present in the matrix gas, for example

$$NO_{(g)} + H_2O_{(g)} \rightarrow HNO_{2(g)} \tag{1}$$

$$NO_{(g)} + O_{2(g)} \rightarrow NO_{2(g)} \tag{2}$$

Simultaneously, instability is compounded by heterogeneous reactions of the NO molecule with the cylinder walls, which may be physical adsorption or chemical absorption of the NO specie. The picture is complicated further by the possibility of desorption from the cylinder walls when the total cylinder pressure is reduced and also by temperature variation. Mathematically, we can postulate a total bulk pressure (P_b) due to the homogeneous gas mixture with

$$P_b x_{NO} = p_{NO} \tag{3}$$

where x_{NO} is the mole fraction of NO molecules in the homogeneous gas phase and p_{NO} the partial pressure of NO. Also, we can assume some saturated equilibrium pressure of NO in the walls of the cylinder (p_{NO}^{sat}), which should be some function of wall surface roughness and the active sites, the activity of which is enhanced probably by bound surface moisture. Regardless of the mechanism, desorption should occur whenever

$$p_{NO} < p_{NO}^{sat} \tag{4}$$

Any attempt to quantify this phenomenon would be futile, due to the varying nature of the cylinder walls and the impossibility of maintaining interior uniformity with compressed gas cylinders.

The results of time-concentration determinations of NO blends in nitrogen are given in Table 1.

It is interesting to observe from these data that mixtures in the range of 5 to 20-ppm NO decreased slightly in concentration ($\sim$0.5 to 1.0 ppm) by the end of 29 days. This loss in concentration is due probably to wall absorption. Concentrations of NO blends 50 to 4000 ppm remained constant and within preparative and analytical tolerance. The results obtained with the helium and argon matrix gases are also of interest because they indicate an effect due to the molecular weight of the matrix gas in the chemiluminescent method of detection. The molecular weights are in the ratio 4:28:40 (helium:nitrogen:argon) and the parts-per-million readings of NO in the ratio 120:100:91, respectively.

The data obtained for the effect of total cylinder pressure in the range 1800 to 150 psig are tabulated in Table 2. Generally, the overall trend appears to indicate that there is no significant effect on concentration of

TABLE 1—*Stability of NO blends in steel cylinders.*

Time in Days	As Prepared Concentration of NO[a]									
	5 ppm	20 ppm	50 ppm	100 ppm	100 ppm[b]	100 ppm[c]	250 ppm	500 ppm	1000 ppm	4000 ppm
1	4.65	19.5	49.5	100	122	91.2	253	518	1030	4220
3	4.55	19.2	49.2	100	120	91.5	253	510	1050	4250
4	4.40	19.3	49.2	100	120	91	252	507	1010	4210
7	4.30	19.2	49.2	100	120	91.5	252	510	1040	4210
11	4.40	19.3	49.2	100	120	91.2	252	508	1030	4200
18	4.20	19.2	49.2	99	121	92	252	515	1040	4250
24	4.10	19.0	49.0	99.5	120	91.2	252	512	1040	4220
29	3.95	19.1	49.2	100	122	91.2	251	513	1040	4220

[a] Nitrogen matrix gas, unless indicated otherwise.
[b] Helium matrix gas.
[c] Argon matrix gas.

TABLE 2—Stability of NO blends: pressure effects in steel cylinders.

Pressure, psig	As Prepared Concentration of NO[a]										
	5 ppm	20 ppm	50 ppm	100 ppm[b]	100 ppm[c]	100 ppm	100 ppm[d]	250 ppm	500 ppm	1000 ppm	4000 ppm
1800	4.05	19.1	49.5	91.2	121	99.5	99.0	252	515	1040	4270
1500	4.20	19.1	49.2	91.0	120	99.5	99.5	251	512	1030	4290
1000	4.15	19.1	49.0	90.5	121	100	99.5	251	512	1030	4300
500	4.05	19.2	49.2	90.5	121	100	99.9	252	512	1030	4300
150	...[e]	20.0	...[e]	90.8	122	...[e]	...[e]	253	512	1030	4270

[a] Nitrogen matrix gas, unless indicated otherwise.
[b] Argon matrix gas.
[c] Helium matrix gas.
[d] Silane treated cylinders in nitrogen matrix.
[e] Values not shown on certain cylinders at 150 psig are due to temperature cycling tests on stability.

NO in the mixture as total cylinder pressure is decreased. The one possible exception may be indicated by the 5-ppm mixture, but, due to the small change involved and the sensitivity of the instrumental analysis, this conclusion is suspect.

For comparative purposes, the stability results of NO blends in stainless steel cylinders and pressure effects are tabulated in Tables 3 and 4.

A significant decrease in NO concentration was observed initially in the range from 5 to 100 ppm. These results are significant because the stainless steel cylinders were not preconditioned. However, the results obtained at 500 and 4000 ppm are interesting in that they show good mixture stability, even though preconditioning was not used. Therefore, we can probably conclude that, due to the surface area and concentrations of NO blends, the effects of absorption have a greater influence on blend stability at the lower concentrations and essentially none at the higher concentrations. Further experiments are planned with stainless steel cylinders, using conditioned cylinders to determine the significance of these results.

TABLE 3—*Stability of NO blends in stainless steel cylinders.*

Time in Days	As Prepared Concentration of NO[a]					
	5 ppm	20 ppm	50 ppm	100 ppm	500 ppm	4000 ppm
1	1.20	10.8	39.9	87.7	492	3950
8	0.90	11.4	40.5	88.0	500	3970
17	1.00	12.2	41.2	80.0	500	4000
22	1.05	12.5	41.5	88.7	500	4000
28	1.05	12.8	41.7	89.0	500	4100
30	1.07	12.8	41.8	88.8	498	4070

[a] Nitrogen matrix gas.

TABLE 4—*Stability of NO blends: total pressure effects in stainless steel cylinders.*

Pressure, psig	Initial Concentration of Nitric Oxide[a]					
	5 ppm	20 ppm	50 ppm	100 ppm	500 ppm	4000 ppm
1700	1.2	10.8	39.9	87.7	492	3950
1600	0.9	11.4	40.5	88.0	500	3970
1500	1.0	12.2	41.2	88.0	500	4000
1100	1.07	12.8	41.8	88.8	498	4070
500	1.20	13.0	41.7	88.8	500	4050
100	...[b]	14.5	...[b]	...[b]	503	4070

[a] Nitrogen matrix gas.
[b] Values not shown on certain blends at 100 psig are due to temperature cycling tests on stability.

Table 4 tabulates the data obtained on the effect of total cylinder pressure on NO concentration in the mixtures. These data indicate a small NO increase in mixture ranges from 5 to 100 ppm. However, it should be noted that generally there is no significant pressure effect on stability of NO blends 50 ppm or greater.

The results with variable conditioning processes are tabulated in Table 5. The most interesting data in these experiments are the results with silane conditioning. Over a period of 64 days of NO determinations, no significant change in NO concentration occurred. These results and other data obtained from production experience indicate that silane conditioning is a viable process for stabilizing reactive gas mixtures. Further experimental data will be determined for other reactive gases in the near future.

The effects of temperature cycling and total cylinder pressure changes on NO concentration are collated in Table 6. These results appear to

TABLE 5—*NO stability in variable conditioning processes.*

Time in Days	Type of Conditioning[a]	
	Normal Conditioned	SiH_4[b] Conditioned
1	100[c]	100
3	100	100
4	100	100
7	100	100
11	100	100
18	99	100
24	99.5	100
29	100	99.9

[a] See experimental section for explanation of conditioning process.
[b] SiH_4-conditioned cylinder was run 64 days and ranged from 99.5 to 100 ppm.
[c] Values are in parts-per-million NO.

TABLE 6—*Stability of NO blends: temperature cycling and total pressure effects.*[a]

Pressure, psig	Steel Cylinder as Prepared Concentration of NO, ppm			Stainless Steel Cylinder as Prepared Concentration of NO, ppm		
	5	50	100	5	50	100
1800 before	3.95	49.2	100	1.05	41.5	88.7
1800 after	4.05	49.5	100	1.05	41.7	89.0
500 before	4.05	49.2	100	1.20	41.7	88.8
500 after	4.15	50.2	100	1.40	42.0	89.0
100 after	4.40	49.7	100	1.77	42.2	89.2

[a] Cylinders analyzed prior to and after temperature cycling. Cylinders were placed in direct sunlight for 8 h at 85°F and then brought inside to ambient temperature (70°F) and analyzed. Matrix gas for all blends was nitrogen.

indicate that, within the range of small temperature cycling, no effects on concentration of NO in the mixtures occurred during the test period.

Conclusion

The model gas mixture system consisting of NO in an inert gas matrix contained in high pressure steel cylinders appears to be a satisfactory method of packaging calibration gases, if certain prescribed procedures are followed. The major contributors to longer shelf life are preconditioning and internal coating of the cylinders. This study suggests that the silane treatment of cylinders may provide an inert coating which will ensure long-term stability of the mixture. Low concentration of NO in mixtures does appear to present problems with respect to the final equilibrium concentration of NO in the mixture. Future studies with an NO model system should explore the range of 1 to 1000-ppm NO mixtures in silane-treated cylinders to determine if complete stability can be achieved over the range. This study suggests also that other reactive pollutants, such as SO_2 and CO should be investigated in a similar manner as the NO mixture system.

Role of the National Bureau of Standards in Calibration

E. E. Hughes[1]

Role of The National Bureau of Standards in Calibration Problems Associated with Air Pollution Measurements

REFERENCE: Hughes, E. E., **"Role of The National Bureau of Standards in Calibration Problems Associated with Air Pollution Measurements,"** *Calibration in Air Monitoring, ASTM STP 598,* American Society for Testing and Materials, 1976, pp. 223–231.

ABSTRACT: The National Bureau of Standards (NBS) produces a limited number of Standard Reference Materials (SRM's) for air pollution and related analyses. The effort involved in the preparation and certification of these standards precludes production in large quantities or of great variety. The requirements for accuracy and stability of samples necessitate a considerable research effort prior to production of the actual SRM's. The decision as to what gas mixtures will be prepared as SRM's is based primarily on a demonstrated need modified by anticipated demand and by other obligations of the SRM program. The demand for these SRM's is increasing, and maintaining stocks of current SRM's must compete with the necessary research prior to issuance of new SRM's.

Comparisons are presented of independent analyses of a number of SRM's currently in use for measurement of automotive emissions.

KEY WORDS: air pollution, analyzing, gas analysis, gases, standards, emission, monitors

The preparation, certification, and distribution of Standard Reference Materials (SRM's) is one of the many functions of the National Bureau of Standards (NBS). There are over 700 SRM's currently available from NBS which are intended for calibration and quality control in almost every area of science and technology. Obviously 700 SRM's cannot meet all of the standardization requirements, nor can new SRM's be produced rapidly enough to satisfy the demands of new analytical problems. Working within the limitations of time, personnel, and money, the list of standards is, however, impressive. In some areas, particularly air pollution, there has been a sudden and rather large increase in the need for accurate measure-

[1] Research chemist, Air and Water Pollution Analysis Section, Analytical Chemistry Division, National Bureau of Standards, Washington, D. C. 20234.

TABLE 1—*Gaseous SRM's.*

SRM Numbers	Description	Concentration	Status
1601-03	CO_2 in N_2	308, 346, 384 ppm	discontinued
1604-09	O_2 in N_2	1 to 1000 ppm, 20%	some discontinued
1610-13	CH_4 in air	1, 10, 100, 1000 ppm	discontinued
1625-27	SO_2 permeation tables	10, 5, 2 cm	in stock
1629	NO_2 permeation tables	...	in stock
1665-69	C_3H_8 in air	3 to 1000 ppm	in stock
1673-75	CO_2 in N_2	1, 7.5, 14.0%	in stock
1677-81	CO in N_2	10 to 1000 ppm	in stock
1683-87	NO in N_2	50 to 1000 ppm	in stock

ments. These measurements require gaseous standards of a relatively higher degree of accuracy than have been available and in a concentration range for which accurate analytical experience has been lacking. NBS is currently engaged in a program to satisfy these requirements as far as it is practical.

The topic of this paper and Dorko's paper[2] deals with the work at NBS concerning SRM's for air pollution analyses. The general philosophy and working details of the program will be discussed.

In 1968, NBS issued the first set of gaseous SRM's intended for the calibration of gas analysis instruments. These consisted of three mixtures of carbon dioxide (CO_2) in nitrogen at concentrations of 308, 346, and 384 ppm and were certified with an uncertainty of ± 1 percent of the amount of CO_2. Since that time, six other sets of gaseous SRM's have been issued, and, in addition, permeation tubes for the calibration of sulfur dioxide (SO_2) and nitrogen dioxide (NO_2) monitors have appeared. These are summarized in Table 1. The sales of these standards indicate a need and a demand that at times seem overwhelming.

The problems relating to the preliminary investigation of a particular series of gas mixtures and the preparation of standards against which the final SRM's are certified are such that the rate of expansion of the gaseous SRM program is necessarily slow. In addition, the rate of increase in the sale of these materials, as shown in Table 2, is such that a major effort of the program is involved with certification and restocking of existing SRM's. As a rough estimate, about 60 to 75 percent of the total effort is required to maintain the current SRM's, and the remaining 25 to 40 percent of the time is available for both preliminary research and production of new materials.

Gaseous materials constitute only 3 percent of the total number of available SRM's. The rate at which new or modified gaseous standards

[2] Dorko, W. D. "Preparation and Evaluation of a Gaseous Standard Reference Material, Carbon Monoxide in Nitrogen," ASTM Symposium on Calibration in Air Monitoring, Boulder, Colo., 4–7 Aug. 1975.

TABLE 2—*Sales of Gaseous SRM's.*

Date	Sales
1968	20
1969	27
1970	21
1971	150
1972	175
1973	405
1974	433
1975	(510)[a]

[a] Estimate based on sales to 30 April 1975.

can be developed is dependent on the requirements for restocking existing standards and on the total demands made upon the SRM program both in terms of budget and manpower. This relatively small portion of the total SRM program is not a reflection of the importance attached to gaseous SRM's but is more a reflection of the degree of difficulty associated with these particular materials.

Production of Gaseous SRM's

The first step in the production of a SRM is a determination of the need for a particular gas mixture or calibrating device. In correspondence and conversations over the years, requests and suggestions have been made for SRM's of literally hundreds of different gas mixtures. A decision must be made at some point as to whether or not the need for a gas mixture is such that an SRM should be issued. The decision may be based on a demonstrated need, as was the case with the gases intended for measurement of automotive emission. Federal regulations specify a rather rigorous analytical procedure based on methods which could not achieve the required degree of accuracy in the absence of accurate standards. The economic importance of the automotive industry and its satellite industries was such that little doubt was felt concerning the need for such standards. Other factors, such as strong interest from a small section of the scientific community, may influence the decision, as it did in the case of the first CO_2 SRM's. In addition, attempts have been made to evaluate needs through market surveys.

All of these inputs are evaluated in competition with many proposals for other SRM's, most of which are of equal and some of which may be of greater importance. After a decision to issue a SRM has been made, there may be a considerable lapse of time before the material is actually available. In the case of gaseous SRM's this is occasioned by the time necessary to complete the required experimental work to assure that the material can be prepared and certified accurately and that the shelf life of the material will not be impractically short.

In general, the pattern followed in the production of a gaseous SRM is as shown in Fig. 1. An extensive investigation of the stability of the material is performed in the concentration range of the intended SRM's. From this study, purchase specifications are developed for the procurement of a large number of commercially prepared samples. Concurrently, a number of primary standards are prepared, usually by gravimetry, which are observed over a period of time to ensure stability. Measurements are made to determine the internal consistency of the entire set of primary standards. Conventional methods of analysis are modified, if necessary, to improve the precision of measurement in order that the eventual intercomparison of the primary standards and the SRM's will not suffer from deficiencies in the method of comparison. An imprecision of intercomparison of ±0.1 to 0.2 percent relative is usually sufficient. In some cases, the quantity of standards required to keep the analysis of the SRM's under adequate control is greater than that available from the primary standards, and it is necessary to prepare a set of secondary or working standards with which to analyze the SRM's.

Finally, the SRM's are analyzed individually. The results of analysis of each lot of 50 or more cylinders is compared. Since each lot represents transfer of 50 or more samples from a single bulk preparation, the agreement between samples is an important factor in assigning the final concentration and the uncertainty to the SRM's. If, for instance, all of the samples in a lot agree with each other to within the limits of imprecision of the measurement, then there is some assurance that the particular mixture is stable, especially if a relatively long time has elapsed between the filling of cylinders and the analysis.

If there is any question about the stability of samples in a lot, or of the entire lot, then a second analysis is performed after a sufficient time interval

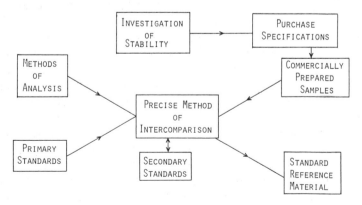

FIG. 1—*General approach to the preparation of a gaseous SRM.*

so that instability can be recognized. The uncertainty of the final certified value is based on the uncertainty of the primary standards and on the imprecision of intercomparison of the secondary standards with the primaries and of the secondaries with the SRM's. The imprecision of intercomparison is represented by the imprecision with which two samples can be compared. The uncertainty of the primary standards is the inaccuracy. A value for the inaccuracy is determined by considering a number of factors. The lack of reproducibility within a set of gravimetric standards at or near the same concentration is the major contributor to the estimate of inaccuracy with which the gravimetric procedure can be performed. The inaccuracy of the analytical technique by which the reagent gases are analyzed must be included in the uncertainty.

In the absence of absolute methods of analysis, it is necessary to utilize as many independent methods of preparation of primary standards as are available. Normally, these include gravimetric preparations, pressure methods, and dynamic dilution methods. While the gravimetric method is potentially the method of highest accuracy, the other methods are quite useful in determining that there are no significant systematic errors due to physical or chemical processes within the cylinder.

Evaluation of Some Gaseous SRM's

The culmination of the effort previously described is a SRM of known accuracy and stability whose use is capable of bringing order to the measurement system. In dealing with gases, this order may be accomplished in one of two ways. First, the ultimate user may purchase a SRM and utilize it for calibration of his analytical system. The number of users then determines the number of SRM's needed. Second, the user may purchase a standard from a commercial supplier specifying that the analysis be peformed by comparison with a SRM. Considering the time and cost involved in each individual SRM, this latter approach is preferable.

If the values that appear on a SRM certificate were accepted without question by the users and if each series of SRM's was internally consistent, then all measurements performed relative to the SRM's would be consistent among themselves. Small systematic errors would be of no consequence, and, if such errors were discovered, adjustments to the entire measurement system could be made. Fortunately, the nature of analytical chemists is such that acceptance of a value offered by anyone is subject to pessimistic scrutiny. Such scrutiny is invaluable in supporting or confirming the accuracy of a number, especially if the scrutinizers base their criticism on measurements performed with independently prepared standards. The following examples, summarized in Tables 3–5, illustrate this point and represent measurements made by a number of competent laboratories of the concentration of the SRM's intended for measurement of automotive emissions.

TABLE 3—*Comparison of results: CO₂—concentration of CO₂ in volume percent.*

		Laboratory Number					
SRM No.	NBS	1	2	3	4	5	6
1673	0.925	0.928	0.928	0.921	0.90	...	0.92
1674	7.01	7.04	7.00	7.09	6.82	...	...
1675	14.03	14.01	14.02	13.95	13.8	13.7	...

TABLE 4—*Comparison of results: propane in air—concentration of propane in PPMV.*

SRM No.		Laboratory Number							
	NBS	1	2	3	4	5	6	7	8
1665	2.95	2.95	2.94	3.07	2.91	2.90	...	2.91	...
1666	9.52	9.80	9.82	9.81	9.49	9.70	...	9.40	9.5
1667	46.5	46.7	46.6	46.2	46.4	46.2	...	...	...
1668	94.2	94.2	94.2	93.3	94.3	94.2	94.2	...	...
1669	477.0	477.0	479.0	477.0	473.0	468.0	...	...	...

TABLE 5—*Comparison of results: CO—concentration of CO in PPMV.*

		Laboratory Number					
SRM No.	NBS	1	2	3	4	5	7
1677	9.7	9.7	10.2	9.7	9.6	9.7	9.8
1678	47.1	47.1	50.7	47.6	49.0	49.0	46.6
1679	94.4	94.4	99.5	95.0	97.4	99.0	94.1
1680	483.0	483.0	492.0	490.0	485.0	488.0	...
1681	958.0	958.0	966.0	958.0	949.0	957.0	...

In general, the agreement between laboratories is rather good with but few exceptions. The most disturbing difference in results is noted for SRM 1666, propane in air. The values appear to be clustered in two groups. The first group at 9.5 ppm consists of NBS, a second government laboratory, a reliable commercial gas company, and a foreign standards laboratory. Group 2 at 9.8 ppm consists of three major domestic automotive company laboratories. The first group prepared standards with which the SRM's were compared entirely independently of each other. There is some question concerning the independence of the standards used by Group 2, and it is likely that the comparison is of the SRM versus a single set of standards. We are not in a position to question these standards but can only offer the results of the two groups for comparison.

A considerable amount of work was done to resolve this problem, and we are convinced that the value 9.5 ppm is correct. This conclusion is

TABLE 6—*Results of analysis of CO grouped by laboratories—average concentration in PPMV.*

NBS	Group 1[a]	Group 2[b]	Group 1 / Group 2
9.7	9.7	9.8	0.990
47.1	47.1	49.6	0.950
94.4	94.5	98.6	0.958
483.0	485.0	488.0	0.994
958.0	958.0	957.0	1.001

[a] Laboratories: NBS, 1, 3, and 6.
[b] Laboratories: 2, 4, and 5.

based on reexamination of the original standards with a new set of standards, the linear relationship of the standards, an independent calibration using a dynamic dilution system starting with pure propane, dilution of SRM 1667 in an exponential diluter. We feel, at this point, that the discrepancies are related to a combination of the different methods of analysis and the composition of the dilution gas in this lot. The oxygen content was measured to be 20.7 which is lower than the oxygen content of any other lot in the series.

The results for carbon monoxide (CO) also appear to fall into two groups, NBS and Laboratories 1, 3, and 7, and Laboratories 2, 4, and 5. The average at each concentration from the two groups is shown in Table 6.

The most recent series of standards, SRM 1683-87, consists of five concentrations of nitric oxide (NO) in nitrogen. Less information has been made available to us by independent laboratories, but the results thus far are very encouraging, especially in view of the nature of NO standards. Many more problems were encountered in the development of this standard than with any of the others.

The results shown in Table 7 represent results from three other laboratories but are not necessarily independent. The results from Laboratory 1 were simply stated to lie within ±2 percent of the NBS values, but the history of the standards used by Laboratory 1 may be related to the standards used by Laboratories 2 and 4. Thus, the results may not represent more than one independent analysis of the SRM's. However, considering the nature of the standards, agreement between two independent laboratories is remarkable. If an estimated uncertainty of ±1 percent is placed on the average value for Laboratories 1, 2, and 4, the average agrees with the NBS value.

The results described represent analyses performed by very competent laboratories, all of which have considerable experience in gas analysis. How then can a laboratory with limited experience and no facilities for the preparation of primary standards relate their analyses to measurements

TABLE 7—*Comparison of results: NO—concentration of NO in PPMV.*

SRM No.	NBS	1[a]	Laboratory Number 2[b] a	b	c	4
1683	45.7	46	44.8	44.9	...	45.9
1684	94.2	94	92.8	93.5	...	...
1685	252.0	250	251.0	250.0	...	252.0
1686	480.0	480	481.0	479.0	456.0	474.0
1687	998.0	998	1001.0	1006.0	984.0	989.0

[a] All values reported to lie within 2 percent of NBS values.
[b] (a) = nondispersive infrared procedures.
  (b) = chemiluminescence procedure.
  (c) = phenol disulfonic acid procedure.

performed in other laboratories? Obviously, they can purchase the appropriate SRM's and assume that the other laboratories will do likewise. This procedure, however, may be economically infeasible if large quantities of gases are required. The alternative is to purchase gas mixtures from commercial suppliers specifying that analyses be performed against SRM's. Table 8 is a summary of analyses, performed in our laboratory, of a series of standards prepared for an industrial laboratory by a commercial supplier who used SRM's to analyze the gases after preparation. The analyses are amazingly consistent, more so because the concentration range extended below the range of available SRM's. This will be readily apparent to anyone who in the past has had occasion to purchase NO in nitrogen standards from commercial suppliers. We hope the practice of using SRM's will eventually extend to all gas suppliers, not only to introduce a common reference point, but also to reduce the demand for these SRM's.

Conclusion

The nature of gaseous SRM's is such that production of a wide variety of standards or of standards in great quantity is not practical. Those which

TABLE 8—*Analysis of commercial mixtures of NO—concentration of NO in PPMV.*

Manufacturer's Claimed Concentration	Analysis by NBS
127.0	126.0
45.0	45.1
22.5	22.2
10.8	10.4

have been distributed appear to justify the effort in terms of the degree of accuracy achieved and the acceptance by analysts in the field of gas analysis.

The reluctance to accept such standards without a critical user evaluation, such as is represented by the results in Tables 3–7, is an analytically healthy attitude. Confidence in a source of standards can only be built on a foundation of reliability, and reliability can only be gained through experience and constructive criticism both from within and without the organization issuing the standard. We welcome any information from users of SRM's, especially where that information reveals problem areas in the analyses for which the SRM is intended as a calibrant. We recognize the peculiar difficulties of standardization in the field of gas analysis and, in particular, those associated with the concentration ranges of interest to the air pollution analyst. Our approach has always been to assume that there is much yet to learn about gas standards and that the learning process does not stop when the standard is issued but must continue as long as the standard is needed.

C. D. Paulsell[1]

Use of the National Bureau of Standards Standard Reference Gases in Mobile Source Emissions Testing

REFERENCE: Paulsell, C. D., "Use of the National Bureau of Standards Standard Reference Gases in Mobile Source Emissions Testing," *Calibration in Air Monitoring*, *ASTM STP 598*, American Society for Testing and Materials, 1976, pp. 232–245.

ABSTRACT: The Mobile Source Air Pollution Control (MSAPC) program has developed a system of primary gas standards which permits commercial gas blends to be named within 2 percent of true value and a computer program which documents the path and traceability relationship of each gas to the National Bureau of Standards (NBS) standard reference material (SRM).

The MSAPC program incorporates gravimetric gas blending as a primary means to verify and extrapolate the work of the NBS. These blends comprise the reference points for a two-point linear interpolation procedure for gas analysis and correlation. The advantages and limitations of this procedure are outlined and quantified.

KEY WORDS: primary standards, gravimetric analysis, motor vehicles, exhaust emissions, gas analysis, calibration, quality control

Gas mixtures are an essential component of the measurement process used to determine motor vehicle emissions. They are used to calibrate sample analysis instruments before and after each analysis and are used also to generate the response versus concentration curve for every analyzer range. Each vehicle pollutant measured requires a specific instrument and a set of nominal operating ranges.

In the early stages of mobile source emission regulation, vehicle exhaust was sampled and analyzed at raw (tailpipe) concentration levels. In 1972, the Environmental Protection Agency (EPA) implemented the constant volume sampling (CVS) procedure [1][2] to permit the determination of vehicle emissions on an absolute mass basis. In the CVS test, the total

---

[1] Quality assurance manager, Mobile Source Air Pollution Control, Ann Arbor, Mich. 48105.

[2] The italic numbers in brackets refer to the list of references appended to this paper.

vehicle exhaust is diluted with room air, a continuously proportional sample of this mixture is collected for analysis, and the total volume of the mixture is measured. The single sample bag CVS procedure simplified the analysis process, but analysis of the lower concentrations of diluted exhaust required more sensitive instruments and lower gas calibration standards.

The CVS test was modified in 1974 [2] to incorporate a weighted calculation from three sample bags. This change, coupled with the lower emission standards of the Clean Air Act, imposed more stringent demands for accurate, stable, standardized, and traceable calibration gases at lower concentrations.

The regulatory program of EPA and the development programs of the industry both needed a common reference for calibration gases. The gas cross checks and interlaboratory correlation programs which had been used in previous years proved very time consuming and were never able to address the question of absolute accuracy. Furthermore, participating laboratories were not compelled to adjust their values to the overall average. Generally, the lack of unquestionable credibility, as well as the lack of a standardized gas analysis procedure, made such arbitrary adjustments difficult to justify.

EPA/NBS Program

In July of 1971, the National Bureau of Standards (NBS) proposed a program to address the problem of standardized calibration gases. As an experienced, unbiased, and recognized "standards" organization of high integrity, NBS was a logical choice as a source of gas standards which could be accepted and used by all organizations working in the field of automotive emissions.

After discussions were held with several organizations to define the requirements for a gas standards program, the Mobile Source Air Pollution Control (MSAPC) program and NBS entered into an interagency agreement in July 1972. The provisions of this agreement were to deliver a set of certified gas standards as shown in Table 1 and to provide an analytical

TABLE 1—*Standard reference gases generated from the EPA/NBS interagency program.*

C_3H_8/air, ppm	CO/N_2, ppm	CO_2/N_2, %	NO_x/N_2, ppm
3	10	1.0	50
10	50	7.5	100
50	100	15.0	250
100	500		500
500	1000		1000

NOTE—All concentrations are nominal. Actual standards had blend tolerance +0 and −10 percent. Accuracy goal of ±1 percent of true value.

system and procedure for intercomparing unknown gases to the standard reference gases.

The four binary blends and eighteen concentrations do not cover adequately the entire spectrum of mobile source analysis requirements, but the values were selected in the initial EPA/NBS program because they would satisfy the critical areas of emissions testing that were anticipated for 1975.

In late July 1972, EPA and NBS sponsored a joint conference at NBS to discuss the proposed program with representatives of the automotive industry and specialty gas manufacturers. From these discussions, it was concluded that NBS should concentrate on developing the technical specifications and certification procedures for the reference materials. The gas blending industry would supply batch blends in large cylinders for NBS to analyze, observe, and certify. This division of responsibility utilized the expertise and capabilities of both organizations, and, at the same time, provided more assurance of standards availability in useable quantities.

Another question which was raised during this conference was the protocol and procedures by which EPA and the automotive industry would accept the values certified by NBS. Skepticism had been voiced by some participants regarding the probability that the program requirements could be satisfied by NBS, or anyone else. Therefore, while NBS was conducting the standards development program, an independent program was conducted at the EPA Mobile Source Laboratory to reproduce, correlate, and extrapolate the work of NBS.

EPA Gravimetric Blending

During its first year as a regulatory function under the Health, Education, and Welfare Department, the MSAPC program had recognized the need for primary gas standards and, prior to the agreement with NBS, had procured the equipment and materials to produce gravimetric blends. Even with the completion of the EPA/NBS program, it was recognized that the number of reference gases being produced by the program was limited in both the scope and intervals of coverage. Since the NBS primary standards were based on gravimetric blending, the EPA equipment provided the opportunity to expand the coverage.

In theory, if a standard is truly a standard, two independent programs that use the same basic method to generate the standard should produce the same result. Therefore, if the EPA gravimetric blending procedure could duplicate the nominal values of the NBS program, and correlate the two blends within 1.0 percent at the 95 percent confidence level, then the entire inventory of EPA gravimetric blends could be accepted and used as primary standards.

TABLE 2—*EPA (MSAPC) gravimetric gas blend inventory.*

C_3H_8/air, ppm	C_3H_8/N_2, ppm	CH_4/air, ppm	CO/N_2 ppm	CO/N_2 %	CO_2/N_2, %	NO_x/N_2, ppm
1	100	3	5	0.5	0.2	25
2	200	10	10[b]	1.0	0.4	50[b]
3[b]	400	25	25	1.5[a]	0.6	75
5	600	50	50[b]	2.5[a]	0.8	100[b]
10[b]	800	75	100[b]	5.0[a]	1.0[b]	240[b]
15	1000	100	150	7.5[a]	1.5[a]	500[b]
25	2000	300	200	10.0[a]	2.0[a]	750
50[b]	3000	1000	250		2.5[a]	1000[b]
75	4000	20000[a] in N_2	500[b]		3.0[a]	1500
100[b]	6000		750		4.0[a]	2000
150	8000		1000[b]		5.0[a]	5000
200	10000[a]		1250		7.0[a,b]	20000[a]
275	15000[a]		1500		9.0[a]	
350	20000[a]		2000		11.0[a]	
500[b]			2500		13.0[a]	
1000			3000		15.0[a,b]	
			4000			

[a] Parent blend.
[b] NBS SRM's.

Table 2 shows the inventory of gravimetric blends that the Mobile Source Laboratory will generate and maintain for all phases of mobile source testing. As of July 1975, all of the mixtures have been blended except the nitric oxide/nitrogen (NO/N_2) and methane/air (CH_4/air).

Figure 1 shows the balance and configuration used to measure the gravimetric differences in cylinder weights at the three filling stages. It is not the purpose of this paper to discuss the details of the gravimetric blending procedure [3], but several aspects of the process should be mentioned because they bear on the overall accuracy of traceability.

If the uncertainty in the calculated gravimetric concentration is to be maintained at 0.1 percent, then a limit must be placed on the mass of the minor component added to the empty cylinder. This limit is a function of the accuracy and precision of the gravimetric balance [4]. It was determined that the MSAPC balance could determine mass differences with a precision of ±2 mg. The accuracy of the mass difference becomes a function of the weights used; the particular weights used in this program were a Class S-1 set which had been checked against a Class M set certified by NBS [5]. Hence, to attain the desired accuracy, the minimum mass of minor component must be greater than 2 g. In practice, filling a cylinder to atmospheric pressure with any of the gases required 5 g or more, so this minimum was specified for all blends. For first and second dilutions, the amount of minor

FIG. 1—*Gravimetric weight differences during the blending process are determined by a 10 kg balance with a vernier chain readout to 1 mg.*

component was often above 20 g. These higher quantities permitted working with positive pressures and assured a 99 percent confidence level on the calculated value, assuming the balance operator has correctly read, added, and recorded the weights. To avoid errors in the calculations, a computer program was developed to convert the recorded gravimetric measurements to volumetric concentrations. The program also generates and maintains a file of all blends. It can later reference that file for the blend mass ratios which are used in the calculations of stepwise dilutions of a parent blend or any previous mixture. Table 3 illustrates the output format.

Once the inventory has been generated, blends can be replenished by using a "cookbook" of specifications. Cylinders are refilled to the nominal mixture concentrations attained when originally produced. This is not only a practical approach, but is recognized as good engineering practice. While gravimetric blending represents the primary step in the establishment of accurate gas standards, the method used to analyze and correlate these primary standards to secondary standards and working gases is equally important.

Standard Correlation

The Mobile Source Laboratory maintains approximately 600 cylinders of calibration gases that make up primary, secondary, and working level

TABLE 3—*Gravimetric gas blend analysis.*

Measured Data

Cylinder	Parent Cylinder	Measured Cylinder Weights, g		
		Empty	After Minor	After Major
H-89456	G-11865	22.552	101.928	478.181
H-89475	H-89456	43.052	70.112	439.822
G-11843	H-89456	93.591	128.682	489.200
G-11848	H-89456	148.156	167.118	569.631
G-11840	H-89456	91.235	103.485	470.723
H-89474	H-89456	32.396	38.953	401.193
H-89469	G-11843	158.577	193.504	450.832
H-89460	G-11843	56.670	67.750	357.891

Calculated Data

Cylinder	Minor Component, g CO	Major Component, g N_2	Mass Ratio	Blend Concentration, ppm	Cylinder Pressure, psi
H-89456	79.376	376.253	0.0028147	2815.347	1595.0
H-89475	27.060	369.710	0.0001920	192.006	1389.0
G-11843	35.091	360.518	0.0002497	249.721	1385.0
G-11848	18.962	402.513	0.0001266	126.660	1475.0
G-11840	12.250	367.238	0.0000909	90.879	1328.0
H-89474	06.557	362.240	0.0000500	50.054	1291.0
H-89469	34.927	257.328	0.0000298	29.844	1023.0
H-89460	11.080	290.141	0.0000092	9.186	1054.0

NOTES—The data was 25 Aug. 1973, the blender, Jk. The major and minor components were N_2 and CO, respectively. Gravimetric values are converted to volumetric concentrations. Mass ratios are stored for use in future stepwise dilutions.

gases in the hierarchy of its reference standards. Primary gases are the EPA gravimetrics, NBS standard reference materials (SRM's), and purchased gases of 1 percent analysis, for which no gravimetrics or SRM's have been generated. Secondary gases are named from primary standards and are used for calibrating instruments and analyzing working gases. Working gases are plumbed to the gas analyzers and are used for calibrating (spanning) the instrument before and after each exhaust sample analysis.

The goal in standards correlation is to quantify the concentrations of all gas mixtures to within ±2 percent of the absolute value. Unfortunately, there are few instruments that can perform quantitative analysis without having a reference point; in other words, all the instruments used in mobile source gas analysis are merely comparators.

As mentioned earlier, this aspect of gas correlation was recognized at the outset of the EPA/NBS agreement, and the comparator and method were specified as part of the program product.

NBS delivered a single instrument package that is capable of comparing propane/air (C_3H_8/air), carbon monoxide/nitrogen (CO/N_2), and carbon dioxide/nitrogen (CO_2/N_2) binary blends. The unit's response comes from a flame ionization detector (FID). The CO and CO_2 blends are reduced catalytically with hydrogen to CH_4 and then analyzed on the FID. The FID, as a detector, has inherent advantages such as fast response, stability, and linear output. Where the number of standards are limited or not adequately spaced for generating calibration curves, use of the linear characteristic of the FID becomes a mandatory requirement.

The Mobile Source Laboratory has not acquired adequate operational experience and sufficient statistical confidence with the NBS comparator to adopt it as the primary standards correlation instrument system. Limited manpower for extra projects in the gas area has been allocated to building a master analysis system (MAS) which will incorporate the NBS comparator as a supplementary instrument.

Although the NBS instrument is not yet in use, the NBS technique of interpolation between two adjacent reference concentrations has been adopted as the MSAPC practice for naming gases. Table 4 illustrates the computer printout of several analyses.

Before the system of gas standards traceability is developed, a few assumptions and limitations regarding the two point analysis procedure need further discussion.

Uncertainty of Analysis

There are several sources of uncertainty which are present in each analysis. One is the uncertainty in the reference gas concentration values. In the case of the gravimetric blend, the overall repeatability in making duplicate samples has been shown, from analysis, to be within ± 0.2 percent. Part of this composite variation is due to the uncertainty in the gravimetric determinations ($< \pm 0.1$ percent), and part is due to the uncertainty in the intercomparison analysis. The accuracy of the gravimetric blend depends also on the purity of the components used in the parent blend. A well-defined offset of 0.358 percent was observed between two, three-bottle sets of parent blends of CO/N_2 made from two pure stocks of CO (both 99.9 percent). One stock was fresh, and the other was two years old. Ironically, the older stock produced higher values. This example has been cited to underscore the importance of using components of quantified purity and integrity in the generation of primary standards.

Once a set of primary standards has been obtained, other gas mixtures of the same type can be named relative to these standards, using an instrument designed to respond to the type and concentration of the unknown mixture. The comparator instrument introduces another source of uncertainty into the analysis. The magnitude of this uncertainty can be minimized by observing a few procedural techniques in the analysis.

TABLE 4—*Gas blend analysis.*

Date of Analysis	Analyzer Train	Analyzer Vendor	Mixture Components		Sample Flow SCFH In. H$_2$O	FID Pressures		Operator Initials
			Minor	Major		Air	Fuel	
16-10-73	21	Beckman	C$_3$H$_8$	air	1.0 10.0	10.0	24.5	PP

Measured Data

Analyzer Setup Data

Cylinder	Nominal Concentration	Low Point		High Point		Cylinder Analysis Meter
		Concentration	Meter	Concentration	Meter	
A-8826	100.0000	74.019	73.4	99.808	99.8	98.0
A-77500	88.6000	74.019	73.4	99.808	99.8	87.7
A-11671	49.3000	43.863	41.8	62.018	60.8	46.3
SG-6895B	42.5000	24.324	22.7	43.863	41.9	40.6
SG-4227B	26.0000	24.324	22.7	43.863	41.9	24.4
SG-173629	10.1000	8.777	34.7	24.324	97.3	40.6
H-89466	74.0190	62.018	60.6	99.808	99.3	72.8
G-4235	93.6000	74.019	73.2	99.808	99.7	93.3
G-4419	46.5000	43.863	41.6	62.018	60.9	44.6

Calculated Data

Cylinder	Analyzed Concentration, ppm	Comments
A-8826	98.050	C$_3$H$_8$/air
A-77500	87.988	C$_3$H$_8$/air
A-11671	48.163	C$_3$H$_8$/air
SG-6895B	42.540	C$_3$H$_8$/air
SG-4227B	26.054	C$_3$H$_8$/air
SG-173629	10.242	C$_3$H$_8$/air
H-89466	73.931	C$_3$H$_8$/air EPA gravimetric
G-4235	93.580	C$_3$H$_8$/air NBS standard
G-4419	46.685	C$_3$H$_8$/air NBS standard

NOTES—(*a*) The value of the unknown gas blend is calculated from a linear interpolation using the high- and low-set points. Each analysis is stored in a file for later reference. (*b*) SCFH = standard cubic feet per hour.

First, an instrument should be used that will produce the most linear response to the concentration range being analyzed. Generally, the non-linearity of a comparator such as a nondispersive infrared (NDIR) analyzer should be limited to less than 15 percent. Nonlinearity is defined as the deviation of the midscale value from the line between zero and full scale, expressed as a percent of full scale. Almost all of the instrument ranges used in the mobile source test program are less than 10 percent nonlinear.

A second procedural technique which should be observed is to make the bracketing analysis in the upper half of the meter response. Normally, instrument outputs can be recorded and interpreted to 0.1 division, which yields an uncertainty of 0.2 percent of point at midscale. This uncertainty does not extend necessarily to the final analysis, because all readings would tend to occur high or be read high for each analysis, thus tending to cancel out an induced error.

Once the proper instrument, range, and output have been obtained, the final procedural precaution is to use the two closest standards available to bracket the unknown within the minimum interval. Generally, the gases used in the test program have nominal concentrations which are near the standards shown in the gravimetric inventory. If the unknown gas is close to a bracketing standard, it does not matter whether the unknown is inside or outside the interval of the standards because the linear analysis error will be minimized in either case.

Figure 2 illustrates graphically the analysis technique and the percentage error induced by not observing the procedural precautions discussed in the previous paragraphs. The instrument used in this error analysis was a 0 to 3 percent CO_2/N_2 analyzer that had assumed values of nonlinearity of 5, 10, and 15 percent. The equation of the nonlinear curve was assumed to follow the form

$$\%CO_2 = A \times d^2 + B \times d \tag{1}$$

where

$d =$ instrument meter response (0 to 100) and
A and $B =$ coefficients of the second order curve.

Having defined the true analyzer curves, several hypothetical two point linear analyses were run. The error induced into the calculated value was then plotted as a percentage of the true value for ten different positions of the unknown on the bracketing interval. As one can see, the error reaches a maximum near the midpoint of the interval and goes to zero at the end points. The maximum error per interval is also observed to increase as the interval increases or moves down scale. Finally, the magnitude of the error increases with increasing nonlinearity.

It should now be obvious why the procedural quality control provisions must be observed to minimize the analysis error. Because these provisions are so critical, they are restated here.

Gas Analysis Quality Control Provisions

1. Use an instrument range with minimum nonlinearity, preferably less than 10 percent.
2. Perform the analysis in the upper half of the meter output.
3. Bracket the unknown with the closest standards available. The interval should not exceed 15 m deflections for nonlinearities of 10 percent.

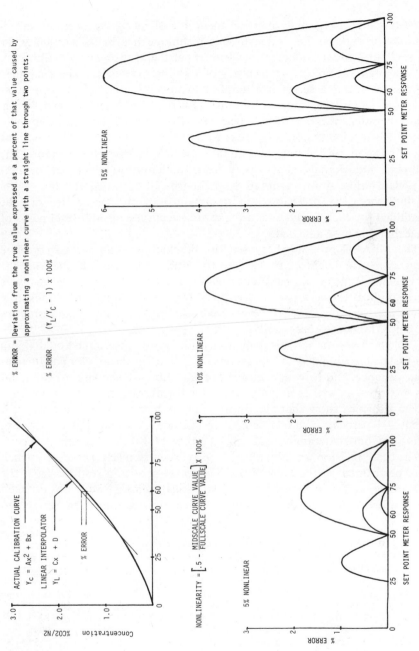

FIG. 2—*Errors induced by approximating a nonlinear curve by a straight line can be minimized by proper quality control provisions.*

4. Develop standards at nominal concentrations close to the values of the working gases used.

At this point, one may question the value of using a procedure so potentially erroneous. The value of this technique lies in its simplicity, its repeatability, and its independence from a particular instrument calibration, recorder calibration, or the accuracy of a calibration curve. The analytical process generates a set of five numbers whose relationship to each other uniquely defines the value of the unknown relative to two known values. The computer program which performs the analysis computations can also perform quality control checks to assure whether the four provisions were followed, or, if not, to estimate the magnitude of the error. The computer file of analyses also provides documentation which can be used to update values if any errors in the standards are revealed at a later date. Furthermore, the precision and uncertainty of the procedure can be quantified for each analysis, and the overall accuracy of multilevel paths of traceability can be assessed.

The MSAPC program has used the bracketing technique to correlate the gravimetric inventory to itself, to the NBS SRM's, and to the MSAPC surveillance contractors calibration gases. In the latter case, the analyses were duplicated on separate analyzers for verification. The bracketing standards were the same for each analysis, but the instrument responses were not duplicated necessarily.

Table 5 shows the statistical analysis of the ratios determined by dividing the first value obtained by the second. The average ratio, standard deviation, variance, and percent coefficient of variation are shown for individual gas mixtures, as well as a composite value for all ratios.

The statistics show that the linear analysis has an overall precision of about ±1 percent at the 95 percent confidence level and that the average ratio of a duplicate analysis is ±0.1 percent of 1.0, as one might expect.

The best precision was obtained in the hydrocarbon (HC) analyses, which were performed on the linear FID. The worst precision resulted from the CO analyses. The data used in this statistical analysis were not checked for conformance with the procedural precautions outlined earlier. How-

TABLE 5—*Statistical analysis of ratios calculated from duplicate gas analyses.*

	C_3H_8/air	CO/N_2	CO_2/N_2	NO_x/N_2	Composite
N	52.0	70.0	46.0	33.0	201.0
ΣX	52.0023	69.9209	45.9588	33.0258	200.9078
ΣX^2	52.0050	69.8455	45.9188	33.0527	200.8220
$\overline{X}$	1.0000	0.9899	0.9991	1.0008	0.9995
σ	0.2788 -2	0.7222 -2	0.5147 -2	0.5883 -2	0.5638 -2
σ^2	0.7772 -5	0.5216 -4	0.2649 -4	0.3461 -4	0.3179 -4
CV, %	0.2788	0.7230	0.5151	0.5878	0.5635

ever, the results on CO support the speculation that the highest probability for error would exist with the CO and CO_2 analyses.

The predicted precision of the nitric oxide (NO_x) ratios should have been similar to the HC data because of the linear response of the chemiluminescent analyzer. However, the NO_x analyses are subject to thermal converter efficiency and flow balance variations. Also, part of these particular samples were not analyzed on different instruments, but rather on two ranges of the same instrument. This very likely introduced a sensitivity variation, which was one of the areas addressed in the procedural precautions.

Now that quantitative assessments of accuracy and precision have been obtained, the system of gas standards traceability and overall uncertainty can be discussed.

Gas Standards Traceability

Since motor vehicle emissions are expressed on a mass rate basis (grams/mile), the measurement process, which includes both volumetric flow (CVS) and gas concentration analysis, must be traceable eventually to a mass standard to assure the desired accuracy. As has been discussed, the mass standards for gas mixtures are the gravimetric blends. Therefore, the concept of traceability includes the path and levels of uncertainty by which all named gases are connected to the primary standards.

Figure 3 illustrates this concept and defines the levels of uncertainty. In an earlier paragraph, the NBS SRM's were named as primary standards. In accordance with Fig. 3, they are actually secondary standards because they have been quantified relative to a gravimetric standard. However, the MSAPC program considers them qualified primary standards because of the way in which they were made and named, the way in which they are used (sparingly), and because of the link that they form between EPA, the automotive companies, and the gas manufacturers.

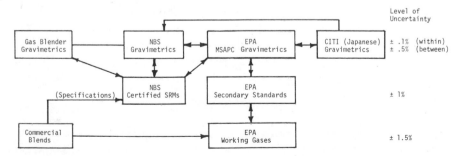

FIG. 3—*Paths of traceability and levels of uncertainty are illustrated for the hierarchy of gases used in mobile source testing.*

If we can be confident that the gravimetric blend is accurate to within ± 0.1 percent, and has demonstrated a ± 1 percent precision on a first level of traceability, then the same should apply to the second level of traceability, which encompasses the day-to-day analyzer working gases. Working gases will, therefore, have a composite uncertainty of ± 1.4 percent ($\sigma_c = \sqrt{1^2 + 1^2}$) relative to the gravimetric blend.

The goal for quantifying gas mixture concentrations has been established at ± 2 percent for most mobile source emissions testing. In practice, this goal can be achieved with the application of quality control provisions within a laboratory's gas standards program. For laboratories with the ability to generate primary standards and the willingness to perform multiple analyses, the achievable accuracy could be closer to ± 1 percent.

Conclusions

The EPA/NBS gas standards program has provided the needed benchmarks for use in automotive emissions testing. The procedure of gas analysis by two point linear interpolation has been shown to be a simple repeatable method for naming gases.

Gravimetric blending of gas mixtures is a highly accurate and precise method for generating primary standards. Correlation of gravimetric blends to the NBS standards and to themselves has provided the assurance needed to accept a complete inventory as primary standards. Component purity and procedural quality control are critical in this area.

Finally, gas mixtures which are blended commercially can be named and shown to be traceable to within ± 2 percent of the true value represented by a primary standard. Four precautions in the naming process must be observed to minimize the induced errors.

Gas Analysis Quality Control Provisions

1. Use an instrument with minimum nonlinearity, preferably less than 10 percent.

2. Perform the analysis in the upper half of the meter output.

3. Bracket the unknown with the closest standards available. The interval should not exceed 15 m deflections for nonlinearities of 10 percent.

4. Develop standards at nominal concentrations close to the values of the working gases used.

Acknowledgments

The author wishes to express his gratitude for the technical assistance of John Kekich in the area of gravimetric blending, for the gas standards correlations performed by Paul Palmer and Gordon Becker, and for the statistical data on replicate analyses compiled by John Shelton.

References

[1] "Control of Air Pollution from New Motor Vehicles," *Federal Register*, Vol. 35, No. 136, Part II, 15 July 1970.

[2] "Exhaust Emission Standards and Test Procedures," *Federal Register*, Vol. 36, No. 128, Part II, 2 July 1971.

[3] "Quality Assurance Guidelines for Mobile Source Measurement Systems—Test Procedures," EPA-650/4-75-024-b, Environmental Monitoring Series, Environmental Protection Agency, June 1975.

[4] Miller, J. E., Carroll, A. J., and Emerson, D. E., "Preparation of Primary Standard Gas Mixtures for Analytical Instruments," Reports of Investigations 6674, U. S. Bureau of Mines, 1965.

[5] "Precision Laboratory Standards of Mass and Laboratory Weights," Circular 547, U. S. National Bureau of Standards, 1954.

S. G. Wechter[1] and H. A. Grieco[1]

Gas Standards, How Standard Are They?

REFERENCE: Wechter, S. G. and Grieco, H. A., "Gas Standards, How Standard Are They?" *Calibration in Air Monitoring, ASTM STP 598*, American Society for Testing and Materials, 1976, pp. 246–254.

ABSTRACT: Not everyone who works with ultra-high purity gases is aware of the difficulties involved in establishing a primary gas standard. The problems associated with the necessary correlation procedures, the instability of certain gases, reaction of gas mixtures, etc., are complicated further by the fact that many firms maintain their own primary standards, with little or no effort given to correlate values with others. It is obvious, therefore, that the only remedy for this haphazard situation is to establish a single repository for primary standards. Because of its history and experience in such matters, the U.S. National Bureau of Standards (NBS) is the only likely choice to serve as this repository. As is commonly known, this is no panacea. All firms involved in the specialty gas business must work continuously to maintain the effectiveness of the primary standards established. An absolute, by definition, is impossible to attain. However, by diligent efforts in correlating gases, we, as an industry, can approach that absolute as closely as possible.

The use of by-weight mixtures is not always as accurate as one may think. This paper intends to point up, by way of specific examples, several correlation techniques we have found necessary in certifying a primary standard, and to point up our present and future needs for standard reference materials supplied by NBS.

KEY WORDS: calibration, gases, standards, air pollution, gas cylinders

Problems of Standardization

Not everyone who works with ultra-high purity gases or critical gas mixtures is aware of the many problems associated with standardization. All too often, what appears as certified on the tag that accompanies the gas cylinder standard is taken as gospel, with little or no investigation as to how the certified value was determined in the first place. Consider this question: how does the calibration gas supplier calibrate the instrumentation he used to certify the cylinder standard? In many cases, the answer may surprise you. Perhaps the following illustrations will help to clarify our point.

[1] Development engineer and general manager, Rare and Specialty Gases Department, Airco Industrial Gases, Murray Hill, N. J. 08077.

TABLE 1—*Certified analyses of NO span gases, ppm.*

Cylinder	NO (certified)	NO (actual)	NO$_2$ (actual)[b]
	GROUP 1 (REJECTED)[a]		
1	52.0	58.0	17.0
2	51.2	67.0	6.5
3	47.2	50.5	20.0
4	53.2	58.0	12.0
5	54.6	60.5	15.0
	GROUP 2 (ACCEPTED)[a]		
1	54.4	54.4	0.7
2	53.2	63.3	1.3
3	52.5	53.2	0.2
4	53.7	54.3	0.0
5	52.8	54.0	2.7

[a] NO average error: Group 1, 14%, Group 2, 4.7%.
[b] Certified: NO$_2$ concentration 1 ppm.

Tables 1 and 2 have been supplied, courtesy of the Texas Air Control Board [1].[2] Table 1 illustrates data obtained from two batches of nitric oxide (NO) standard cylinders prepared by the same vendor. Both batches were certified to have the reported NO concentrations and to contain less than 1 ppm of nitrogen dioxide (NO$_2$). As can be seen, the agreement between certified and actual values was somewhat less than satisfactory.

Table 2 represents results obtained from interlaboratory testing of two primary standard cylinders containing methane/carbon monoxide (CH$_4$/CO). Both primary standard cylinders were prepared by the same vendor, who was aware that they were to be used as primary standards. The results illustrated in Table 2 speak for themselves.

Table 3 is yet another example of what can happen when a group of suppliers is working in an area, with some having their own standards, and others working without either standard reference materials (SRM's) or the proper analytical equipment to make the required measurement [2]. In this particular example, a shipment of zero air was ordered from six gas suppliers. Each order requested zero air certified to 0.1-ppm total hydrocarbons as CH$_4$. As can be seen from Table 3, only two out of the six suppliers actually met the certified analysis ordered. We believe that this situation is not unusual.

Table 4 represents, once more, an example of standard discrepancies that can be found commonly among suppliers. A 10-ppm water (H$_2$O) in nitrogen (N$_2$) certified moisture standard was purchased again from six different sources. As can be seen, the accuracy varied substantially among the various suppliers [3].

[2] The italic numbers in brackets refer to the list of references appended to this paper.

TABLE 2—*Interlaboratory test of "primary" CH_4/CO standard.*

Laboratory	CH_4, ppm	CO, ppm
CYLINDER 1		
A	14.0	42.0
B	14.0	42.0
C	10.5	24.5
D	26.4	20.0
A	14.0	43.0
E	12.0	32.0
C	15.0	24.0
F	14.0	26.0
Mean	15.0	32.0
CYLINDER 2		
A	14	40.0
B	14	40.5
C	14	36.0
A	14	44.0
C	15	37.0
F	14	43.0
Mean	14	40.0

TABLE 3—*Certified 0.1 ppm max zero air.*

Source of Supply	Actual Total Hydrocarbons, ppm[a]
Supplier A	0.065
Supplier B	0.099
Supplier C	0.120
Supplier D	0.190
Supplier E	0.210
Supplier F	0.550

[a] All tests were based on NBS hydrocarbons-in-air standards, were performed on a flame ionization detector hydrocarbon analyzer (Beckman Model 400), and were confirmed by an independent test laboratory. Two NBS standards were used: one at 1.02-ppm total hydrocarbons in air, and the other at 107-ppm total hydrocarbons in air.

TABLE 4—*Comparison of cylinder moisture standards obtained from various suppliers (10 ppm H_2O in N_2).*

Source of Supply	Suppliers Reported Value, ppm	Analysis at Full Cylinder Pressure, ppm
Supplier A	14.0	14.0
Supplier B	6.5	8.0
Supplier C	9.0	75.0
Supplier D	10.1	30.0
Supplier E	13.0	17.0
Supplier F	11.5	14.0

Problems of Stability

One very serious problem associated with certified standards, especially among standards related to the air pollution industry, is that of stability. Stability is the ability of a gas mixture to maintain its original concentration with time or as the temperature or pressure of the cylinder changes. A certified standard which can change is not a standard at all. To illustrate the problem, refer to Fig. 1. Figure 1 represents the stability of low part-per-million CO mixtures prepared in steel (Department of Transportation (DOT)-3AA) cylinders. These data were supplied by the National Bureau of Standards (NBS) and demonstrate the fact that CO mixtures in low concentrations are not stable in steel [4–6]. This stability problem has prompted the NBS to use a wax-lined cylinder for the CO SRM. If an order was placed for a certified cylinder standard at low part-per-million CO in N₂ from a supplier, it would be received probably in a steel cylinder with no mention of the stability problem.

Another problem area very common in the air pollution control industry involves the use of NO and NO_2 standards. These reactive gases are also unstable in steel cylinders [4,6], and this fact has been recognized by most reliable suppliers. One of the most popular methods of combatting the problem is to precondition the cylinder with a high concentration of the gas with which it is to be filled. The theory here is that any of the reactive gas that is going to react with, or be absorbed into, the cylinder walls will do so during the conditioning period. The problem occurs, however, when one realizes that what absorbs can also desorb, especially when dealing with low part-per-million concentrations.

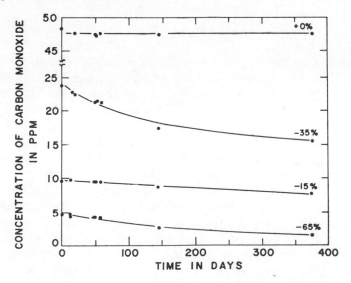

FIG. 1—*Stability of CO mixtures in steel cylinders (DOT-3AA)*

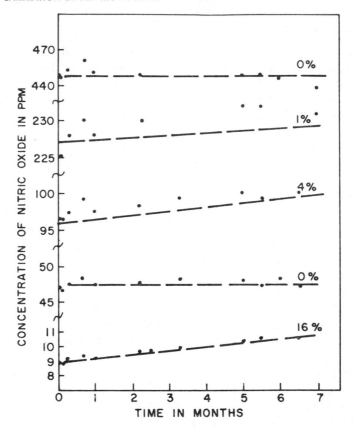

FIG. 2—*Stability of NO mixtures.*

Figure 2 is an illustration of this behavior and has been supplied courtesy of the NBS. It depicts the stability of NO mixtures in conditioned steel cylinders (DOT-3AA). As can be seen, the desorption effects were quite drastic at the lower concentrations. Because of possible sorption effects, the new SRM's for NO were prepared in conditioned steel cylinders, but at concentrations not lower than 45 ppm. Also, these particular SRM's are not certified for more than six months, nor at cylinder pressures below 500 psig. However, if you were to order a 1-ppm NO in N_2 from many suppliers, you would get it in steel, with no mention of a stability problem.

As we have illustrated, there are some very real problems associated with the preparation of certified cylinder standards. Avoiding the problems, as they now exist, will lead only to more serious misunderstandings. Unwarranted vendor claims of stability and accuracy, as well as unrealistic buyer specifications, have served only to compound the problem. Continuous updating of analytical competence and technique, as well as a more honest and open interaction between vendor and customer, is necessary if we are to reestablish rapport.

Need for Central Authority

The problems associated with gas standardization procedures, the instability of certain gases, reactions of gas mixtures, etc., are complicated further by the fact that many private industries maintain their own arbitrary primary standards. Our situation as a supplier is certainly not unique in finding that representatives from a particular company will provide their own standards to be used by vendors in the certification of product. In many cases, however, the standards that have been supplied do not agree from one company to another within the same industry!

Clearly, the only remedy for such a haphazard situation is to be able to refer to a single repository or central authority. Because of its excellent experience and history in such matters, the U. S. NBS is the only likely choice with the ability to serve as this repository.

The very proficient work undertaken by the NBS certainly deserves much appreciation. The SRM's produced thus far have gone a long way in eliminating many current standardization controversies. The number of SRM's available, however, is still too few. Due to lack of personnel and the inordinate demand for standards, the NBS has just not been able to provide SRM's required for all the gases. It is within these areas, where SRM's are not available, that great care must be taken in providing certified cylinder standards. In light of past history, can the specialty gas industry provide reliable, accurate standards where no reference exists? We believe it can. By using state-of-the-art analytical capabilities and sophisticated correlation techniques, coupled with substantiated stability evaluation, reliable and accurate cylinder standards can be supplied.

Correlation of Internal Standards

In the absence of SRM's, some method of establishing internal standards must be devised. One very common method used is to make a set of "primary standards" by weight. These primary standards are then used to calibrate analysis methods used in cylinder certification. But just how good are these by-weight primary standards? As can be seen by the examples cited thus far, this is a valid question. The question becomes especially critical when we speak of reactive gases, such as those required by the air pollution control industry. What is put into a cylinder very carefully by weight may not always come out at the concentration expected. Without a suitable container, which will afford stability to the mixture being made by weight, this so-called primary standard is useless. Also, anyone familiar with weight filling systems available today is aware of the possible errors in technique, which can go unnoticed and lead to inaccuracies.

What, then, is the solution to obtaining a primary standard? We propose that, rather than use any single method, a series of correlations, with many different chemical and physical methods, be undertaken. To illustrate what is meant by correlation of methods, the following techniques were used to compare internal standards for the oxides of nitrogen prior to the availability of applicable SRM's.

Two sets of standards containing six cylinders each were prepared with NO_2 concentrations, using treated aluminum cylinders [6]. The first method of preparation was by weight, using a high precision balance (Voland Model HCE-50). The second method of preparation was to blend the same concentrations by pressure, using an MKS baratron manometer. The two sets of cylinders were then analyzed by chemiluminescence, looking for relative values. A correlation between the two methods was obtained to within 2 percent. The next correlation sought involved the use of an ultraviolet photometric analyzer (duPont Model 411). This analyzer is supplied with an optical calibration filter, with a simulated concentration based on known molar absorptivities for the gases being measured. When the photometric analyzer was calibrated with this filter and the cylinders analyzed, a correlation was obtained to within 2 percent of the by-weight value previously determined. At this point, two additional sets of six cylinders, each containing NO, were prepared again by weight and by pressure. After correlation between them was completed, the chemiluminescence analyzer was calibrated with these newly prepared NO standards. The NO_2 cylinders were then analyzed by a chemiluminescent convertor, using a NO calibration. In this way, a correlation between the two sets of NO cylinders and the NO_2 cylinders was obtained to within 2.5 percent. The higher error here was attributable probably to the extra step required in determining the chemiluminescent convertor efficiency by gas phase titration. The final correlation was obtained by calibrating measurement instrumentation with permeation tubes and noting analysis results. A correlation to within 3 percent of the by-weight cylinders was obtained using this method. In the end, it could be said that mixture concentrations were correlated with:

1. Filling cylinders by weight.
2. Filling cylinders by pressure.
3. Optical calibration correlation.
4. Conversion correlation (NO_2 to NO).
5. Permeation calibration correlation.

After correlation, a primary standard value can be assigned with confidence. This policy of correlation should be undertaken in the verification of all primary standards, rather than rely on a single method of verification, which may contain inherent errors that could go unnoticed.

It is interesting to note that the NBS also used a similar correlation approach to verify primary standards produced for the NO SRM's. A comparison between sets prepared by the NBS and us showed less than a 2 percent disagreement, which is well within the analytical accuracy of the equipment utilized.

Conclusions and Recommendations

In conclusion, it can be said that the need for SRM's is immediate and of great consequence for uniformity. It is up to the specialty gas manufacturers and industry, as a whole, to support the NBS as the central authority. Disagreements or problems encountered should be dealt with and not simply ignored. In our experience, the NBS has been more than cooperative in remedying problems to the benefit of all concerned.

For the users of certified calibration gases, we offer the following recommendations:

1. Inquire as to how your supplier is certifying a standard and determine what reference he is using. Verify his analytical capability.

2. When a supplier claims traceability to the NBS, verify that he used applicable SRM's and not just mixtures prepared by weight. The weights used in the preparation may be traceable to the NBS, but the mixture made is not, unless it is further correlated against an SRM gas mixture.

3. In the case of reactive gas mixtures, ask the supplier if he is aware of any stability problem and what steps have been taken to rectify them. Can data be provided to support and verify stability claims?

4. Ask also if the supplier has more than one analytical method available to verify an analysis.

5. Use caution in obtaining primary standard mixtures prepared by weight which have not been analyzed. Errors in technique will not be detected unless the mixture is verified by analysis.

6. Be skeptical of accuracy claims of better than 1 percent for gas mixtures. It is all but impossible to verify analytically to better than 1 percent accuracy, especially if the analysis method being used must also be calibrated. When SRM's are being used, 2 percent accuracy is a more realistic figure.

7. Lastly, but, perhaps, most importantly, establish a dialog with your supplier. Let him know what you are doing with his product. Many times, your supplier can save you time and money if he knows your intended use. Visits to each other's facilities will be valuable in determining solutions to common problems, as well as in establishing confidence in your supplier's capability.

References

[1] Johnson, D. R. and Richardson, R. L., "Assuring High Quality Data from Air Quality Monitoring Networks," Paper No. 75-10.1, presented at the Air Pollution Control Association, June 1975.

[2] Grieco, H. A. and Hans, W. M., *Industrial Research*, March 1974, p. 39.

[3] Wechter, S. G. and Kramer, F., "Evaluation of Gas Phase Moisture Standards Prepared in Treated Aluminum Cylinders," presented at the 21st National Symposium Analysis Instrumentation Division of the Instrument Society of America, 8 May 1975.

[4] Hughes, E. E., "Development of Standard Reference Materials for Air Quality Measurement," Paper 74-704, Instrument Society of America, New York, 19 Oct. 1974, pp. 3-5.

[5] "Development of Technical Specifications for Standard Gas Diluent Mixtures for Use in Measurement of Mobile Source Emissions," Report EPA-650/4-74-020, Environmental Protection Agency, June 1974, pp. 5-13.

[6] Wechter, S. G., this symposium, pp. 40-54.

J. H. Elwood[1]

A Calibration Procedural System and Facility for Gas Turbine Engine Exhaust Emission Analysis

REFERENCES: Elwood, J. H., "A Calibration Procedural System and Facility for Gas Turbine Engine Exhaust Emission Analysis," *Calibration in Air Monitoring, ASTM STP 598*, American Society for Testing and Materials, 1976, pp. 255–272.

ABSTRACT: This paper is directed toward those individuals and organizations who, in the process of being regulated, are, or have been, required to develop their own standard reference materials, to establish the analytical procedures necessary to develop and maintain these materials, and to evolve a calibration methodology for using these standard materials in day-to-day operations, as well as for compliance testing.

In the *Federal Register*, (Vol. 38, No. 136, Part II, 17 July 1973) the Environmental Protection Agency (EPA) promulgated "Emissions Standards and Test Procedures for Aircraft." Maximum allowable emission levels were established for smoke, carbon monoxide, hydrocarbons, and oxides of nitrogen; and, in addition, criteria were established for the measurement of these constituents. Requirements were also set for the measurement of carbon dioxide to be used in determining the representativeness of the sample. At that time, only a few selected standard reference materials, developed for the automotive industry, were available. These were three concentrations of carbon dioxide in nitrogen and five concentrations of propane in air, all certified to ± 1 percent over a 95 percent confidence interval. The EPA required that all calibration gases would be known to ± 2 percent without specification of the confidence interval. There was no suggestion as to a source of these relatively high accuracy gases, how to guarantee the accuracy of assay, or how they were to be maintained, monitored, and used. Generally poor experience with gas vendor's abilities to consistently supply gases within 2 percent of the certified analysis, and the demonstrated instability of some mixtures in the cylinder led, in part, to the decision to develop a standard reference materials laboratory in support of our emissions measurement technology programs. This standards laboratory was charged with:

1. Providing a bank of standard reference gases for use in all emissions measurement technology programs at Pratt and Whitney Aircraft.

2. Where analytical procedures for making high accuracy determinations of gas concentrations were lacking, to develop this capability.

3. Develop procedural systems necessary to make this reference bank of standards available for day-to-day instrumentation calibration, and 30-day detailed calibrations as required by the EPA.

[1] Project engineer, Engineering Department, Pratt and Whitney Aircraft, Division of United Technologies, East Hartford, Conn. 06108.

4. Determine, insofar as practicable, our ability to perform analyses and assign concentration levels in comparison with the rest of the industry.

5. As National Bureau of Standards standard reference materials become available, to adopt these standards and phase them into our program.

These goals have been met in essentially all respects. In addition, it has been determined that the practically achievable precision and accuracy of measurement is significantly different from that implied by the EPA, and it is highly unlikely that their high accuracy requirements can be met.

KEY WORDS: calibration, instruments, standards, gases, accuracy, aircraft, regulations, emission, air pollution, measurement

Background

In the late 1950's, the Los Angeles County Air Pollution Control District conducted a test program to assess the impact of jet powered aircraft on the air pollution burden in Los Angeles County [1].[2] The methods of measurement were admittedly freely adapted from standard practices for measuring emissions from combustion sources, as were the methods of calibration. For all practical purposes, no further formal program was conducted to assess emissions from gas turbine engines or attempts made to standardize methods of measurement or calibration until 1968, with the formation of the Society of Automotive Engineers (SAE) E-31 committee on Measuring Emissions from Aircraft Gas Turbine Engines.

However, it should be mentioned that a number of groups within the aerospace industry, including our own at Pratt and Whitney Aircraft (P&WA) in early anticipation of having to address the engine emissions problem, had been making measurements by whatever means were available. Many of these methods were either wet chemical manual methods or adaptations of laboratory chromatographic methods, which were totally unsuitable for the testing of gas turbine engines because of the amount of time required to obtain a viable sample and, more importantly, because the accuracy and precision of these procedures was unacceptable.

The aircraft industry became regulated with the issuance of a *Federal Register* document [2]. This document, in addition to setting levels and times for complying with these levels, also specified methods of measurement for demonstrating compliance, including detailed calibration procedures. These regulations were anticipated by P&WA and by the industry and technical community, in general, as early as 1967, leading in 1968 to the formation of the just mentioned SAE committee. The specific charter of the E-31 committee was written with regard to formulating standard methods of measurement of aircraft gas turbine emissions, acceptable to both the governmental and private sectors, in anticipation of influencing the federal regulations. This was done through the issuance of two Aero-

---

[2] The italic numbers in brackets refer to the list of references appended to this paper.

space Recommended Practices, ARP 1179, "Aircraft Gas Turbine Engine Exhaust Smoke Measurement" and ARP 1256, "Procedure for the Continuous Sampling and Measurement of Gaseous Emissions from Aircraft Turbine Engines." At the time of the writing of these practices, there was still little direct experience, either within the industry or in other sectors, in the sampling and analysis of pollutants from gas turbine engines. The major source of experience was in the measurement of smoke, which had been of concern to the military for some time. Some additional experience was derived from the measurement of combustion by-products for the inference of combustion efficiency and gas stream temperature and for the requirement to demonstrate the quality of engine supplied air used in the pressurization of the aircraft cabin. There were neither standard nor uniform practices within the industry. There were no suitable standard reference materials (SRM's) available, and there was little confidence in the ability of commercial gas suppliers to provide calibration gases of known assay and stability of the gaseous mixture in the bottle.

Introduction

At the beginning of our program, we asked ourselves the following questions:

1. What SRM's were needed and to what accuracy of assay?
2. Were they available and where?
3. Where not available, how could they be obtained?
4. What analytical procedures were required, and did we have the necessary resources and capabilities?
5. How do you use these SRM's, and would they be sufficient to meet the needs of:
    (a) Development programs necessary to meet the regulations?
    (b) Compliance testing requirements?
6. What guidance could we expect from:
    (a) Government agencies?
    (b) Experience derived in other industries?
    (c) Common experience within our own industry?

The answers to these questions were somewhat disquieting, to say the least.

The reference materials needed were those required for field calibration of the analytical instruments, those for guaranteeing traceability to some primary standard or to an in-house fixed standard, and those required for the analytical procedures used to generate an in-house fixed standard. In the latter case, they could be, for example, the chemical reagents and balance weights for making wet chemical determinations of nitrogen oxide (NO_x). However, the major portion of SRM's required are gases with a relatively high accuracy of assay, which leads to the second question: were they available? The answer was, much to our concern, no. Gases could be obtained from the various suppliers with a certified analysis to 1 or 2 percent, but these assays simply could not be believed [3,4]. It took a considerable amount of time, money, and frustration to determine this. The reasons for this situation are not many. In some instances, the suppliers did not have the analytical capabilities to provide the required accuracy and did not know it. In others, the supplier did not have the manufacturing capabilities to prepare the product and did not know it. And, of course, we were, and are, faced with the ubiquitous problem of gas mixture instability in the cylinder. In spite of considerable work over the years in many sectors, this problem continues to plague us. It is my belief that, as long as cylinders continue to be filled and refilled, as long as special linings are not uniformly applied, or deteriorate, and as long as quality control over the gas mixtures cannot be absolutely assured, we will continue to have a problem.

Because the required gases were not available in any acceptable sense, we had to determine how they could be acquired, since the requirements were still there. A number of alternatives were open to us. We could undertake the task of preparing mixtures ourselves, in much the same way as the vendors did, but, hopefully, with increased quality control or, as other testing agencies faced with the same problem were doing, for example, volumetric, pressure, or gravimetric blending. We could continue to buy gases to a certified assay and, in some fashion, verify the vendor's analysis, or, alternatively, buy gases to a nominal composition and make the analytical determinations ourselves. This would require us to develop analytical capabilities which we had available only in part. Finally, we could generate our own set of standard gases, which would provide us with an internal, self-consistent, and high accuracy bank of primary standards to serve as a point of reference for all of our emissions technology programs. We could then use these standards to generate transfer and working standard gases. Doing this would also require us to develop and improve our analytical capabilities. Regardless of which option was chosen, there remained open the question of how to use these standard gases once they became available. Since these were to be primary standards rather than working standards, some procedural system had to be devised whereby traceability could be ensured without compromising the primary standards and which would accommodate both compliance testing and development programs. Development programs at P&WA typically require a considerable amount of total engine running time, which is very expensive. As a result, every effort is made to reduce engine running time, with minimum compromise to the measurement. Compliance testing, because of its somewhat unique nature, does allow frequently for some compromise in cost, engine running time, and efficiency.

The problem of the availability of SRM's was not, of course, confined to the aircraft industry. The automotive industry had been suffering from the same lack of standards for many years. In July 1972, a National Bureau of Standards/Environmental Protection Agency (NBS/EPA) joint conference was held to lay the groundwork for a program to authorize the NBS to develop a set of SRM's suitable for the development and compliance testing of automobile engines [4]. These were to be: carbon monoxide (CO) in nitrogen (N_2), 10 to 1000 ppm; carbon dioxide (CO_2) in N_2, 1 to 14 percent; nitric oxide (NO) in N_2, 2 to 100 ppm; and propane (C_3H_8) in air, 3 to 500 ppm. The concentrations were to be known to an accuracy of ± 1 percent of the true value. In very large measure, these gases and their range of concentrations were also suitable for gas turbine engine testing, the most notable deficiency occurring with CO_2. Aircraft gas turbines operate extremely lean, and CO_2 concentrations seldom exceed 5.0 percent, which meant that there would be only one suitable standard reference gas. Of all of the gases under consideration, CO_2, in our estimation, is the easiest to assay, and it was not felt that the lack of a complete set of applicable CO_2 standards would constitute a serious handicap.

Requirements

As previously mentioned, at the inception of this program in 1968, NBS had not undertaken the task of developing standard reference gases suitable for use in gas turbine engine emission analyses. Accordingly, it was decided that we at P&WA would have to develop our own set of primary reference materials which would be used to provide us with a single, continuing point of reference for all emissions technology programs. If, at some future time, national reference standards became available, as is now the case, our primary standards could be compared with them, and appropriate adjustments in our data could be made, if warranted. Primary standards, in the context of our program, means high accuracy gases which remain in the laboratory and are used to generate transfer standard gases, which, in turn, are used to generate working standard and span gases for use in field testing. In this sense, the primary standards have relatively low volume usage, the transfer standards, somewhat higher volume usage, and the working standards and span gases, very high volume usage. To provide a high accuracy assay for each standard in each category would be prohibitively expensive and time consuming and would place an unreasonable burden on any analytical chemistry laboratory. For example, to meet our requirements, we currently have some 1200 gas cylinders in inventory, all of which are analyzed before use. Most of the analyses are a simple comparison against a transfer standard, using analytical instrumentation to be described in a subsequent section.

TABLE 1— *Calibration gas requirements.*

Carbon Monoxide	
Range, ppm	Calibration Gas, ppm
0 to 100	30, 60, 90
0 to 500	150, 300, 450
0 to 2500	750, 1500, 2250

Carbon Dioxide	
Range, %	Calibration Gas, %
0 to 2	0.6, 1.2, 1.8
0 to 5	1.5, 3.0, 4.5

Oxides of Nitrogen[a]

Hydrocarbons[b]

Instrument Response

Range, ppm C-scale	Calibration Gas, Propane, ppm C-scale
0 to 10	5, 9.5
0 to 100	50, 95
0 to 1000	500, 950
0 to 2000	1000, 1900

Instrument Linearity

Range, ppm C-scale	Calibration Gas Propane, ppm C-scale
0 to 10	3, 6, 9
0 to 100	30, 60, 90
0 to 1000	300, 600, 900
0 to 2000	600, 1200, 1800

Response to Classes of Compounds

Range, ppm C-scale	Calibration Gas, Propylene, Toluene, *n*-Hexane, Propane, ppm, C-scale
0 to 100	20 to 50[a]

[a] The EPA specifies no instrument range but requires calibration gases of 50 and 95 percent of each range used.

[b] One calibration gas of each named compound within this range.

The major penalty incurred by adopting this approach is, of course, the introduction of uncertainty at each step of the calibration hierarchy. Dieck has described the net effect of this error propagation on typical calibration gas accuracies in an earlier paper [5].

The EPA requires a detailed calibration of each instrument every 30 days. Although no specific listing of calibration gases is made in the *Federal Register*, the required gases and their concentrations can be inferred from the specified calibration procedures and the tabulated instruments and ranges, for example, nondispersive infrared (NDIR) instruments are to be calibrated with gases having concentrations of 30, 60, and 90 percent of full scale for each range. Hydrocarbon (HC) and NO_x analyzers are to be calibrated with gases having concentrations of 50 and 95 percent of full scale for each range. No specific ranges are detailed for the chemiluminescent NO_x analyzers, but if we assume that two ranges are required and include the need for three high accuracy (± 1 percent) gases to determine the oxygen effect, and four HC compounds to determine the effect of compound on the flame ionization detector (FID) analyzers, then we need a minimum of 34 standard reference gases. These gases must all be assayed to ± 2 percent except, for some reason, the three oxygen effect verification gases, which must be assayed to ± 1 percent. Inasmuch as the NBS standard reference gases are certified to ± 1 percent, this is an unrealistic requirement. Table 1 lists the calibration gases required by the EPA. Table 2 lists

TABLE 2—*NBS standard reference gases.*

Constituent	SRM[a]	Concentration[b]
C_2H_8 in air	1665	2.8 ppm
	1666	9.5 ppm
	1667	48 ppm
	1668	95 ppm
	1669	475 ppm
CO_2 in N_2	1673	0.95%
	1674	7.2%
	1675	14.2%
CO in N_2	1677	9.74 ppm
	1678	47.1 ppm
	1679	94.7 ppm
	1680	484 ppm
	1681	957 ppm
NO in N_2	1683	50 ppm
	1684	100 ppm
	1685	250 ppm
	1685	500 ppm
	1609	20.95%

[a] SRM-standard reference material.
[b] Nominal concentrations.

those standard reference gases currently available from NBS. These reference gases are issued in small volumes, 31 ft³ at standard temperature and pressure conditions, and are limited in supply. As a result, it is strongly recommended that they not be used as working standards but rather as primary standards used in the preparation of transfer and working standards.

Analysis

The gases of interest in assessing pollutant levels from gas turbine engines, that is, those required by the EPA [2] are CO_2, CO, total hydrocarbons (THC), reported as equivalent carbon but referenced to C_3H_8, and NO_x, which are considered to consist of NO and nitrogen dioxide (NO_2). In addition, we have a self-imposed requirement for the measurement of oxygen which is used, in part, to evaluate the "goodness" of the measurement. Prior to the availability of NBS standard reference gases, analytical procedures had to be developed to provide for an accurate assay of our primary standards. Since the NBS automotive standards are not sufficient to meet the needs of the aircraft industry, some of these procedures are still required. Many problems were encountered in the development of suitable analytical procedures which are described in detail elsewhere [6] and will be summarized here.

Oxides of Nitrogen

The EPA requires the use of a chemiluminescence analyzer for the measurement of total NO_x, and the SAE recommends the use of a NDIR analyzer and a nondispersive ultraviolet (NDUV) analyzer for the simultaneous but separate determination of NO and NO_2. Calibration of the chemiluminescence analyzers requires standards of NO in N_2 plus an ancillary NO_2 generator to check the NO_2 to NO converter efficiency. The converter is required because the chemiluminescence method is NO specific, depending upon the reactions

$$NO + O_3 \rightarrow NO_2^* + O_2 \tag{1}$$

$$NO_2^* \rightarrow NO_2 + h\nu$$

The NDIR and NDUV instruments require calibration standards of NO in N_2 and NO_2 in air.

NBS now has available standards of NO in N_2. Laboratory transfer standards and, subsequently, working standards are prepared through comparison with the NBS gases by means of a chemiluminescence analyzer. Prior to the availability of the NBS standards, primary standards were assayed by means of replicate analysis using the phenol disulfonic acid (PDS) wet chemical procedure. However, when we first began to use the PDS procedure, we found it to have significant problems, making it difficult to obtain reproducible results. In particular, we have modified the procedure [7], from that recommended by the EPA [8] or the ASTM Test for Oxides of Nitrogen in Gaseous Combustion Products (Phenol Disulfonic Procedure) (D 1608-60 (1967)) as follows:

1. The borosilicate glass vessels etch after repeated use, and this etching leads to the formation of a precipitate which compromises the measurements. We use these vessels only once.

2. Sodium hydroxide (NaOH) is added only to the neutral point with no excess.

3. Ammonium hydroxide (NH_4OH) is added in excess to a total of 15 ml.

4. The absorbance of the final solution is read at 405 nm.

It should be mentioned also that there continues to be some concern over the stability of NO mixtures in the cylinder.

Hydrocarbons

Both the EPA and the SAE require the use of a FID HC analyzer for the measurement of THC. These instruments are calibrated using mixtures of C_3H_8 in air and the instrument response reported as equivalent carbon or, alternatively, as equivalent methane (CH_4). This latter practice should be avoided because of the difference in relative response FID's have to CH_4 in comparison to other paraffinic HC's.

Two problems occur in the use and calibration of FID's, both of which are addressed by the EPA and SAE. The first is concerned with the oxygen effect, or so-called oxygen synergism, whereby the response of the FID is dependent upon the oxygen concentration in the sample. The instruments are calibrated using C_3H_8 in air, whereas the actual concentration of oxygen in the gas turbine exhaust varies between 15 and 20 percent, which are nominal values. The second problem occurs because, with a THC analyzer, there is a tacit assumption made that the instrument responds equally to all classes of HC, which is, of course, not true [9].

The SAE permits a maximum deviation in response of 5 percent to the average response of the instrument to propylene (C_3H_6), toluene (C_7H_8), and n-hexane. The EPA, on the other hand, requires that the response to C_3H_6, C_7H_8, or n-hexane differ by not more than 5 percent from the response to C_3H_8. Contrast this with a required instrument accuracy of 1 percent on the 0 to 2000 ppm C-scale or 5 percent on the 0 to 10 ppm C-scale and a required accuracy of assay for the calibration gas of 2 percent for the EPA and 1 percent for the SAE. The SAE is currently reviewing these requirements as perhaps being overly restrictive.

Aside from the just mentioned considerations, the calibration of FID's in our ranges of interest are neither difficult nor troublesome, and the handling of the gases poses no special problems. Our current practice with respect to these standards is to:

1. Use NBS standards and a gas chromatograph, with a FID, to establish a set of laboratory transfer standard gases.

2. Use these laboratory transfer standard gases and a THC analyzer to generate working standard gases for field test instrumentation.

3. Calibrate the field test instrumentation.

Carbon Monoxide

Both the EPA and the SAE require the use of NDIR instrumentation for the measurement of CO. These instruments are calibrated using mixtures of CO in N_2. Laboratory analysis, for concentrations above 100 ppm at P&WA is done usually by gas chromatograph, using a thermal conductivity detector. Below 100 ppm, the gas is hydrogenated catalytically to CH_4 and measured chromatographically using an FID. With the NBS standards, direct comparison of laboratory transfer standards to the NBS standards is possible. Because the NBS standards do not cover our complete range of interest (we require calibration standards up to 7 percent by volume), an alternative procedure had to be developed to extend the ranges of our standards and still maintain traceability to NBS. The approach which we decided upon was to use an exponential dilution flask, [6] to define the linearity of the gas chromatograph thermal conductivity detector, and extrapolation of the high concentration gases to the NBS standards. Figure 1 shows a typical straight line response curve using the exponential dilution flask.

The calibration procedures used at P&WA for CO are:

1. For concentrations of CO below 100 ppm, use methanation of CO, measurement by gas chromatograph with a FID and comparison with NBS standards to generate laboratory transfer standards.

2. Establish laboratory transfer standards for concentrations between 100 and 1000 ppm by gas chromatographic analysis, using a thermal conductivity detector and comparing with NBS standards.

3. For concentrations above 1000 ppm, laboratory transfer standards are established using an exponential dilution flask together with a gas chromatograph, with a thermal conductivity detector, and comparison with NBS standards.

4. Working standard gases are established, using an NDIR analyzer with linearizing electronics and the laboratory transfer standard gases.

5. Field test instrumentation is calibrated, using the working standard gases.

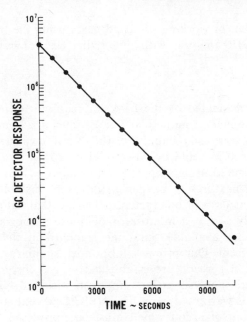

FIG. 1—*Exponential dilution of CO with N_2.*

Carbon Dioxide

Both the EPA and the SAE require the use of a NDIR analyzer for the measurement of CO_2. The instruments are calibrated, using mixtures of CO_2 in N_2. The reason for requiring the measurement of CO_2, which is not considered normally to be a pollutant, is to provide a means for ensuring that a representative exhaust sample has been taken. The procedure by which this is done is detailed in a subsequent section. Unlike CO and NO_x, CO_2 does not pose any particular stability problems in the concentrations of interest, nominally 0.5 to 5.0 percent, and analysis proceeds in a relatively straightforward fashion, using either gas chromatograph or a mass spectrometer.

One problem does exist, however, because the NBS standards address more nearly the needs of the automotive industry than those of the aircraft industry. NBS provides SRM's in nominal concentrations of 1, 7, and 14 percent. Only one, the 1 percent SRM, is directly applicable to our needs.

Our present procedure consists of:

1. Establishment of primary CO_2 standards by chromatographic and mass spectrometric analysis.

2. Establishment of laboratory transfer standards by chromatographic analysis and comparison with the primary standards or NBS standards where appropriate.

3. Establishment of working standard gases using the transfer standard gases and a NDIR analyzer with linearizing electronics.

Oxygen

Although not mandated by the EPA, or required by the SAE, oxygen measurements are made routinely at P&WA during all emission tests and the data used to assess the reliability of the overall measurement. How this is done is explained in detail by Alwang et al [10].

Oxygen is measured using amperometric analyzers, and the instruments calibrated, using mixtures of oxygen in nitrogen. Instability and drift in these analyzers, as used in our systems, demand that calibrations be performed frequently and at a number of points over the range of interest. Currently NBS has available only one standard in the percent range, nominally 21 percent. Our primary laboratory standards, for concentrations other than 21 percent, are established by gas chromatographic and mass spectrometric analysis and comparison with the NBS standard. A word of caution is warranted here. The NBS 21 percent standard contains the normal amount of argon which must be considered when making a chromatographic separation.

Our current calibration procedure is to:

1. Establish primary laboratory standards through chromatographic and mass spectrometric analysis and comparison with the NBS 21 percent standard.

2. Establish working standards and span gases by chromatographic analysis and comparison with the primary laboratory standards. Transfer standards are not required because of the small volumes of gas consumed in analysis by chromatography.

On-Stand Validation

Making measurements on large gas turbine engines is both time consuming and expensive. Real-time, or almost real-time, validation of emissions measurement data serves to reduce the time and expense of gathering data, minimizes the necessity for having to repeat tests, and goes a long way toward the establishment of credibility in the data. We consider the validation of the data to be an integral part of the overall calibration procedure. Real-time validation of emissions measurement data is made possible through the availability of an on-line data processing computer and is handled in three ways:

1. Calculation of the fuel-to-air ratio, as determined from measured fuel and air flow and comparison with the fuel-to-air ratio calculated from the measured species.

2. Inspection of empirically derived smooth functional relationships between the various gaseous constituents.

3. Calculation of the standard error of estimate (SEE) for each measured species and comparison both with the SEE as it changes during the day and with the cumulative SEE over all past testing since the inception of the computerized surveillance program.

The calculation of fuel-to-air ratio proceeds in a straight forward fashion, using a procedure adopted by the SAE which uses the following approximation

$$F/A \approx \frac{\dfrac{CO}{10^4} + CO_2 + \dfrac{C}{10^4}}{207 - \dfrac{2\,CO}{10^4} - CO_2} \qquad (2)$$

where

F = fuel flow,
A = air flow,
CO = concentration of CO in ppm (wet),
CO_2 = concentration of CO_2 in percent (wet), and
C = concentration of HC in ppm as carbon (wet).

This expression assumes a hydrogen to carbon ratio, for the fuel, of two. Typical F/A comparisons for turbojet and nonmixed flow turbofan engines fall within ±5 percent.

At high engine power, the concentration of CO and HC is very small relative to the concentration of CO_2, and the calculated F/A is almost entirely dependent upon the measurement of the CO_2. A disadvantage in relying solely upon a carbon balance fuel-to-air ratio calculation is that, in large measure, only one constituent is being measured, CO_2, and this constituent, although important in assessing the representativeness of the sample, does not reflect the accuracy of the other instruments.

Experience has shown us that there are a number of useful smooth relationships between many of the species measured. For example, there is a straight line relationship between O_2 and CO_2, which can be derived from consideration of the reaction of complete combustion with excess air (Fig. 2)

$$XCH_\alpha + \gamma O_2 + 4\gamma N_2 \rightarrow k_1 CO_2 + \frac{\alpha}{2} k_1 H_2 O + k_2 O_2 + k_3 N_2 \qquad (3)$$

where

X = initial moles of fuel;
α = hydrogen to carbon ratio of the fuel = 2;
γ = initial moles of oxygen;
k_1, k_2, k_3 = number of moles of CO_2, O_2, and N_2 in the final mixture; and
CH_α = equivalent molecular formulation.

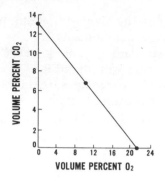

FIG. 2—CO_2 versus O_2 for CgH_{18} fuel.

Alwang et al [10] have shown that this leads to an equation of the following form

$$\eta CO_2 = 1/8 - 5/8 \eta O_2 \tag{4}$$

where η = Mole fractions.

By plotting a least squares fit to the CO_2–O_2 data and performing a linear regression on the curve, a good estimate of the measurement variability of these species is obtained. For the situation of incomplete or fuel rich combustion, suitable correction factors must be applied to compensate for nonnegligible quantities of HC and CO.

Although smooth relationships also exist between other species, for example, CO_2 versus log NO_x, log CO versus log THC (Fig. 3), CO_2 versus log CO, and CO_2 versus log THC, no simple derivation of these relationships is possible. CO, THC, and NO_x are present in very small quantities and vary in a complex fashion with combustor design and operating conditions. However, since smooth relationships do exist, having been empirically determined over many thousands of tests, they can be used to draw attention to shifts in instrument calibration or erratic behavior.

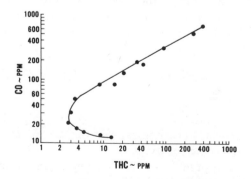

FIG. 3—Log CO versus log THC (as measured).

As with the CO_2–O_2 curve, standard error data is used to estimate goodness, and any points deviating more than two standard deviations from the smooth curve are suspect.

The most useful tool for assessing instrument uncertainty is the SEE. This is recalculated automatically each time an instrument is calibrated, both for the day and over all testing. Nominal guidelines, or bounds, derived from past experience as to the normally anticipated uncertainties, are programmed into the computer, which compares the immediate SEE with the expected level, and, if the expected level is exceeded, the data are flagged automatically on a computer graphic scope display and on the hard copy printout. The operator can exercise his own judgement as to continuing with the test or pausing to resolve the discrepancy. The SEE's, taken over the 95 percent confidence interval, are determined from the gain setting data. Each time an instrument is calibrated or spanned, the gain setting is recorded before and after adjustment and the data fed into the computer for calculation. In addition, the individual instrument calibration curves, checked every 30 days, are programmed into the computer, with the appropriate SEE for the curve and the particular working standard gas values in daily use. If one of these standards should change during a test, because of depletion, for example, the operator can change values in the computer program on the test stand by means of a manual keyboard. This approach to the monitoring of individual instrument uncertainty has given us valuable insight into the practially achievable precision and accuracy in using these types of analytical instruments and has led to the following conclusions:

1. Linear interpolation of instrument drift as determined from post-test calibration will not, in general, improve the data.

2. Instrument precision varies widely from day to day.

3. Instrument precision can be inferred from calibration-to-calibration data.

4. Instrument precisions required by the EPA are optimistic and are not typically achieved.

Comparative Testing

Early in our program, we decided that, to establish a calibration facility, we would attempt to compare, insofar as practical, our analytical capabilities and assigned values for our reference gases with others working in the field. Our thinking, of course, was that although there existed the possibility of suffering some temporary embarrassment, the time to determine deficiencies in our analytical capabilities or standard reference gases or both, if any, would be in the beginning of the program, where the impact would be the least. In addition to establishing a bench mark in the beginning, we also decided that this type of comparison would be a healthy thing on a continuing basis. Our particular situation, with a single laboratory testing our own company's products, created an insular situation in which it would be quite possible to introduce an unknown bias into our measurements which would be difficult to determine, particularly before the availability of NBS SRM's. Initially, the means we took to accomplish this was to participate in a number of collaborative testing programs under the auspices of the SAE and the Coordinating Research Council. These programs were intended to evaluate instruments and instrumental procedures, but also offered the opportunity for comparing calibration gases. For a number of years now, we have been participating in the Scott Research Laboratories calibration gas cross reference service [11]. This service, which has subscribers from a good cross section of industry, government, and private laboratories, enables participants to check their analytical procedures and capabilities on a variety of gas mixtures, each of which is designed to address a specific problem area. For example, there are five cross reference services which include mixtures concerned with diesel exhaust, automotive exhaust, NO_x, constant volume sampling (CVS), and atmospheric monitoring. Mixtures of these gases are supplied four times a year, and, for each service and each quarterly mixture, a detailed report listing results, with a statistical analysis of the results, is provided each participating laboratory. Inasmuch as each participating laboratory is free to choose whichever analytical technique it wants, some judgements can be made also as to the efficiency and accuracy of the various procedures. Of course, it should be pointed up that demonstrating your ability to assay your reference gases accurately is no guarantee that you will preserve this capability in the field. Real-world accuracy of field test instrumentation is obviously dependent upon many factors which are likely to be obtained outside of the laboratory [12]. Restricting consideration of accuracy to that assigned to the calibrating materials only is both naive and misleading.

Accuracy

Standard reference gases and methods of instrument calibration are essential to the making of accurate and precise measurements. However, they form only one aspect of the practically achievable precision and accuracy of the measurement. For gas turbine engines, as well as other sources, the real-world accuracy of the measurement is considerably different from that implied by the restrictions placed upon the accuracy of the calibration gases and the analytical instrumentation. In addition to the considerable effort which has gone into establishing a set of standard reference gases and a procedural system for their use, an even greater effort has gone into understanding the practically achievable precision and accuracy in measuring emissions from gas turbines, into understanding and assessing the significance of the basic components of the error propagation model used to calculate the total uncertainty in the measurements, and into evaluating the implications of this uncertainty on both development and compliance testing [12–14]. In summary, the sources of error, in addition to standards and calibration gases, include instrument uncertainty, engine performance measurement uncertainty, and sampling error.

Sampling error, because of the spatial distribution of the gases, constitutes the single largest source of uncertainty and, in fact, for mixed flow turbofan engines, dominates the total uncertainty.

As shown by Dieck (Table 3), even when testing an infinite number of points, the total uncertainty is always considerably greater than that required by the EPA. Reliance on the care taken in calibrating the instrumentation and on the insurance of traceability to NBS can be misleading.

Conclusions

1. A bank of standard reference gases, now traceable to the NBS has been established.
2. A procedural system has been developed to make these standard reference gases available for daily instrument calibration requirements, as well as the 30-day detailed calibrations required by the EPA.

TABLE 3—*Typically achievable EPA accuracy in percent of point.*

Number of Single Point Samples	1	12	100	∞
Excluding Sample Error—PWA Instruments				
NO_x	7.62	4.10	3.70	3.68
HC	9.30	3.83	3.17	2.43
CO	4.17	2.52	2.34	2.31
Including PWA Sample Error—T2 Class Engine				
NO_x	17.3	6.0	4.03	3.68
HC	75.7	22.0	7.95	2.43
CO	36.0	10.4	3.59	2.31
Including FAA[a] Sample Error—T3 Class Engine				
NO_x	160.0	46.0	16.0	3.68
HC	96.0	28.0	10.0	2.43
CO	203.0	59.0	20.0	2.31
Utilizing Only EPA Required Accuracy				
NO_x	2.16	2.01	2.00	2.00
HC	2.41	2.04	2.01	2.00
CO	2.41	2.04	2.01	2.00

[a] Estimated due to missing take-off data.

3. Analytical techniques for making high accuracy analyses of calibration gases have been improved or developed or both.

4. We have satisfied ourselves that the accuracy of our measurements is favorably comparable to the accuracies achieved by the rest of the industry.

5. The accuracy of our original bank of internally established standard reference gases has been verified through comparison with NBS standards.

6. Considering only the calibration gas and instrument accuracy in estimating the total uncertainty in the measurement can be misleading.

7. It is unlikely that the high accuracy requirements, implied by the EPA, can be met in practice.

References

[1] George, R. E. and Burlin, R. M., "Air Pollution From Commercial Jet Aircraft in Los Angeles County," Los Angeles County Air Pollution Control District, April 1960.

[2] "Control of Air Pollution from Aircraft and Aircraft Engines," *Federal Register*, Vol. 38, No. 136, Part II, 1973.

[3] Grieco, H. A., Hans, W. M., and Patel, K., "Ultra-pure Gases and Gas Standards," presented at the Pittsburgh Conference on Analytical Chemistry and Applied Spectroscopy, Cleveland, Ohio, 5 March 1974.

[4] "Report of the NBS-EPA Joint Conference on Problems in the Development of Standard Reference Gases for Mobile Source Emissions Measurement," National Bureau of Standards, 7 Aug. 1972.

[5] Dieck, R. H., this symposium, pp. 16–39.

[6] Elwood, J. H., Robertson, D. J., Groth, R. H., and Gardner, D. G., "Problems in Establishment of Standard Reference Gases and Analytical Procedures for Use in Gas Turbine Exhaust Measurements," Paper 75-03.4, 68th Annual Meeting of the Air Pollution Control Association, 15–20 June 1975.

[7] Robertson, D. J., Groth, R. H., and Glastris, E. G., *Environmental Science and Technology*, Vol. 9, No. 10, Oct. 1975, pp. 979–981.

[8] *Federal Register*, Environmental Protection Agency, Method 7, Vol. 36, 23 Dec. 1971.

[9] Jackson, M. W., "Analysis for Exhaust Gas Hydrocarbons—Non-Dispersive Infrared Versus Flame-Ionization," *Journal of the Air Pollution Control Association*, Vol. 2, No. 12, 1966.

[10] Alwang, W. G., Campbell, N. T., and Groth, R. H., "Empirical Validation of Turbine Engine Exhaust Measurements," Paper 75-03.3, 68th Annual Meeting of the Air Pollution Control Association, 15–20 June 1975.

[11] Souza, A. F., "A Calibration Gas Cross-Reference Service," International Instrumentation Conference, Instrument Society of America, New York, 28–31 Oct. 1974, pp. 74–634.

[12] Elwood, J. H. and Dieck, R. H., "Real World Accuracy of Field Instrumentation," 21st International Instrumentation Symposium, Instrument Society of America, Philadelphia, Pa., 21 May 1975.

[13] Dieck, R. H. and Elwood, J. H., "The Assessment of Emission Analysis Accuracy," 67th Annual Meeting of the Air Pollution Control Association, Denver, Colo., 9–13 June 1974, pp. 74–91.

[14] Dieck, R. H., "Gas Turbine Emission Measurement Uncertainty," International Instrumentation Conference, Instrument Society of America, New York, 28–31 Oct. 1974, pp. 74–639.

Ultra-Low-Level Problems
and Techniques

W. E. Scott[1] *and J. T. Marrin*[1]

Problems with Zero Gases for Ultra-Low Level Measurements of Air Pollutants

REFERENCE: Scott, W. E. and Marrin, J. T., **"Problems with Zero Gases for Ultra-Low Level Measurements of Air Pollutants,"** *Calibration in Air Monitoring, ASTM STP 598*, American Society for Testing and Materials, 1976, pp. 275–281.

ABSTRACT: The replacement of wet-chemical methods of measuring air pollutants by more sophisticated instruments has introduced a number of new problems. Most of the new analytical instruments do not give absolute results. Instead, their measurements are relative to a reference standard containing a "known" concentration of the pollutant of interest and to a "zero" standard containing neither the pollutant of interest nor interfering components. As the attempt is made to measure pollutants at very low levels, it becomes more difficult not only to produce reference standards, but also equally difficult to establish the zero level.

The specific requirements for ultra-pure zero gases, including carrier gases employed in chromatographic measurements, are illustrated for many instruments in use today. Problems in the handling of zero gases are discussed. Results of tests demonstrate the ease of contamination of zero gases by regulators, sample lines, syringes, etc. Solutions to many of these handling problems are presented.

KEY WORDS: calibration, instruments, gases, air pollution, standards, monitors, measurement

In order to obtain results on an absolute basis, most analytical instruments for the measurement of air pollutants require reference standards, one containing a known concentration of the pollutant of interest, and a second containing none of the pollutant. These reference standards are commonly called "span" gases and "zero" gases. The need to monitor many pollutants at lower and lower concentrations in the atmosphere has resulted in the availability of instruments of higher and higher sensitivities. The concentrations of pollutants in the required standards are now one to two orders of magnitude lower. Specialty gas suppliers are not accustomed to producing standards at the lower levels required, and, when they try, they find that stability is difficult to attain, especially with the so-called "reactive" gases, such as nitrogen dioxide (NO_2), carbon monoxide (CO), hydrogen sulfide (H_2S), etc.

[1] President and vice president, respectively, Scott-Marrin, Inc., Riverside, Calif. 92507.

The requirement for low level standards is more critical for zero gases than for span gases. Where a prepurified grade was previously satisfactory, now one may find an ultra-high purity grade unsuitable, not only as a zero gas, but as the diluent for a span gas. A minimum purity of 99.999 percent does not tell us what we need to know; a more detailed analysis of trace impurities is required. What is a zero gas? How does one obtain a suitable zero gas? How can a user determine whether a zero gas is good enough, particularly for measurements of ultra-low levels of pollutants? What precautions are necessary in using this zero gas, once you have it? The objective of this paper is to answer these questions and many related ones, thereby assisting those carrying out ultra-low level measurements to obtain a desired accuracy.

Definition of Zero Gas

For practical purposes, a zero gas is a gas which, when introduced into a pollution monitoring instrument, produces no detectable change in response relative to absolute zero on the instrument scale selected for measurements. This definition is independent of the type of analytical instrument, continuous or chromatographic, being calibrated.

The purity of the zero gas, that is, the absence of the pollutant being measured and, equally important, of any possible interfering component, is dependent on the concentration level being measured. Obviously, it follows that the higher the sensitivity of the instrument and the lower the concentration to be measured, the higher the purity of the zero gas required. For measurements at ultra-low levels, which we can specify roughly as less than 1 ppm, the zero gas purity more closely approaches the absolute zero.

For chromatographs, the zero gas is the carrier gas. Therefore, the lower the concentration to be measured, the higher the purity of the carrier gas required. If a sample of a gas of higher purity is injected, and a detectable response in the form of a vacancy or negative peak is obtained, then the carrier gas is not what we will call a zero carrier gas. Again, carrier purity refers not only to its content of the pollutants to be measured, but also of possible interfering trace components, including components such as water which would cause deterioration of columns, or components which would destroy the efficiency of a catalyst or produce a new product by catalytic reaction that might interfere with the measurement of the pollutant of interest.

Applications of Zero Gases

Zero gases are of basic importance. The name, zero gas, originated from the practice of using a high-purity gas to set the zero scale deflection of continuous analyzers. Today, the name is used to indicate high purity with respect to specific trace components.

A supplier of span gases in cylinders for low-level measurements must use a diluent gas of high purity, that is, the diluent must be a zero gas for the trace component to be measured. Such diluent gases are also required for static and dynamic dilution and permeation tube calibrators. As mentioned previously, carrier gases for chromatography are zero gases.

Trouble shooting, another important application of a zero gas, will be discussed in a following section on measuring the purity of zero gases.

Sources of Zero Gases

There are many suppliers of zero gases in cylinders. A sample of the specifications for common zero gases, selected from suppliers catalogs, is shown in Table 1. The table also shows results of analyses by Scott-Marrin, Inc. (SMI) for some additional components not covered by the specifications. The table shows that some zero gases are available that are suitable for ultra-low level measurements. However, most of those in the table have a specification for total hydrocarbon (THC) but nothing else. If the measurement application is for CO, sulfur dioxide (SO_2), or nitrogen oxide (NO_x), there may be suitable nitrogen or hydrogen zero gases available, but these components are not specified, and, therefore, there is no assurance that the cylinder purchased will be a suitable zero gas. Furthermore, the trace component composition is variable. For example, the CO content of

TABLE 1—*Specifications for common zero gases in cylinders.*

	Specifications	Other Data (SMI)
Air:		
Ultrapure	THC, CO, NO_x <10 ppb	CO_2 3 to 8 ppm
	SO_2 <1 ppb	H_2O 10 to 20 ppm
HC-free	THC <0.1 ppm	...
Zero	THC <2 to 4 ppm	CO <4 ppm
		SO_2 <1 ppb
Zero-vehicle emissions	THC, CO 1 ppm max	...
	NO 0.1 ppm max	...
	CO_2 300 ppm max	...
Nitrogen:		
O_2-free	O_2 <0.2 to <5 ppm	...
Ultra zero	THC <0.1 ppm	...
Zero	THC <0.5 ppm	CO <4 ppm
		NO_x <10 ppb
Hydrogen:		
Zero	THC <0.5 ppm	CO <10 ppb to 0.25 ppm
		CO_2 3 to 4 ppm
Ultra-high purity	min purity 99.999 %	...
	typical THC <0.5 ppm	...
Helium:		
Zero	THC <0.1 ppm	...

TABLE 2—*Analyses of certified 0.1-ppm-max zero air.*[a]

Source of Supply	Actual Total Hydrocarbons, ppm
Supplier A	0.065
Supplier B	0.099
Supplier C	0.120
Supplier D	0.190
Supplier E	0.210
Supplier F	0.550

[a] Reference *1*.

the hydrogen used in our laboratory varies from less than 10 to 250 ppb. Buying an expensive ultra-high purity grade with a guaranteed minimum purity of 99.999 percent does not guarantee a hydrocarbon-free (HC) or CO-free gas. The 10 ppm maximum impurity may be half CO or HC. A prepurified grade with a lower guaranteed purity may have the same or lower THC or CO content. Many times a lower priced grade is as good as a higher priced one, especially if you are only interested in a specific pollutant not covered by the gas specification, such as SO_2 or NO_x, and other trace components, which may be present, do not interfere.

It is costly to purify and analyze gases at ultra-low concentrations. Unless suppliers publish specifications on other trace components in addition to THC, then specifications must be written by the buyer. Analysis and purification by the buyer may be necessary because suppliers do not always meet their published specifications or the buyer's. Recently Airco Industrial Gas made a study [*1*][2] of zero air with a specification of less than 0.1-ppm THC obtained from different suppliers. The results, shown in Table 2, illustrate the point that specifications are not always met.

The suppliers did not know their products were being used in the study, nor did Airco's analytical department know anything about the program. Airco believes that the results are not unusual. Without detailed knowledge of the capabilities of individual suppliers, the data indicate that some suppliers either have bad standards, inadequate handling, or analytical techniques, or possibly all of these problems.

Cylinder gases, if not sufficiently pure for use as a zero gas, can be purified by various means. Table 3 lists several gas purifiers used for removing pollutants or impurities. Air purification has been described by Nelson [*2*]. The portion of this reference on water vapor removal has extensive tables covering the effectiveness of various dessicants. A detailed study has been made of the effectiveness of silver wool for removal of H_2S in the measurement of sulfur compounds [*3*]. The DEOXO[3] purifier listed

[2] The italic numbers in brackets refer to the list of references appended to this paper.
[3] Trademark of the Engelhard Industries.

TABLE 3—*Means for removing specific trace components.*

Pollutant	Gas	Removal By
THC, CO	air	catalytic combustion
NO	air	ozonator + Ascarite
NO_2	air, N_2	soda lime or Ascarite
SO_2	air	activated charcoal
H_2S	air	silver wool
CO_2	air, N_2, H_2	Ascarite
H_2O	air, N_2, H_2	Molecular Sieve 5A
O_2	N_2	DEOXO purifier, Model C
All	H_2	palladium diffusion

in Table 3 is copper which is converted to copper oxide in removing oxygen. The purifier can also be used to remove hydrogen and CO by the reverse reaction [4].

Palladium diffusion units generally are incorporated in hydrogen generating equipment but can also be purchased separately for use with cylinder hydrogen. Hydrogen generators supply dry, HC-free gas but are reported to have a high failure rate [5].

Measuring Purity of Zero Gases

At ultra-low levels, establishing that a zero gas is suitable is often difficult. The simplest procedure consists of comparing the zero gas of unknown suitability to a cylinder of zero gas known to contain no detectable quantities of the pollutant to be measured or any known interferants.

A zero gas standard in a cylinder is also useful for determining the purity of a carrier gas by looking for negative peaks when the zero standard is injected.

If absorption scrubbers are used to purify a carrier gas, it is easy to check the performance of the purifier by injecting a zero gas of known high purity. If the carrier contains a significant concentration of the pollutant of interest relative to the zero gas, a negative peak (or vacancy chromatogram) will result. Similarly, catalytic purifiers commonly used in air monitoring stations to purify air for THC-methane (CH_4)-CO instruments, can be checked by injecting air zero gas from a cylinder. Reference 5 shows how this technique provides an early warning system for oxidation catalyst failure. A zero gas, especially one free of all pollutants of interest and possible interfering components, thus becomes an essential troubleshooting tool in the operation of an air monitoring station.

A second method of measuring the concentration of a pollutant in a zero gas is to use an absolute analytical method having a sensitivity sufficiently high to measure the level of interest in the intended application. An example is the use of the Saltzman method to measure NO_2.

A third method commonly used to determine the purity of carrier gases is the use of enrichment or concentration techniques. For example, a volume of the carrier gas 100-fold greater than the volume of the sample normally injected for analysis, is passed through a packed cold trap, concentrating the pollutants if any. Subsequent injection of the concentrated sample into the chromatograph reveals any contaminants in the carrier [6].

Handling Zero Gases

Zero gases for ultra-low level measurements require special handling to avoid contamination. All components of a system used to carry the gas to the measuring instrument must be free of the pollutant being measured. Regulators, valves, sample lines, pumps, flasks, syringes, or other components used to contain or control the zero gas must be leak-tight. Fittings and pumps frequently are found to leak [7]. If the system can be pressurized, it can be checked for leaks with soap solution. Regulators and valves with diffusion resistant metal diaphragms should always be used. Sample lines should also be diffusion resistant. Some plastic sample lines will allow diffusion of oxygen and water into carrier gases, thereby damaging sensitive chromatographic columns. Purging with zero gas and evacuating all sample handling components, at elevated temperatures if possible, reduces the possibility of contamination by pollutants adsorbed on the surfaces of the components. The cleanliness of the component should always be checked by analyzing the zero gas flowing through it or by analyzing a sample of the zero gas removed from a container which is part of the handling system. Table 4 shows the HC contamination of Ultrapure Air by regulators and a cylinder before and after cleaning by evacuation at an elevated temperature.

Sample handling components exposed to high concentrations of the pollutant to be measured, should be recleaned before using with a zero gas. Table 5 shows that cleaning the internal sample handling parts of a continuous sulfur analyzer by purging with zero gas is a slow process after

TABLE 4—*Contamination of Ultrapure Air by sample handling components.*

Component	CH$_4$ Concentration, ppm	
	Before Cleaning	After Cleaning[a]
Two stage regulator with stainless steel diaphragms (new)	0.075 to over 1	<0.01
Single stage regulator with stainless steel diaphragm (new)	0.041 to 0.122	<0.01
Aluminum cylinder	0.089	<0.01

[a] Cleaning by baking under vacuum and purging with Ultrapure Air.

TABLE 5—*Time required to purge SO₂ analyzer after exposure to various SO₂ concentrations.*

Sample Concentration, ppb[a]	Duration of Sampling, min	Time to Purge to 10 ppb with Ultrapure Air, min[b]
65	30	1
		13 (to 3 ppb)
900	60	16
6200	20	90

[a] In treated aluminum cylinders.
[b] Sample flow rate approximately 200 ml/min.

exposure of the instrument to high concentrations of SO_2. Exposure to a high level should be avoided if measuring only very low levels. The time to purge the analyzer becomes increasingly important if automatic zeroing and spanning operational modes are used.

Conclusions

Although zero gases for ultra-low levels of measurement are in some cases difficult to obtain, sufficient techniques are available for removing specific impurities, verifying that the impurity has been removed, and handling the resultant zero gas.

References

[1] Grieco, H. A. and Hans, William, *Industrial Research*, Vol. 16, No. 3, March 1974, pp. 39–41.
[2] Nelson, G. O., *Controlled Test Atmospheres*, Ann Arbor Science Publishers, Ann Arbor, Mich., 1971, Chapter 2.
[3] Baumgardner, R. E., Clark, T. A., and Stevens, R. K., *Analytical Chemistry*, Vol. 47, No. 3, March 1975, pp. 563–566.
[4] Data Sheet, Engelhard Industries Division, Systems Department, Engelhard Minerals and Chemicals Corp., East Newark, N. J.
[5] Richardson, R. L., Paper No. 74–56, presented at the 67th Annual Meeting of the Air Pollution Control Association, Denver, Colo., 9–13 June 1974.
[6] Stephens, E. R. and Burleson, F. R., *Journal of the Air Pollution Control Association*, Vol. 19, No. 12, Dec. 1969, pp. 929–936.
[7] Hilborn, J., *Journal of the Air Pollution Control Association*, Vol. 24, No. 10, Oct. 1974, p. 983.

J. N. Harman III[1]

Electrochemical Generation
of Pollutant Standards

REFERENCES: Harman, J. N. III, "**Electrochemical Generation of Pollutant Standards,**" *Calibration in Air Monitoring, ASTM STP 598*, American Society for Testing and Materials, 1976, pp. 282–300.

ABSTRACT: Six common ambient air pollutant species (ozone, nitric oxide, chlorine, carbon monoxide, sulfur dioxide, and hydrogen sulfide) have been electrolytically generated at the parts-per-billion to parts-per-million level in a scrubbed ambient air carrier. Theoretical background and practical aspects of this technique are discussed, and the difference in pollutant output to that expected theoretically is reviewed. Under the conditions of the work reported, the desired theoretical output was not achieved. As a result, this technique does not appear feasible as a primary technique for the production of these species. However, the approach may serve as a convenient, low-cost means to produce secondary or working standards for the calibration of ambient level air pollution analyzers.

KEY WORDS: calibration, carbon monoxide, chloride, coulometry, electrochemistry, evaluation, hydrogen sulfide, nitric oxide, nitrogen dioxide, ozone, performance, sulfur dioxide

Continuous ambient air quality monitoring is now conducted nationwide to assess local, regional, and national concentrations of gaseous species for which primary and secondary Federal standards were promulgated in the Clean Air Act of 1963 and the Air Quality Act of 1967 and the Clean Air Amendments of 1970. Primary standards were set to provide a level of air quality sufficient to protect the public from any known or anticipated effects of a pollutant. Gaseous species designated as pollutants for which these standards were set include photochemical oxidants (predominantly ozone (O_3)), carbon monoxide (CO), sulfur dioxide (SO_2), and reactive hydrocarbons (HC). Reference methods for the determination of these concentrations were detailed by the Environmental Protection Agency (EPA) and equivalent methods for these concentration determinations were allowed, provided that it could be proven that the equiv-

---

[1] Senior chemist, Beckman Instruments, Inc., Fullerton, Calif. 92634.

alent methods bore a known, constant relationship to the reference method.

To ensure the validity of the data collected, it is necessary to check instrument calibration periodically. Dynamic calibration is preferred to a static technique, as it actually exercises the instrument in an operational condition with a synthetic standard. Calibration standards may be prepared by dynamic dilution, blending of a standard gas mixture in a suitable cylinder, the use of permeation tubes, gas phase titration (GPT), or by electrochemical generation from an appropriate medium. Dilution and permeation tube techniques are discussed by the Intersociety Committee [1][2] along with general precautions to be employed in calibration activities. Permeation devices are treated fundamentally by O'Keefe et al [2] and Scaringelli et al [3]. A theoretical and practical review of all conventional methods of producing known test atmospheres has been presented by Nelson [4].

Hughes [5] and Grieco et al [6] treat the limitations inherent with the use of calibration cylinders and Grieco et al detail the advantages of using aluminum cylinders treated with a proprietary coating. GPT techniques for chemiluminescent O_3 and nitrogen oxide (NO_x) analyzers used for the measurement of ambient levels of O_3 and oxides of nitrogen have been discussed by Rehme et al [7] and in the *Federal Register* [8].

A potential means of generating pollutant standards is the electrochemical generation of the pollutant species by a coulometric process. The amount of pollutant generated by such a process, and thus the concentration of pollutant, even if diluted with a diluent gas, may be determined by reference to reaction stoichiometry and the fundamental quantities of molecular weight, time, and the Faraday (96 493 C). This paper addresses the questions of potential systems of significance for the calibration of ambient air quality analyzers used to monitor species for which ambient air quality standards exist or which may be of concern to industrial hygienists, the practicality of this approach and the limitations to be expected of this technique.

A primary purpose and significant contribution of this work is to critically evaluate the argument, conveyed in the literature, that electrolytic generation of pollutants for standardization purposes is a routine procedure sufficiently developed to offer an accurate, stable, and precisely controllable standards.

Background

Theoretical System

Coulometric generation of pollutant standards is a potentially attractive means to calibrate ambient level pollution monitoring equipment because

---

[2] The italic numbers in brackets refer to the list of references appended to this paper.

the pollutant is generated on site at the time of calibration and the technique can generate the pollutant for long periods of time. Moreover, temperature coefficient sensitivity of the technique is minimal, and changes in pollutant concentration may be made rapidly by changing the generating current. In an ideal system, the amount of pollutant generated and the concentration of the pollutant in a carrier gas stream may be computed theoretically. The ideal theoretical model relies upon the stoichiometry of the electrode reaction, the flow rate of the carrier gas, and Faraday's law.

Faraday's law of electrolysis states that the quality of material oxidized or reduced at an electrode is directly proportional to the amount of charge passing the electrode/solution interface and that the relative amounts of different species oxidized or reduced by the same quantity of charge are in direct proportion to the equivalent weights of the species. Using notation employed by Nelson [4], the pollutant production rate in the ideal theoretical system is related to generation current by

$$ i = \frac{znF}{t} = zF_{q_e} \tag{1} $$

where

i = current in amperes,
z = number of electrons involved in the reduction or oxidation process,
n = number of moles liberated in the electrolytic process,
t = time in seconds,
q_e = rate of gas production (mole/s), and
F = Faraday's law (96 493 C).

If the pollutant standard is diluted with a carrier gas flow of q_d (mole/s)

$$ C = 10^6 \left(\frac{q_e}{q_d}\right) = \left(\frac{10^6}{z f_{q_d}}\right) \tag{2} $$

Equation 1 becomes, at 20°C, converting from mass flow units to volume flow units

$$ C = \left(\frac{14.96}{z_{q_d}}\right) i \tag{3} $$

where

C = pollutant concentration in ppm,
i = generation current in mA,
q_d = diluent gas flow rate in litre/min, and
z = number of electrons involved in electrode process.

Theoretical behavior of the generating system must be ideal if the coulometric nature of the process is to be relied upon for predicting the concentration of the generated species from the applied current. To achieve the ideal, theoretical behavior, certain aspects of the generating system must be known or carefully controlled:

1. The stoichiometry of the electrode reaction which generates the gaseous product must be known and must remain constant during the time and conditions of the electrolytic pollutant generation reaction.

2. All the current applied to the working electrode which generates the product must be utilized in generating the pollutant of interest—no side reactions are permissible.

3. Loss of the generated product must be prevented; losses can occur by solubility in the electrolyte, diffusion in the electrolyte to the other cell electrode where reaction may occur, gas phase reactions in the carrier gas creating a new undesired species (such as nitric oxide $\rightarrow$ nitrogen dioxide ($NO \rightarrow NO_2$) conversion in an air carrier) or by physical losses in the downstream sample handling system between the generating cell and the analyzer.

Practical Systems

In practical systems, the foregoing conditions may not be satisfied and the actual pollutant yield may be less than the theoretical yield desired. In this case, Eq 3 must be modified to

$$C = (Y) \left(\frac{14.96}{z_{q_d}} \right) i \qquad (4)$$

where Y = a yield factor or coefficient having a value between 0 and 1, and a yield factor of unity corresponds to ideal behavior.

To improve the chances of meeting the foregoing criteria for constructing a system for generating a pollutant standard from a cell which behaves ideally, certain precautions should be observed:

1. Adequate depolarizer should exist in the electrolytic cell such that the possibility of concentration polarization is minimized; if insufficient depolarizer is present, the applied input current may result in undesired electrode processes.

2. The electrolyte should have a low resistance, due to the depolarizer concentration or the addition of a nonelectroactive supporting electrolyte, so that the applied current is sufficient to drive the working electrode to the potential of the desired electrode process (minimal polarization voltage losses due to the flow of generating current through resistance present in the cell).

3. The cell should be stirred either with a gas stream or with some other stirring device to prevent mass transport limitations if an inadequate supply of depolarizer is available.

4. A current-voltage curve of the system under operation should be taken; this should be done in order to monitor the working electrode potential during electrolysis meaningfully.

5. The working electrode should have sufficient area to support the maximum applied input current and should be positioned such that pollutant generated has the maximum chance to escape.

The constancy and absolute value of Y in Eq 4 over a range of generated pollutant concentrations must be determined by an independent technique to assess whether the system is behaving according to ideal behavior.

To assess the degree of conformance of a particular generating cell system to ideal behavior after the system has been optimized, one may perform the following tests:

1. Determine the open circuit contribution. In the ideal system this should be zero.

2. Vary the input current to the cell and note pollutant output—ideal behavior is a linear relation of output pollutant concentration to input current over the whole range of desired pollutant concentrations.

3. Determine the coulometric yield factor Y, by use of Eq 3—ideal behavior is $Y = 1$; useful behavior is observed if Y is constant over the range of normal operating conditions.

4. Determine the stability of pollutant output over a useful time period.

5. Determine the repeatability of the pollutant generation process over a reasonable number of cycles.

In the system where the yield is less than that expected theoretically, the technique of electrolytic generation may be of value as pollutant preparative technique, but any utility as a primary standard is lost.

Certain practical problems are inherent with the electrochemical generation approach. These have been treated extensively by Hersch [9,10].

1. Only limited quantities of pollutant are generated conveniently, of the order of microlitres per minute; this sets the profile of the maximum concentration available for an instrument sample requirement.

2. The generated standard contains significant quantities of water vapor; this may present a problem of interference to certain physical analytical techniques [for example, interference in the nondispersive infrared technique (NDIR), possible water (H_2O) vapor quenching in chemiluminescence and fluorescence techniques]. Attempts to remove H_2O vapor may result in loss of the generated pollutant.

3. Carrier gas flow rate and generating currents must be precisely monitored and maintained constant.

4. The apparatus employed is typically glassware, complex and fragile.

5. The carrier gas should be presaturated with H_2O vapor to reduce or eliminate evaporation at the electrode/solution interface. Such evaporative

losses can change the operating potential of the electrode by charging current density changes or can cause interruption of the electrolytic contact at the working electrode/solution interface.

Benefits to be derived from this approach are that:

1. System is low cost.
2. Pollutant may be generated for long-time periods.
3. Ambient air background gas may be spiked with the pollutant of interest.

Experimental

Experimental work reported here is limited to the generation of those species for which ambient air quality standards exist or which may be of concern to industrial hygienists. Specifically, pollutants generated coulometrically for this investigation and the systems used are as follows.

Ozone (O_3)—Anodic electrolysis (oxidation) at a platinum microelectrode of concentrated sulfuric acid (H_2SO_4) electrolyte.

Nitric Acid (NO)—Cathodic electrolysis (reduction) at a platinum microelectrode of the nitrosyl ion, NO^+, in a concentrated H_2SO_4 electrolyte containing sodium nitrite $(NaNO_2)$.

Nitrogen Dioxide (NO_2)—Generation of NO by reduction of NO^+ as just detailed with subsequent oxidation in the gas phase of the NO to NO_2 with oxygen or O_3.

Chlorine (Cl_2)—Anodic electrolysis (oxidation) at a platinum microelectrode of chloride ion in a potassium chloride (KCl) solution.

Carbon Monoxide (CO)—Anodic electrolysis (oxidation) of water at a platinum microelectrode to produce H^+ which reacts with sodium formate (HCOONa) present in solution to form CO.

Sulfur Dioxide (SO_2)—Anodic electrolysis (oxidation) of H_2O at a platinum electrode to produce H^+ which reacts with dissolved sulfite anion $(SO_3)^=$ in a sodium sulfite $(Na_2S_2O_3)$ solution to form SO_2.

Hydrogen Sulfide (H_2S)—Anodic electrolysis (oxidation) of H_2O at a platinum electrode to produce H^+ which reacts with dissolved sulfide anion $(S^=)$ in a sodium sulfide solution to form H_2S.

Preliminary experiments were performed to establish that the pollutant of interest was generated actually from the chemical/electrode system being investigated, and then tests were conducted to establish the following system performance criteria:

1. Linearity of pollutant output concentration with the current applied to the electrolytic cell.
2. Stability (time) of the pollutant generation process.

3. Magnitude of the coulometric yield factor Y.

4. Response time for changes in pollutant production with changes in cell input currents.

5. Maximum pollutant concentration output which may be consistently and conveniently generated.

6. Special considerations for a given cell system, such as air oxidation of the electrolyte or background contribution from the electrolyte.

Electrolysis was conducted in the cell shown in Fig. 1. This cell was adapted from the cell described by Hersch [10] and offers the desired geometrical and operational properties. The electrolytic generation current was supplied by an electronically regulated constant current power supply (J. T. Fluke Co., Model 351A); current flow in the generating cell was monitored with an electrometer (Keithley 610 B). All chemicals employed in this investigation were reagent grade. A schematic diagram of the pollutant preparation system is shown in Fig. 2.

Results of experiments conducted on the specific systems just detailed are summarized in Table 1, and discussed in detail next.

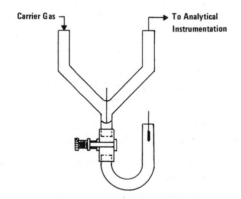

FIG. 1—*Electrolytic generation cell.*

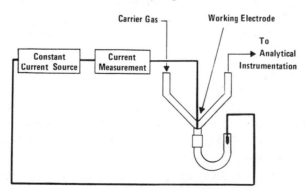

FIG. 2—*Schematic of pollutant preparation system.*

TABLE 1—*Summary of experimental results.*

Pollutant	Medium	Range of Concentrations	Yield Factor	Remarks
Ozone	concentrated H_2SO_4	10 ppb to 1 ppm	$\sim 10^{-4}$	
Nitric oxide	nitrosyl sulfuric acid	10 ppb to 0.8 ppm	$\sim 10^{-2}$	open circuit evolution of NO_2 objectionable
Chlorine	saturated KCl	20 ppb to 1.7 ppm	$\sim 10^{-1}$	
Carbon monoxide	$1 M$ HCOONa	1 to 50 ppm	$\sim 10^{-3}$	
Sulfur dioxide	$2M$ Na_2SO_3	20 ppb to 1.4 ppm	$\sim 10^{-2}$ to 10^{-3}	possible air oxidation of $SO_3^=$ history effects
Hydrogen sulfide	saturated Na_2S	100 ppb to 5 ppm	$\sim 10^{-2}$	300 ppb background contribution

Ozone—Anodic electrolysis of $12M$ H_2SO_4 produced O_3 in concentrations of from 20 ppb to 1.2 ppm with input currents from 1.2 to 150 mA at a carrier gas flow rate of 300 cm^3/min. The O_3 output as a function of applied input current is shown in Fig. 3. The yield factor Y_{O_3}, is of the order of 10^{-3} over the acid electrolyte concentration range of 0.01 to $12M$; this may be explained by the following postulated mechanism for the O_3 production at the anode.

$$2H_2O \rightarrow 2OH^- + 2H^+ + 2e^-$$
$$2OH^- \rightarrow H_2O + O$$

$$O + O \rightarrow O_2$$
$$O_2 + O \rightarrow O_3$$

The instrument used to detect the O_3 was a chemiluminescent O_3 analyzer (Beckman Model 950) calibrated by reference to a coulometric instrument (Beckman Model 908) sampling from an ultraviolet (UV) discharge O_3 source. Calibration of this instrument was checked by the O_3–NO GPT technique described by Rehme [1]. Response time of changes in measured pollutant concentration when the applied input current was changed was of the order of 20 s.

Despite good long-term stability of the O_3 production rate at constant current, on the order of 1 percent/h, the electrochemical generation of O_3 cannot be considered a primary standard because of the low value of Y and the potential problem of O_3 loss due to solubility in the electrolyte if cell electrolyte level variations occur. However it may serve adequately as a secondary standard or source of moderate long-term stability.

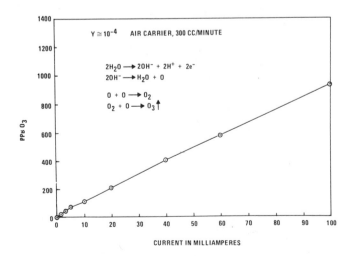

FIG. 3—*Generation of O_3.*

Nitric Oxide—Cathodic electrolysis of $1M$ $NaNO_2$ dissolved in 30 weight percent H_2SO_4 produced concentrations of from 5 ppb to 1 ppm with input currents from 5 to 200 μA at a carrier gas flow rate of 1000 cm^3/min. The NO output as a function of applied input current is shown in Fig. 4. The yield factor Y_{NO} observed was 0.02 and response time of the change in measured pollutant (NO + e^- → NO related) concentration when the applied input current was changed was of the order of 10 to 30 s. No background contribution of NO from the electrolyte was observed when the generating current was terminated under these conditions; from 200 to 400-ppb NO_2 was evolved from the solution even on open circuit continuously. Long-term stability of this NO production technique was of the order of 1 percent/h. NO was detected with a Beckman Model 952 chemiluminescent NO_x analyzer standardized by the previously mentioned GPT technique.

Further refinement of this system and optimization of the experimental conditions might give a yield factor $Y = 1$. With the present system, NO is generated to serve easily as a secondary source, but future investigation must be conducted to demonstrate the constancy of Y with varying operating conditions before it would serve as a reliable secondary standard. Under no conditions may this technique be regarded at present as a primary technique.

Nitrogen Dioxide—the NO output of the previously mentioned generating system may be conveniently reacted in the gas phase with molecular O_2 or O_3 to form an equivalent amount of NO_2. The part-per-million levels of NO generated do not have sufficient residence times in practical systems for full conversion in the gas phase with air as a carrier [11,12]; so, either pure O_2 must be used as the carrier or the doped output of the generation

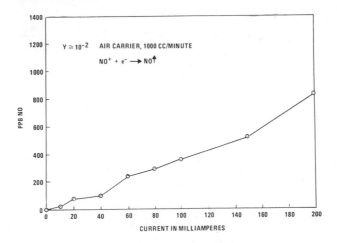

FIG. 4—*Generation of NO.*

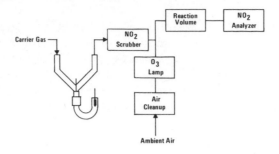

FIG. 5—*Gas phase conversion of electrolytically produced NO to NO₂.*

cell must be passed through a UV discharge source of O_3 for conversion of NO to NO_2. The residual NO_2 produced from the generating cell even an open circuit is removed with a downstream argentous oxide (Ag_2O) or silver carbonate (Ag_2CO_3) scrubber which quantitatively transmits the NO produced. A schematic diagram of the system used for NO_2 production is shown in Fig. 5. No significant work was done with the system because of limitations of the NO production system and because the quantitative nature of the NO → NO_2 gas phase conversion has been well established [2,3].

Chlorine—Anodic electrolysis of $1M$ KCl produced from 20 ppb to 1.7 ppm Cl_2 with input currents of from 10 to 155 μA at a carrier gas input flow rate of 150 cm³/min. The yield factor Y_{Cl_2} was ~0.65. This species was of secondary concern; so, no extensive testing program was conducted. A plot of the Cl_2 output as a function of applied input current is shown in Fig. 6.

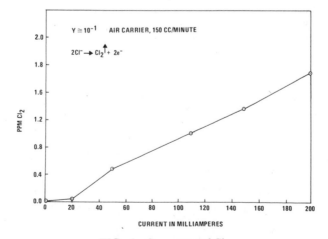

FIG. 6—*Generation of Cl₂.*

Cl_2 measurements were conducted with a coulometric oxidants analyzer (Beckman Model 908) in which Cl_2 oxidized I^- in the cell electrolyte to iodine (I_2) which was detected by cathodic reduction. No calibration was required because of the inherent coulometry of the detector system.

Carbon Monoxide—Anodic electrolysis of $1M$ HCOONa produced concentration of from 1 to 50-ppm CO with input currents from 20 to 1000 mA at a carrier gas input flow rate of 500 cm^3/min. The CO output as a function of applied input current is shown in Fig. 7. The yield factor Y_{CO}, was in the range of 1×10^{-3} to 5×10^{-3} based on a stoichiometry

$$2H_2O \rightarrow H_2O + O + 2H^+$$

$$2H^+ + HCOONa \rightarrow HCOOH \rightarrow CO^\uparrow + H_2O$$

Response time of pollutant output to step changes in the applied input current was in the range of 1 to 3 min. Long-term stability of this pollutant production system is in the range of 1 percent drift/h and is limited by evaporative losses from the cell.

The CO produced from this system was detected with a M865 NDIR analyzer which had been calibrated with standard CO/air blends traceable to the National Bureau of Standards (NBS). CO is undoubtedly the species being produced due to the inherent selectivity of this mode of analysis.

Sulfur Dioxide—Anodic electrolysis of $2M$ sodium sulfite ($Na_2S_2O_3$) produced concentrations of from 20 ppb to 1.4-ppm SO_2 with applied input currents of the 100 μA to 1.5 mA at a carrier gas input flow rate of 150 cm^3/min. The SO_2 output as a function of the applied input current is shown in Fig. 8. The yield factor, Y_{SO_2}, was variable, from 2×10^{-3} to 6×10^{-2}, depending on the applied input current. The variable yield is

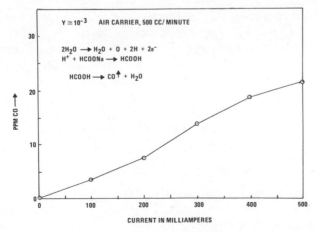

FIG. 7—*Generation of CO.*

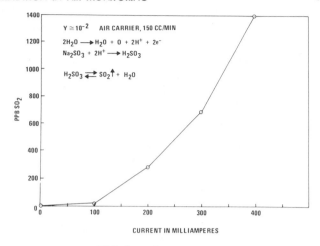

FIG. 8—*Generation of SO₂.*

due to the extreme solubility of the evolved SO_2 in the aqueous electrolyte. Reduction of this solubility by use of nonaqueous solvent might be helpful in obtaining better coulometric yields. Response time of pollutant output to step changes in the applied current was 2 to 5 min; this long response time is caused by the high solubility of the evolved SO_2 in the electrolyte. These results were taken with a virgin platinum electrode at which the anodic oxidation of water was conducted. After generation of several hundred microampere hours, SO_2 generation became impossible at the electrode, even though currents as large as 500 mA were passed through the generating cell. It is thought that the bulk of the current passed through the anode was now being preferentially routed to oxidation of the $SO_3^=$ to $SO_4^=$ and thus not available for the production of H^+ to release the desired SO_2.

This system produces SO_2 indirectly by local formation of H^+ at the anode concurrent with the production of molecular O_2; the H^+ reacts with the dissolved $SO_3^=$ to form gaseous SO_2. With no applied input current, no SO_2 is detectable in the carrier gas; no oxidation of $SO_3^=$ by O_2 dissolved in the electrolyte was noted. The generating volume used in the SO_2 production must be small, as response time for pollutant production rate changes was of the order of 1 min when the applied input current was changed. The electrode and chemical reactions which occur are as follow

$$H_2O \rightarrow 2H^+ + O + 2e^-$$
$$Na_2SO_3 + 2H^+ \rightarrow SO_2^{\uparrow} + H_2O$$

The SO_2 produced from this system was detected with a Model 906A coulometric SO_2 analyzer. No standardization of this device was required as coulometric ideality has been tested to establish that the device has a known output of 18.49-μA/ppm SO_2 at 150 cm³/min sample input flow rate.

Based on the variability and low value of the observed yield factor (Y_{SO_2}) for the experimental system considered, SO_2 generation by the coulometric technique does not appear practical or seem to offer any significant promise.

Hydrogen Sulfide—Anodic electrolysis of H_2O at a platinum electrode to produce H^+ which reacts with dissolved $S^=$ in a Na_2S solution to liberate H_2S was investigated. A significant problem associated with this approach if low level H_2S standards are to be generated is the aqueous hydrolysis of the $S^=$ in the electrolyte to yield H_2S on open circuit. Typical levels observed for a saturated H_2S electrolyte were 0.3 ppm at ambient temperature.

H_2S concentrations of from 100 ppb to 5 ppm were produced with applied input currents of from 0.1 to 5 mA at carrier gas input flow rate of 200 cm^3/min. H_2O output as a function of applied input current is shown in Fig. 9. The yield factor, Y_{H_2S}, was $\sim 3 \times 10^{-2}$. Response time of pollutant output to changes in the applied input current was from 3 to 5 min. The H_2S was detected with a membrane covered polarographic H_2S sensor which had been calibrated on fresh H_2S samples prepared by dynamic dilution of a high level H_2S/N_2 gas blend.

Severe sample handling problems occur when transporting H_2S standards due to adsorption and desorption. These limitations detract from the utility of the approach for the preparation of H_2S standards.

Additional Experimental Work

In the preceeding investigations, several deficiencies of the technique which could be related to cell design were noted:

1. The yield factor, Y, ranged from 2×10^{-3} to 0.63 and was in no case theoretical.

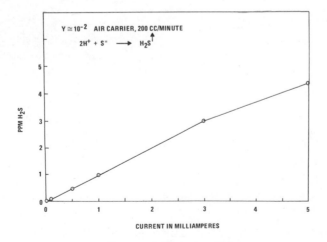

FIG. 9—*Generation of H_2S.*

2. Response time of the pollutant output to a step change in input current ranged from 0.3 to 5 min.

3. Pollutant output stability at constant input current was poor and ranged from 1 to 3 percent/h drift, probably due to evaporative losses.

All of these observations could be related to the solubility of the evolved gas in the electrolyte and the change in the electrode/electrolyte interface level. To minimize the effect of changes in the electrode/electrolyte level, a cotton wick consisting of sleeving placed over the working electrode was evaluated in two systems, Cl_2 (highly soluble), and NO (slightly soluble). Addition of the wick to the cell resulted in a working electrode which should be bathed in a constant small volume of electrolyte, independent of the level of the miniscus in the cell; this change should result in minimum solubility of the evolved gas in the electrolyte, minimum response time to changes in applied input current, and maximum stability of pollutant output due to the independence of the exposed electrode area on evaporative losses.

A possible scheme to improve on the yield factor is to generate a gas electrolytically and react the generated gas quantitatively with a heated chemical (elemental) bed to yield the desired pollutant species. Both H_2 and O_2 may be coulometrically generated with an ideal yield ($Y = 1$); O_2 thus generated can be reacted with elemental carbon to give CO, and H_2 may be reacted with elemental sulfur to give H_2S. Preliminary work indicates that this approach is marginal due to kinetic limitations involved in conversion of parts-per-million level input gases, variability of the degree of conversion, and the high vapor pressure of the sulfur in the H_2S and SO_2 preparative techniques which leads to condensation of sulfur in the system and a high level of elemental sulfur in the analyzer input gas stream.

Discussion

In all systems investigated the coulometric yield factor, Y, is significantly less than the theoretical value of 1. Possible causes for the low values observed include:

1. Solubility of the evolved gas (especially H_2O soluble gases).
2. Current consumption due to oxidation or reduction of the working electrode surface.
3. Reaction in the gas phase of the evolved pollutant with water vapor.
4. Side reactions which produce undesired species at the working electrode.
5. Kinetic limits of the pollutant producing reaction.
6. Mass transport limitations.

In order to investigate the role of mass transport limitation, a rotating electrode was tried in two systems, (Cl_2 and NO) (soluble and insoluble).

Essentially identical yield factors were obtained as in the unstirred solutions. Results supported the view that low yield factors at high electrolyte concentrations were due to solubility losses or kinetic limitations rather than mass transport limitations.

In an attempt to control the problem of gas solubility and electrode/electrolyte interface variation, these systems were also explored with a cell similar to that in Fig. 1, but incorporating a wick over the working electrode. The wick performs the function of defining a constant, small volume electrolyte layer over the working electrode. This cell configuration improved the stability of pollutant output but did not significantly change the yield factor or decrease the response time of pollutant production changes to changes in the applied input current.

The contribution of these findings is that coulometric generation of the pollutant standards characterized under the experimental conditions of this work cannot be considered as a primary technique. Further improvements in the experimental conditions or combination of electrode/electrolyte may result in systems in which the expected theoretical yield may be achieved, but with consideration of the optimization of conditions used in this work, the chances of success seem small. No systematic regimen has been found to obtain the correct theoretical yield, but precautions to be observed and critical parameters which should be controlled have been identified.

Although the results of this work show that, for the systems studied, a theoretical yield was not achieved, and thus the technique, employed under these experimental conditions, may not be considered a primary technique; under suitable conditions it may have potential as a secondary technique for the convenient preparation of a wide range of species to serve as secondary or working standards. Further work in electrolyte optimization by use of nonaqueous electrolytes could achieve improvements in pollutant yield by minimizing the solubility of highly water soluble gases such as Cl_2, SO_2, and O_3. Particular weaknesses of this technique are evident in Table 2 which compares pertinent performance criteria of this technique to the GPT, gas blend, and permeation tubes calibration techniques.

Practical difficulties encountered which detract from the use of this approach as a secondary standard "pollutant source" are:

1. The change in pollutant concentration for a given increment change of input current is not a linear function of the applied current over the whole range of pollutant concentrations of interest. At low applied input currents, especially with highly soluble desired gas species, lesser amounts of pollutant are transferred to the effluent gas phase.

2. Evaporative losses change the level of the electrode/solution interface sufficiently to change the pollutant output rate due to current density and gas solubility changes and on the long term may break the electrode/electrolyte contact. A presaturator upstream of the generating cell may help,

TABLE 2—*Overview of calibration sources.*

	Electrolytic	Gas Blend	Permeation Tube	Gas Phase Titration	Dynamic Dilution	Bag Samples
Accuracy	if yield is constant, accuracy 1% typical (flow measurement)	1% typical	1% typical	1% typical	2% typical	1% typical
Stability	1%/h typical	short-term stability good, long-term stability poor for reactive gases	stable at constant temperature	2%/day (O_3 lamp stability, NO source stability, flow stability)	stable if flows are stable	stable with most constituents
Pollutants available	SO_2, Cl_2, NO, NO_2, O_3, CO, H_2S	all—single or multicomponent blends possible	SO_2, Cl_2, NO, H_2S, HF, HC's, no NO	O_3, NO, NO_2	all	
Required operator attention	high	low	moderate	moderate	moderate	moderate
Temperature effects	low	moderate—adsorption/desorption	high; 3%/°F typical	low	low	low
Advantages	capable of generating many species dynamically on site	inexpensive, convenient portable	portable, inexpensive	flexible, three parameters available in one	inexpensive, use of pure constituents, simple	inexpensive, use of pure constituents, simple
Limitations	cumbersome, technique not fully developed	reactive gases, adsorption/desorption, cylinder history effects, surface conditioning, hazardous	humidity effects, carrier gas problems, tube storage conditions	only three species capability developed	flow stability critical	possible bag reactivity, leaks in bag

but system hydrostatic pressure variations and potential reactions of the generated pollutant with water in the gas phase are a potential problem.

3. High gas evolution rates yield a noisy pollutant output; dead volume can be added to the system downstream of the cell to minimize the excursions, but a system response penalty is paid and possible losses on the added downstream dead volume material may occur.

Future work will include polarographic analysis to determine the optimal electrode potential at which side reactions are minimized.

By characterizing the current-voltage behavior of the electrode/electrolyte system, it should be possible to identify undesired electrode processes occurring at the working electrode, such as oxidation or reduction of the electrode material or oxidation or reduction of an undesired species at the electrode potential where the desired reaction is occurring. By taking the current-voltage curve of the electrode/electrolyte system while observing the rate of pollutant output into the gas phase with the appropriate instrumentation, one may be able to assess the dependence of the yield factor on electrode potential and also obtain information on the actual mechanism of pollutant production occurring within the generating cell.

Conclusion

Although a number of important air pollutant species may be generated electrolytically for calibrating of parts-per-million level air pollutant monitoring instrumentation, yields obtained do not approach the theoretical yield which must be obtained for this generation technique to be used as a primary calibration technique. The technique does offer promise as secondary pollutant standard source. Potential advantages are low cost and simplicity of apparatus for field use. However, much more work must be done to fully characterize and optimize the systems, particularly with regard to use; minimizing solubility losses of the evolved gas to the electrolyte and optimizing of the cell geometry.

Once studies have been conducted of the fundamental characteristics of potential systems, a development effort should be undertaken to suitably package and field test calibrations based upon the electrolytic generation concept. Cross comparison of this approach should be conducted against the other calibration techniques currently available.

References

[1] *Methods of Air Sampling and Analysis*, Intersociety Committee, American Public Health Association, Washington, D. C., 1972.
[2] O'Keefe, A. E. et al, *Analytical Chemistry*, Vol. 38, 1966, p. 760.
[3] Scaringelli, F. P. et al, *Analytical Chemistry*, Vol. 42, 1970, p. 871.
[4] Nelson, G. O., *Controlled Test Atmospheres, Principles and Techniques*, Ann Arbor Science Publishers, Ann Arbor, Mich., 1971.

[5] Hughes, E. E., "Development of Standard Reference Materials for Air Quality Measurement," Paper 704, presented at the International Instrumentation and Automation Conference and Exhibit, Instrument Society of America, New York, 1974.
[6] Grieco, H. A. et al, *Industrial Research*, 1974, p. 39.
[7] Rehme, K. A. et al, "The Application of Gas Phase Titration in the Simultaneous Calibration of NO, NO_2, NO_x, and O_3 Atmospheric Monitors," presented at the 164th National American Chemical Society Meeting.
[8] *Federal Register*, Vol. 38, No. 110, 12 Oct. 1973, p. 28438.
[9] Hersch, P. A. et al, "Electrolytic Calibration of Gas Monitors," paper presented at the 9th National Instrument Symposium, Houston, Tex., 1963.
[10] Hersch, P. A., *Journal*, Air Pollution Control Association, 1969, p. 164.
[11] "Selected Methods for the Measurement of Air Pollutants," Publication No. 999-AP-11, Interbranch Chemical Advisory Committee, Public Health Service, 1965, p. C-7.
[12] Smith, J. H., *Journal*, American Chemical Society, Vol. 65, 1943, p. 74.

D. P. Lucero[1]

Ultra Low-Level Calibration Gas Generation by Multistage Dilution Techniques

---

REFERENCES: Lucero, D. P., "**Ultra Low-Level Calibration Gas Generation by Multi-Stage Dilution Techniques,**" *Calibration in Air Monitoring, ASTM STP 598*, American Society for Testing and Materials, 1976, pp. 301–319.

ABSTRACT: More precise and accurate parts-per-billion level calibration gases are obtained dynamically from concentrated sources such as permeation tubes and pure pressurized gases. Calibration gas production is accomplished by multistage dilution steps, comprised of combinations of pneumatic and diffusion processes. Zero air is defined relative to an analyzer response including interferent molecular response. Dilution precision and stability can be obtained within ±1 percent over ±15°C variations with pneumatic/pneumatic and pneumatic/diffusion networks. Nitric oxide calibration gas is generated from a nitrogen dioxide permeation tube and a molybdenum converter. Dilution factors larger than one billion are obtained with multistage pneumatic/diffusion techniques. The parametric relationships at each dilution stage are defined and the theoretical performance limits of multistage dilution techniques established.

KEY WORDS: calibration, gases, analyzers, permeability, stability, air pollution

Nomenclature

C Calibration gas concentration, ppm

q_s Gas blend calibration gas flowrate, ml/min

q_a Pneumatic/pneumatic dilution zero air flowrate, ml/min

L Permeation device tube length, cm

P_m Permeation device tube wall material permeability coefficient, ml/s-cm²-torr/cm

P_o Permeation device tube wall material reference permeability coefficient, ml/s-cm²-torr/cm

p_v Permeation device liquid gas vapor pressure, torr

q Pneumatic/diffusion zero air flowrate, ml/s

r_o Permeation device tube outside diameter, cm

r_i Permeation device tube inside diameter, cm

[1] Chief engineer, Monitor Laboratories, Inc., San Diego, Calif. 92121.

E Permeation device tube wall material permeability activation energy to calibration gas, cal/mol

R Universal gas constant, 1.986 cal/mol-K

T Temperature, K

p_j Sample calibration gas vapor pressure at reference temperature T_j, torr

ΔH_e Calibration gas average molar heat of evaporation over temperature range T_i to T_j, cal/mol

c Constant equal to $[\Delta H_e/RT_j]$, dimensionless

t Time, s

t_c Pneumatic/diffusion stage time constant, s

$_1$ and $_2$ Subscripting, denoting 1st and 2nd dilution stages, respectively

Due largely to more stringent monitoring regulations and the advent of analyzers with greater sensitivity, requirements for ultra-low level (<10 ppb) calibration gas sources are becoming rapidly more widespread. Field-proven automated continuous flame and flameless gas phase chemiluminescent analyzers are attaining parts-per-billion and sub-parts-per-billion sensitivity levels. Analyzer calibration is imperative at these levels to ensure performance specifications and the reliability of field data obtained. Most of these analyzers are calibrated at levels in excess of 100 ppb and their response characteristics extrapolated to parts-per-billion levels. Accurate, stable, and reliable calibration systems are required for these purposes.

Five fundamental problems are associated with the generation of ultra-low level calibration gases: (1) high-quality zero air production, (2) flowrate control, (3) calibrator/analyzer pneumatic interface, (4) primary calibration gas source accuracy and stability, and (5) pneumatic/diffusion dilution control. These considerations define design and operating constraints peculiar to the calibration gas species and the analyzer response characteristics, and therefore operating conditions for ultra-low level calibration.

Zero Air Production

Zero air, or "zero air purity," assumes a more specific and limited definition for ultra-low level calibration applications. In defining zero air purity, it is essential to consider the specific type of analyzer under calibration. This aspect is important in that, not only must the particular pollutant molecule concentration level be reduced to levels below the analyzer noise, but, also, it may not be necessary to reduce impurities to parts-per-billion levels for molecules which do not promote an analyzer response. Analyzers employing different operating principles can display entirely different response characteristics to the source of zero air. This is

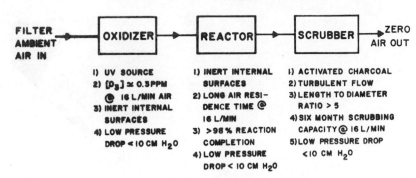

FIG. 1—*Oxidizer/scrubber zero air module.*

evidenced by the air monitoring equivalency regulations [1–3][2] regarding interferent molecules for a host of analyzer types, as shown by Table 1. For example, interferent responses of a flame photometric detector (FPD) sulfur dioxide (SO_2) analyzer can arise from hydrogen sulfide (H_2S) at low levels (100 ppb) and from carbon dioxide (CO_2), water (H_2O) vapor, and carbon monoxide (CO) at relatively high levels. While for spectrophotometric wet chemical, electrochemical, conductometric, and spectrophotometric (gas phase) SO_2 analyzers, interferent responses can arise from hydrochloric acid (HCl), ammonia (NH_3), H_2S, nitrogen dioxide (NO_2), ozone (O_3), and *m*-xylene at relatively low concentrations (<0.5 ppm). Further examination of Table 1 shows also similar interferent variation for several types of O_3 analyzers.

Thus, it is clear that the term zero air possesses a meaning related, not only to the molecular pollutant response of the analyzer, but also to its interferent molecular response. For ultra-low level applications, it may be the only practical meaning.

Zero Air Production

Figure 1 shows the basic elements of a zero air generator and illustrates some of its fundamental operating parameters. It is suitable for 99 percent removal of nitric oxide (NO), NO_2, SO_2, H_2S, and other pollutant and analyzer interferent gases. Ambient air flows through the oxidizer, reactor, and scrubber elements. Near 100 percent scrubbing efficiencies are attained by designing the module elements with respect to criteria prescribed in Fig. 1.

An activated charcoal scrubber with a length-to-diameter ratio of 6, where $L = 22.8$ cm, $D = 3.8$ cm, eliminates typical ambient air gases, listed previously, to 1-ppb levels, with the exception of NO. Fully turbulent flow is attained at a modified Reynolds number above 100 [4]

$$N_{Re}' = D_p G/\mu \tag{1}$$

[2] The italic numbers in brackets refer to the list of references appended to this paper.

TABLE 1—*Ambient air analyzer [1]: interferent test concentration levels, parts per million.*[a]

Pollutant	Analyzer Type[b]	HCl	NH₃	H₂S	SO₂	NO₂	NO	CO₂	C₂H₄	O₃	M-Xylene	H₂O	CO	CH₄	C₂H₆
SO₂	flame photometric (FPD)			0.1	0.14^d			750				$20\,000^c$	50		
SO₂	gas chromatography (FPD)			0.1	0.14^d			750				$20\,000^c$	50		
SO₂	spectrophotometric-wet chemical (pararosaniline reaction)	0.2	0.1^c	0.1	0.14^d	0.5		750		0.5					
SO₂	electrochemical	0.2	0.1^c	0.1	0.14^d	0.5	0.5		0.2	0.5					
SO₂	conductivity	0.2	0.1^c		0.14^d	0.5	0.5	750				$20\,000^c$			
SO₂	spectrophotometric gas phase				0.14^d	0.5	0.5			0.5	0.2				
O₃	chemiluminescent			0.1^c				750		0.08^d		$20\,000^c$			
O₃	electrochemical		0.1^c		0.5	0.5				0.08^d		$20\,000^c$			

Analyzer type										
O₃ spectrophotometric-wet chemical (potassium reaction)	0.1[c]	0.5	0.5	0.5[c]			0.08[d]			
O₃ spectrophotometric-gas phase		0.5	0.5	0.5[c]			0.08[d]			
CO infrared					750			20 000	10[d]		
CO gas chromatography with flame photometric detector								20 000	10[d]		0.5
CO electrochemical	0.1			0.5		0.2		20 000	10[d]		
CO catalytic combustion thermal detection					750	0.2		20 000	10[d]	5.0	0.5
CO infrared fluorescence					750	0.2		20 000	10[d]		0.5
CO mercury replacement-ultraviolet photometric						0.2			10[d]		0.5

[a] Concentrations of interferent listed must be prepared and controlled to ±10 percent of the stated value.
[b] Analyzer types not listed will be considered by the Administrator as special cases.
[c] Do not mix with pollutant.
[d] Concentration of pollutant used for test. These pollutant concentrations must be prepared to ±10 percent of the stated value.

where

N_{Re}' = modified Reynolds number, dimensionless,
D_p = average particle diameter, cm,
G = air superficial mass velocity based on empty cartridge cross section, g/s-cm², and
μ = air viscosity, poise.

This is with an air flowrate of 16 litre/min at 25°C, where D_p = 0.254 cm and N_{Re}' = 22. Although the flow is not fully turbulent, it is removed sufficiently from the laminar region (N_{Re}' < 10) to ensure efficient use of the charcoal.

The pressure drop across a densely packed cartridge at 16 litre/min is less than 1-cm H_2O [5]. Thus, most of the pressure loss is incurred by the cartridge end fittings or whatever fluid conduit is utilized.

Activated charcoal scrubs pollutant gases by an absorption mechanism [6,7]. Its absorption capacity is a function of temperature and pollutant concentration and species. For example, as temperature increases and pollutant concentration level decreases, activated charcoal absorption capacity decreases. The absorption life of the scrubber just described, utilizing absorption criteria for Pittsburgh granular activated carbon, is considerable. Operating continuously with an ambient air flowrate of 16 litre/min, carrying 50-ppb SO_2 [8] and 10-ppb H_2S at 25°C, its absorption life is 840 and 8450 h for SO_2 and H_2S, respectively. Assuming a 1 h/day calibration run and an equal amount absorption capacity required for NO_2, NH_3, etc., the scrubber absorption life is in excess of six months.

The oxidizer and reactor elements of Fig. 1 are employed to preprocess NO molecules for absorption by the scrubber element. O_3 is produced by the oxidizer, which oxidizes NO to NO_2, which is absorbed subsequently by the scrubber. This is a requisite because the activated charcoal absorption capacity for NO is nil. Oxidation by ozone is prescribed since the process is practically independent of ambient temperatures and humidity variations. In addition, the NO oxidation is predictable. The oxidizer produces approximately 0.3-ppm O_3 with air flowrate of 16 litres/min at 23°C and 70 percent relative humidity. Higher O_3 concentration levels can be attained by employing more ultraviolet (UV) sources. It is essential that all internal surfaces of the oxidizer chamber and the reactor are inert so that O_3 concentration level is not reduced by interaction of the O_3 and chamber active surfaces.

A reactor chamber is required for this zero air generator because the NO/O_3 oxidation process proceeds at a relatively slow rate. The chamber permits a time period for the oxidation reaction to occur to completion. Thus, nearly all the NO carried by ambient air is oxidized to NO_2 prior to entering the scrubber. With a 0.3-ppm O_3 concentration level and kinetic data for the NO + O_3 = NO_2 + O_2 reaction reported in the literature

[9–12], approximately 13.2 s are required to attain 98 percent oxidation. In-house Monitor Labs, Inc. experimental design data show that the oxidation reaction is 98 percent complete after 3.8 s. Thus, the reaction chamber volume is 1 litre.

For ambient air carrying 50-ppb NO, the zero air produced by the 98 percent efficient zero air generator of Fig. 1 contains a maximum concentration of 1 ppb as it enters the scrubber. Thus, the calibrator zero air NO concentration level is approximately 1 ppb. This is a conservative representation of the zero air, which can be produced in most parts of the United States, since average ambient NO levels rarely exceed 100 ppb and are usually below 50 ppb [13–14].

Flowrate Control

Dilution calibration systems require a flowrate network. Minimally, they are comprised of either a two-stream network incorporating a pneumatic dilution stage, such as that employed to dilute NO/N_2 gas blends by air; or a pneumatic/diffusion dilution stage, as in passing zero air over a permeation device. It is imperative to maintain relative and absolute flowrate control of all gas streams comprising the dilution network or both over ambient temperature and upstream pressure variations. Pneumatic-pneumatic dilution networks require volumetric flowrate control. These distinct fundamental requirements arise because the gas emission rate from a diffusion dilution stage, such as a permeation device or the gas flow through a semipermeable membrane, is mass flowrate controlled. Thus, the dilution gas must also be mass flowrate controlled to avoid inaccuracy and instability arising from ambient temperature and pressure variations. Conversely, a purely pneumatic system requires only volumetric flowrate control. For example, in a pneumatic network, such as that employed to dilute a gas blend of NO/N_2, two streams from separate pressurized gas sources are mixed. Each stream pressure is regulated upstream of a pneumatic impedance element and mixed downstream. Ambient pressure and temperature variations have a negligible effect on the flowrate ratio of one stream to the other. However, pressure regulators which are referenced to the same ambient pressure and display reasonably matched temperature coefficients must be used on each stream. In addition, the pneumatic impedance elements must respond to temperature variations in identical parametric fashion. For example, capillary and porous plug elements display an impedance change inversely proportional to the 3/2 power of absolute temperature, while orifice and valve elements change inversely in proportion to the 1/2 power. Thus, pneumatic network temperature control can be avoided while obtaining ±1 percent dilution stability over 25 ± 15°C temperature range. It is essential only that all branches of the network are within 10°C of each other, and temperature changes of all branches are within ±3°C of each other, regardless of the magnitude of the temperature change.

Mass flowrate control is attained by utilizing a pressure regulator with a small temperature coefficient ($\simeq 1.36 \times 10^{-4}$ atm/°C) and temperature controlling the impedance element. Temperature regulation within ±3°C yields mass flowrate control within ±1 percent, providing the ambient pressure is constant. Since ambient pressures are relatively constant and change mainly with altitude, the mass flowrate can be easily corrected for altitude variations.

It is possible to obtain mass flowrate control, regardless of altitude, by use of a mass flowrate controller, utilizing a feedback signal. However, the author is not aware of temperature coefficient data on these devices and is unable to state whether or not temperature control of the mass flowrate controller is required.

Calibrator/Analyzer Pneumatic Interface

A very important aspect of ultra-low level calibration is the calibrator/analyzer pneumatic interface. Precautions in design, setup, and operation must be instituted to minimize the effects of back-diffusion, line outgassing, and surface absorption.

Back-Diffusion

The pneumatic interface requires a vent line for calibrators whose gas is exhausted under pressure. The calibration gas flowrate is usually in excess of the analyzer gas flowrate. Thus, a portion of the calibration gas must be vented to the atmosphere to reduce the gas pressure to the atmospheric level and to eject the excess gas. Improper venting can cause severe problems in the calibration gas stability, accuracy, and repeatability. The magnitude of these problems is magnified in working with ultra-low levels. Atmospheric gas back-diffusion through the vent line promotes these problems. It is absolutely essential that the vent line gas flow is sufficiently high to minimize back-diffusion to insignificant levels. Of course, if the velocity is excessively high, a pressure difference is developed in the line, which changes the gas pressure at the analyzer input port.

At the present time, there is no theoretical or analytical basis which defines the following venting parameters: (1) vent gas velocity, (2) vent line dimensions, and (3) vent gas pressure. Thus, the calibrator designer and user must establish common ground rules for the vent.

It is noted that back-diffusion problems are eliminated entirely for a calibration flow network that operates at induced pressures. More specifically, the analyzer gas input port is connected directly to the output of the calibrator network. With this arrangement, the zero air flowrate is controlled directly by the analyzer. Thus, there is no excess calibration gas to vent and no excess pressure to reduce. The arrangement is illustrated by connecting an analyzer at the output of the NO generator of Fig. 2. Since the analyzer ingests the entire zero air flowrate, this arrangement is limited to those calibration networks which can operate at the analyzer flowrate. However, it is also an advantage because much less zero air is required.

Line-Outgassing

Another interface problem with ultra-low level calibration is line-outgassing. Pneumatic lines leading to the analyzer detector module may outgas sample gas molecules at rates which can yield an ultra-low level response equivalent to or larger than the response to calibration gas. It occurs after the analyzer has been in the monitoring mode with relatively high level sample. Thus, outgassing from the pneumatic lines will occur over extended periods of time, when the analyzer is on zero air or on ultra-low level calibration gas.

For ultra-low level applications, the zero air and calibration input ports to the analyzer must be as close as possible to the detector module to minimize the outgassing time. Usually, the zero air and calibration gas inlet ports are at bulkhead fittings on the rear panel and meet subsequently at a common point, such as a solenoid valve. If this arrangement is employed, the length of common line from the solenoid valve to the detector module must be minimized.

Surface Adsorption

The problems of surface adsorption are very similar to those of line outgassing. Identical precautions must be taken in design and calibrator/

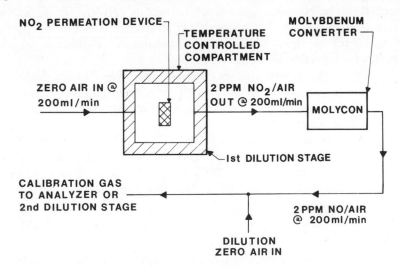

FIG. 2—*NO generator.*

analyzer setup. In this case, however, more attention must be devoted to the materials used. Surface adsorption can be reduced significantly whenever it is possible to utilize "inert" materials such as fluorinated ethylene propylene (FEP) or tetrafluoroethylene (TFE) and glass. For example, replacement of stainless steel fittings and lines with TFE or FEP equivalents can reduce significantly the calibration gas hold-up time of ultra-low levels.

Calibration Gas Primary Source

There are three basic sources of span gases: (1) permeation devices [15–17], (2) gas blends, and (3) generators and reactors [12].

Permeation Devices

For typical pollutant gases such as NO_2, SO_2, and H_2S, permeation device technology has advanced to a stage where reliable and controlled stability and output are routine. Several commercial enterprises are based on permeation tube products. Stable operation of permeation devices is based on maintaining the device at a constant temperature ($\pm0.1°C$) to control the calibration gas diffusion rate through its semipermeable wall, and on flowing zero air over it under controlled conditions. The two gases mix and formulate the low-level calibration gas. The single most important advantage of permeation devices is that reliable and repeatable dilution factors in excess of one million can be obtained with less than 1 litre/min zero air flowrate and ±1 percent stability. Requirements for relatively small amounts of zero air are also a large advantage in itself. In addition, the calibration gas emission rate of SO_2 and NO_2 permeation devices are traceable to the National Bureau of Standards (NBS). The spectacular success of permeation devices as a calibration gas primary source is partially responsible for the rapid development of automated continuous gas phase air pollution analyzers in recent years.

Although working with pure gas sources and large dilution factors has a significant advantage, permeation devices require relatively long initial stabilization times [17]. Increasing their dilution factors to one billion by increasing thickness dimensions is, in some cases, impractical, since much larger quantities of zero air are required, and the stabilization times increase logarithmically. For example, to increase the dilution factor of a permeation device operating at 50°C by a factor from 3 to 300 million, increases its stabilization from seven days to several years. Clearly, this is somewhat impractical.

Blended Gases

In cases where permeation devices are not practical, such as with NO, pressurized blended gases are available from gas manufacturers, which are traceable to NBS standards. Cylinders can be NBS certified at specific concentration levels in given carrier or diluent gases. Some disadvantages are associated with stability and operator mishandling. For example, the inadvertent introduction of oxygen or air into the tank can occur when hooking up pressure regulators and other pneumatic connections to the tank; long-term stability of the tank concentration levels are sometimes questionable when this occurs. Other problems are associated with gas adsorption on the tank walls, which occurs preferentially for some pollutant gases.

It is essential that blended gases are given enough time to stabilize after the original blend is mixed. This may last as long as 9 to 15 weeks, depending on the gas and the conditions under which it was mixed. Zero air or zero diluent gas is as essential to the blend as is zero gas, which is employed to dilute the blended concentration to lower levels. Usually, relatively high concentrations are employed in order to ensure accuracy and stability. These levels range from 50 to 500 ppm. Thus, the use of a blended gas to produce ultra-low level span gas will still require a dilution of approximately 50 to 200 000.

An interesting variation of a permeation device is suggested, which can be employed with a gas blend to produce low levels and relatively small zero air flowrates. It is comprised of a pressurized cylinder whose outlet port is stuffed with a leak-tight plug of some inert, thick, semipermeable material such as TFE or FEP. The stabilization time of the plug is reduced by immersing the plug in an equivalent gas blend and heating to an elevated temperature ($\simeq$200°C). At this temperature, the stabilization time can be reduced by at least 100. Thus, the plug can be allowed to saturate to concentration levels equivalent to that produced by the concentration of the gas blend at room temperature. It is then inserted into the gas blend cylinder outlet port. This procedure is proposed to circumvent the preposterous stabilization times.

Gas Generators and Reactors

For some molecular species it is possible to obtain calibration gases only from on-site generators. This requirement is most common for O_3 sources. O_3 is generated from zero air by irradiation with a UV light source [18]. The UV light source temperature, gas flowrate, and its electrical current level must be controlled within narrow limits to provide the stability required. Zero air requirements are different from those for most other pollutant calibration gases. The zero pollutant and other reactive gas concentration levels, such as NO and H_2S [19], must be maintained below 1 ppb to avoid side reactions with O_3, which will diminish its concentration to unknown levels after it is generated. Also, H_2O vapor must be removed from the zero air to 25 percent relative humidity levels at 25°C. With these circumstances, O_3 output concentration is maintained within $\pm$2 percent.

An important technique for producing NO span gas from NO_2 permeation devices is also available. Figure 2 shows the schematic network for this process. It is comprised of an NO_2 permeation device, contained within a temperature controlled compartment, and a molybdenum converter pneumatically in series. Zero air, at a flowrate less than 300 ml/min, flows into the compartment. NO_2, emanating from the permeation device, is mixed with the zero air stream and flows into the molybdenum converter. The NO_2 is quantitatively converted to NO. Downstream of the molybdenum converter, additional zero air is introduced to dilute further the NO calibration gas generated, and to provide also sufficient air for the analyzer intake and any venting action which may be required at the analyzer-calibrator pneumatic interface.

Using a permeation device to generate NO via a molybdenum converter has the primary advantage of being traceable directly to NBS standards. The permeation device output is traceable directly to an NBS standard for permeation tube output. A molybdenum converter's efficiency may be traceable also to an NBS standard by similar means. The standard NBS NO_2 tube must equal the NO response of tube with an in-line converter. This system is free of all the interferences and operator misuse problems which can occur with blended gases. This is a relatively simple calibrator for NO and NO_2. The molybdenum converter can be bypassed, through the action of solenoid valves, to produce only NO_2, or it may be injected directly to produce NO. Of course, the key to its success in the field depends upon the life and efficiency of the molybdenum converter.

Figure 3 shows the converter efficiency characteristics, under varying conditions of operating temperature, flowrate, and concentration level. As shown, the converter efficiency for 300 and 600 ml/min extends to 11 and 6-ppm NO_2, respectively. The selected operating temperature is 315°C, with flowrate 300 ml/min. Under these conditions, the molybdenum converter life is in excess of 6000 ppm h at 300 $\pm$ 15 ml/min, at a concentration level of 11 $\pm$ 0.1 ppm. NO_2 passed through the converter for 45.7 days and operated at an observed 100 percent efficiency during this time. Thus, by reducing the flowrate to 200 ml/min and a concentration level of 2 ppm NO_2, the converter efficiency will operate at 100 percent efficiency in excess of 6000 ppm h. It is estimated that the life of the converter, under these conditions, will be approximately 9000 ppm h, or one year.

A variation of the network of Fig. 2 is to introduce a second molycon in series. This arrangement can be applied periodically to check the converter efficiency.

Multistage Dilution

The two most widely used dilution techniques are those utilizing the methods of pneumatics and diffusion dilution. These are primarily the

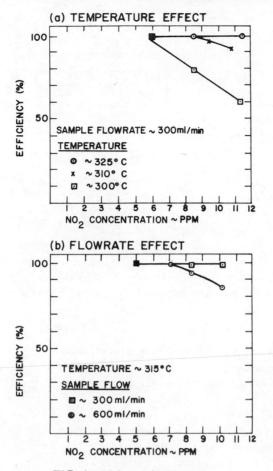

FIG. 3—*Molycon characteristics.*

straight pneumatic dilution, whereby two streams are mixed under controlled flowrate conditions, and the pneumatic/dilution techniques, whereby a highly concentrated gas such as the vapor over a liquefied gas is diluted by a permeation device and mixed with zero air.

Pneumatic Multistage Dilution

Figure 4 shows the network for a multistage, purely pneumatic dilution system. It is the simplest network to implement for low-level calibration, when using gas blends which are reasonably stable. The primary air and calibration source output pressures are controlled by pressure regulators. The impedance of the two lines are left virtually untouched, and their temperature is not controlled, for reasons described previously.

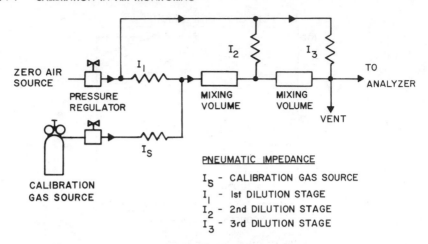

ZERO AIR SOURCE

PRESSURE REGULATOR

CALIBRATION GAS SOURCE

MIXING VOLUME

MIXING VOLUME

VENT

TO ANALYZER

I_1

I_2

I_3

I_S

PNEUMATIC IMPEDANCE

I_S - CALIBRATION GAS SOURCE
I_1 - 1st DILUTION STAGE
I_2 - 2nd DILUTION STAGE
I_3 - 3rd DILUTION STAGE

FIG. 4—*Pneumatic/pneumatic dilution.*

The calibration gas concentration at the second stage is described by the equation

$$C_2 = 10^6(q_s + q_{a_1} + q_{a_2})/q_s \tag{2}$$

The nomenclature for this and subsequent equations is described in the Nomenclature section.

As with all purely pneumatic dilution systems, temperature control is not required, for reasons cited earlier. Figure 4 shows also the presence of mixing volumes downstream of each fork in the network. In some cases, the mixing volume shown is equivalent to a given tube length or the connections and fittings normally used to accomplish the circuit. However, in some cases, the mixing volume or, rather, a delay volume, may be required to produce a homogeneous mixture. Table 2 tabulates the dilution factors obtained, as well as the concentration parameters and equilibrium response at the first and second stages. The dilution operating conditions are listed also.

Diffusion/Pneumatic Multistage Dilution

Figure 5 shows the network for a multistage dilution system employing two diffusion dilution stages and two pneumatic dilution stages. The first stage is comprised of a typical permeation device dilution system, employing a pressure regulator common to the dilution zero air for both stages. Zero air flows through a temperature controlled pneumatic impedance (I_1) into the temperature compartment and over the permeation device. At this stage, the calibration gas concentration for a permeation device with cylindrical geometry is described by the equation

$$C_1 = (2 \times 10^6)\pi L_1 P_{m_1} p_v/q_1 \ln (r_o/r_i)_1 \tag{3}$$

TABLE 2—*Multistage dilution characteristics.*

Dilution Technique	Dilution Factor			Concentration Parameters		Equilibrium Response (time constant)	
	1st Stage	2nd Stage	Total	1st Stage	2nd Stage	1st Stage	2nd Stage
Pneumatic/pneumatic 1. 1st stage flowrate (q_{a1}) = 10 litre/min 2. 2nd stage flowrate (q_{a2}) = 100 litre/min 3. Gas blend = 100-ppm NO/N_2 4. Calibration gas flow-rate (q_s) = 10 ml/min 5. Mining volume (V_m) = 1 litre	1001	10	10 010	$C_1 = \dfrac{q_s + q_{a1}}{q_s}$ C_1 = 100 ppb	$C_2 = \dfrac{q_s + q_{a1} + q_{a2}}{q_s}$ C_2 = 10 ppb	$T_{c1} = (V_m/q_a)_1$ T_{c1} = 6 s	$T_{c2} = (V_m/q_{a2})$ T_{c2} = 0.6 s
Pneumatic/diffusion 1. 1st stage (a) Calibration gas source-NO_2 (b) permeation tube r_o = 0.277 cm r_i = 0.0712 cm L_1 = 0.526 cm $P_m = 1.33 \times 10^{-9}$ ml/s-cm²-torr/cm $D = 4.03 \times 10^{-7}$ cm²/s T = 50°C P_v = 3600 torr (c) First stage flow-rate (q_1) = 0.2 litre/min	3.32×10^6			$C_1 = \dfrac{(2\pi \times 10^6)L_1 P_1 P_m P_v}{q_1 \ln(r_o/r_i)}$ C_1 = 3500 ppb		$T_{c1} = \dfrac{(r_o^2 - r_i^2)_1 \ln(r_o/r_i)_1}{2\,D_1}$ $T_{c1} = 1.21 \times 10^6$ s	
2. 2nd stage—TFE tube (a) r_o = 0.318 cm r_i = 0.292 cm L_2 = 25.4 cm $P_m = 2.8 \times 10^{-5}$ ml/s-cm²-torr/cm $D = 4.54 \times 10^{-5}$ cm²/s T = 200°C P_v = 760 torr (b) Second stage flow-rate (q_2) = 0.5 litre/min		1.6×10^3	5.32×10^9		$C_2 = \dfrac{(4\pi^2 \times 10^6)L_1 L_2 P_{m1} P_{m2} P_{v1} P_{v2}}{q_1 q_2 \ln(r_o/r_i)_1 \ln(r_o/r_i)_2}$ C_2 = 2.18 ppb		$T_{c2} = \dfrac{(r_o^2 - r_i^2)_2 \ln(r_o/r_i)_2}{2\,D_2}$ T_{c2} = 15 s

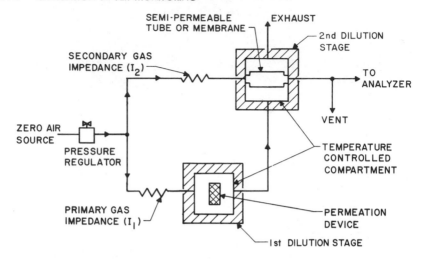

FIG. 5—*Two-stage pneumatic/diffusion dilution.*

The effect of temperature on P_{m_1}, and p_v is

$$P_{m_1} = P_o \exp(-E/RT) \qquad (4)$$

$$p_v = p_j \exp(-\Delta H_e/RT - c) \qquad (5)$$

As shown, temperature effects only the permeation device permeability coefficient (P_{m_1}) and the vapor pressure (p_v) of the liquefied gas within the permeation device. 'It is a significant effect. A $\pm0.1°C$ change will promote a ±1 to 2 percent change in SO_2 calibration gas concentration at 30 to 50°C operating temperatures. The temperature effect is more significant with gases possessing larger molar heats of evaporation (ΔH_e) because it is additive to the permeation device activation energy (E). This effect is not present in the second dilution stage since a liquid gas is not used.

The second stage is comprised of a heated and temperature controlled semipermeable tube or membrane diluter. Calibration gas from the output of the first stage flows over the outside surface of the tube and is exhausted from the system. Zero air flows through a second temperature controlled pneumatic impedance (I_2) into the second stage dilution stage compartment, and through the semipermeable tube. Calibration gas from the outside of the tube diffuses through the tube wall at a prescribed and controlled temperature, and mixes with the second zero air stream. The calibration gas concentration level at the exit of the second zero air stream is

$$C_2 = \frac{(4\pi^2 \times 10^6)L_1L_2P_{m_1}P_{m_2}P_Tp_v}{q_1q_2 \ln(r_o/r_i)_1 \ln(r_o/r_i)_2} \qquad (6)$$

$$P_{m_2} = P_o \exp(-E/RT) \qquad (7)$$

As seen by Eqs 6 and 7, only the tube material permeability coefficient (P_{m_2}) is affected by temperature, while both the permeation device permeability coefficient (P_{m_1}) and the calibration gas molar heat of evaporation (ΔH_e) are affected in the first stage as shown by Eq 3. Thus, temperature control requirements are not as stringent in the second stage as in the first stage, even at elevated temperatures. For example, a $\pm 1°C$ variation at a 200°C level will promote a ± 1 percent variation in calibration gas concentration at the second output.

Equations 3 and 6 will be examined further later in reviewing Table 2.

The multistage pneumatic/diffusion network of Fig. 5 is adapted to provide NO calibration gas by simply inserting a molybdenum converter in the line between the first and second dilution stages. It is illustrated by Fig. 6. All parameters remain unchanged in Eqs 3, 6, and 7, with the exception that the second stage permeability coefficient (P_{m_2}) is now the coefficient for NO, not NO_2. At 200°C, the permeability coefficients for NO and NO_2 are within 10 percent of each other, when using TFE.

A characteristic of all permeation devices, as used to produce span gas, is their time rate of response characteristic, which arises from the time required to saturate the permeation material to an equilibrium level. Steady-state operation of a permeation device is achieved after it experiences a transient stage, which follows the charging of the permeation device with the liquefied calibration gas, or after a temperature change, or after a zero air flowrate change through the first stage. The exact same condition applies to the diffusion material of the second stage. The only exception is

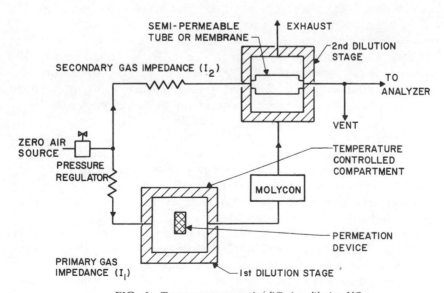

FIG. 6—*Two-stage pneumatic/diffusion dilution NO.*

that the saturation level is much less than that of the first stage, because the concentration level is much lower. In both stages, however, the total equilibrium time is determined primarily by the time required to saturate the tube wall with sample to its equilibrium concentration level, for whatever reason. For radial diffusion in both stages, the time dependent calibration gas concentration is

First stage

$$C_1 = \frac{(2\pi \times 10^6)L_1 P_{m_1} p_v}{q_1 \ln (r_o/r_i)_1} [1 - e^{-t/t_{c_1}}] \tag{8}$$

$$t_{c_1} = (r_o^2 - r_i^2)_1 \ln (r_o/r_i)_1/2D_1 \tag{9}$$

Second stage

$$C_2 = \frac{(4\pi^2 \times 10^6)L_1 L_2 P_{m_1} P_{m_2} P_T p_v}{2q_1 q_2 \ln (r_o/r_i)_1 \ln (r_o/r_i)_2} \times f(t) \tag{10}$$

$$f(t) = [1 + \{y_1 - 1\} e^{-t/t_{c_1}} + y_2 e^{-t/t_{c_2}}] \tag{11}$$

$$t_{c_2} = (r_o^2 - r_i^2)_2 \ln (r_o/r_i)/2D \tag{12}$$

$$y_1 = t_{c_1}/(t_{c_2} - t_{c_1}) \tag{13}$$

$$y_2 = t_{c_1}/(t_{c_1} - t_{c_2}) \tag{14}$$

Table 2 shows the application of Eqs 3–14 for the operating conditions listed.

An NO_2 permeation device, with the dimensions shown, operating at 50°C, will dilute the gas by a factor of 3.32×10^6, with 200 ml/min zero air flowrate. The NO_2 concentration at the first stage is 3500 ppb. At the second stage, a TFE tube, with the dimensions shown, at 200°C and a 500 ml/min zero air flowrate, dilutes the sample further by a factor of 1600 to 2.18 ppb. The overall dilution factor is 5.32×10^9. It is accomplished with a total zero air flowrate of only 700 ml/min. The two-stage diffusion/pneumatic dilution system removes a large burden from the zero air supply module. For example, an equivalent two-stage pneumatic/pneumatic dilution system requires approximately 110 litre/min.

The requirement for relatively small amounts of zero air permits the analyzer to be connected directly to calibration gas output of the second stage of Fig. 5, eliminating the secondary impedance element (I_2), and also back-diffusion and venting problems. Because of the relatively low first-stage zero air flowrate, the pressure regulator can be eliminated and the flow induced by a vacuum pump.

Table 2 summarizes the equilibrium response characteristics of the multistage dilution systems. The pneumatic/pneumatic system response is relatively fast. Neglecting pneumatic line outgassing and surface adsorptions effects described earlier, the time constant of the system is approximately 6.6 s.

The two-stage pneumatic/diffusion system responds much more slowly. However, it is only the permeation device of the first stage. It has a time constant of approximately 1.4 days. This time constant, however, is not involved in the response of the system, since the permeation device temperature is held constant during operation. It is a part of the equilibrium response only on initial charging of the device with liquid NO_2 and warm-up from room temperature to 50°C or both.

The time constant of the second dilution system is 15 s.

Acknowledgments

The author wishes to thank V. E. Modzeleski of the Monitor Labs calibration laboratory for performing kinetics experiments on the NO/O_3 oxidation reaction, P. A. Griffith for establishing the molybdenum converter efficiency levels, and J. D. Byrne and E. F. Szabo of the Monitor Labs air engineering department, whose designs of multistage dilution devices contributed to the development of low-level calibrators.

References

[1] "Ambient Air Monitoring Reference and Equivalent Methods," *Federal Register*, Vol. 40, No. 33, Part 2, 18 Feb. 1975, pp. 7042–7078.

[2] Hauser, T. R. and Shearer, S. D., *Environmental Science and Technology*, Vol. 9, 1975, p. 539.

[3] "Guidelines for Determining Performance Characteristics of Automated Methods for Measuring Nitrogen Dioxide and Hydrocarbons Corrected for Methane in Ambient Air," EPA-650/4-74-018, Environmental Protection Agency, Nov. 1974, p. 21.

[4] Leva, R. H. in *Fluidization*, McGraw-Hill, New York, 1959, p. 49.

[5] Perry, R. H., Chilton, C. H., and Kirkpatrick, S. D. in *Chemical Engineers' Handbook*, 4th edition, McGraw-Hill, New York, 1969, pp. 5–50.

[6] Rinehart, T. M., Scheffler, G. H., Helbig, W. A., and Truemper, J. T., *A Symposium on Activated Carbon*, ICI America Inc., 1968.

[7] Lovett, W. D. and Poltorak, R. L., "The Use of Activated Carbon for Controlling Odorous Air Pollutants," Air Pollution Control Association Specialty Conference on the State-of-the-Art of Odor Control Technology, Pittsburgh, Pa., 7–8 March 1974.

[8] "Air Quality Criteria for Sulfur Oxides," Publication No. AP-50, National Air Pollution Control Administration, Jan. 1969, p. 36.

[9] Clyne, M. A., Thrush, B. A., and Wayne, R. P., *Transactions of the Faraday Society*, Vol. 60, 1964, p. 359.

[10] Clough, P. N. and Thrush, B. A., *Transactions of the Faraday Society*, Vol. 63, 1967, p. 915.

[11] Redpath, A. E. and Menzinger, M., *Canadian Journal of Chemistry*, Vol. 49, 1971, p. 3063.

[12] Stefferson, D. M. and Stedman, D. H., *Analytical Chemistry*, Vol. 46, 1974, p. 1704.

[13] "Air Quality Criteria for Nitrogen Oxides," Publication No. AP-84, Air Pollution Control Office, Jan. 1971, p. 6–1.

[14] Williamson, S. J. *Fundamentals of Air Pollution*, Addison-Wesley, Reading, Mass., 1973, p. 298.

[15] O'Keefe, A. E. and Ortman, G. C., *Analytical Chemistry*, Vol. 38, 1966, p. 760.

[16] O'Keefe, A. E. and Ortman, G. C., *Analytical Chemistry*, Vol. 39, 1967, p. 1047.

[17] Lucero, D. P., *Analytical Chemistry*, Vol. 43, 1971, p. 1744.

[18] *Federal Register*, Vol. 38, 8 June 1973, p. 11015174–1518.

[19] Hales, J. M., Wilkes, J. O., and York, J. L., *Atmospheric Environment*, Vol. 3, 1969, p. 657.

A. H. Pradzynski[1] *and J. R. Rhodes*[2]

Development of Synthetic Standard Samples for Trace Analysis of Air Particulates

REFERENCE: Pradzynski, A. H. and Rhodes, J. R., "**Development of Synthetic Standard Samples for Trace Analysis of Air Particulates,**" *Calibration in Air Monitoring, ASTM STP 598*, American Society for Testing and Materials, 1976, pp. 320–336.

ABSTRACT: Synthetic, "homogeneous," and particulate standard samples in the form of deposits on filters have been developed for use in quality control of analytical methods and for calibration of X-ray emission spectrometers.

The standards for X-ray emission spectrometer calibration comprise membrane filters with single element or multielement solutions homogeneously deposited and dried, and membrane filters with known amounts of single mineral powders of well-defined particle size ranges deposited and fixed on them.

For quality control of analytical methods and laboratories, synthetic standards for sulfates, nitrates, and trace elements have been developed. The standards for sulfates, nitrates, and volatile trace elements were deposited in the form of solutions on glass fiber filters and dried. The standards for nonvolatile trace elements were prepared from -10-μm quartz powder spiked with compounds of the elements and deposited from air suspension.

KEY WORDS: air pollution, analyzing, sulfates, nitrates, trace elements, instruments, calibration, quality control, X-ray spectrometry, standard samples

A growing demand for rapid, instrumental, multicomponent analysis of large numbers of air particulate samples has been created by the recent increased emphasis on air pollution measurement and control. Preferred methods of elemental analysis of air particulates are those that do not require dissolution of the sample or any other time-consuming sample preparation. Such methods are almost always instrumental and are not absolute. Calibration standards are required in order to relate the instrument signal to the element mass or concentration in the sample.

Another application, for which standards are needed, is quality assurance of analytical methods and performance evaluation of laboratories that analyze air particulate samples.

[1] Research Associate, University of Texas Nuclear Reactor Teaching Laboratory, Austin, Tex. 78712.

[2] Manager, Applied Research Division, Columbia Scientific Industries Corp., Austin, Tex. 78766.

In order to satisfy some of these current needs, synthetic standards of three types have been developed in our laboratories: (a) "homogeneous" single element and multielement samples, (b) particulate deposits made from single minerals or standard reference materials, and (c) particulate deposits made from multielement spiked quartz matrices.

The methods of preparation, the applications, and some problems involved in preparation and use of these standard samples will be discussed in this paper.

Natural and Synthetic Standards

It is widely accepted that the best standards are those made of homogenized natural materials, analyzed by different methods and by several independent laboratories. Standard reference materials (SRM's) have been developed or certified or both by the National Bureau of Standards (NBS) since 1906. Other organizations such as the U. S. Geological Survey and foreign geological surveys also produce and certify SRM's. The NBS has developed several SRM's certified for trace elements, such as orchard leaves, bovine liver, glass, and fly ash. At least one ambient air particulate SRM is under development and will be certified for trace metals [1].[3] However, it may take several years before such SRM's become available for distribution [2]. The process of development and certification of real air particulate SRM's is long and expensive. Even when available, they will satisfy only a part of the overall requirements. Each one will represent only a single type of air pollution particulate, and several may be needed to cover the number and concentration ranges of trace elements found. They will not be suitable for instrument calibration, since each trace element will be certified at one concentration only. Also, they will not be suitable for calibration of a given method for elements that interfere when that particular method is used. Clearly, separate standards for each mutually interfering component would then be needed.

Since the ambient air particulate SRM's will be in the form of loose powder, they will not accurately represent samples collected on a filter, for example, from a high volume sampler. It should be emphasized that, in the specific case of air particulates, beside the need for standard reference materials, there is a need for standard reference samples. Finally, since air particulate SRM's are difficult to collect, they will be available only in limited amounts. Therefore, their use in large-scale quality control will not be practicable.

Synthetic standards can be well characterized, independently of a given analysis technique, by preparation from pure materials using absolute gravimetric or volumetric methods. Specific properties can be controlled

---

[3] The italic numbers in brackets refer to the list of references appended to this paper.

to allow instrument calibration for one parameter at a time. For example, single element standards and noninterfering multielement standards can be made for calibration of X-ray emission spectrometers. Particulate samples of predetermined particle size and composition can also be made. Furthermore, synthetic standard samples can be manufactured in a form similar to that of the unknown and at the same time compatible with the analytical instrument to be calibrated or evaluated. Since air particulates are usually collected on filters, the standard samples should be prepared on various filter substrates. Finally, synthetic standards or reference samples can be produced in practically unlimited quantities for large-scale quality assurance programs.

Standards for Calibration of X-Ray Emission Spectrometers

X-ray spectrometry has proved to be a very suitable method for elemental analysis of air particulates, mainly because it is rapid and does not require sample preparation [3,4]. The majority of air particulate samples are collected by drawing the air through a filter. The sample then constitutes a thin layer of particles uniformly spread on the surface or impregnated in the filter with a certain concentration profile. Such samples can be analyzed directly on an X-ray spectrometer. Other air particulate samples, collected by impactors, may require some pretreatment, such as spreading uniformly on a filter before analysis.

It was indicated by Winslow and Liebhafsky [5] as early as 1949 that interelement effects due to absorption and enhancement inherent in X-ray spectrometry are minimized when the analyzed sample is thin. Other advantages of the use of thin samples are: linear instrument response to element mass per unit area over a wide range of concentration; simplified corrections for particle size effects where necessary [6,7]; and increased fluorescent-to-scattered ratio of X-ray intensities, which is especially important in energy dispersive X-ray spectrometry.

The use of the thin sample method in air particulate analysis has been discussed by the authors of this paper with specific reference to energy dispersive X-ray fluorescence analysis of air particulates [8]. For a thin homogeneous sample the count rate I_x of characteristic X-rays from an element x is

$$I_x = S_x m_x \tag{1}$$

where

S_x = "sensitivity factor" for element x, (counts/s per $\mu g/cm^2$), and
m_x = mass per unit area of element x, ($\mu g/cm^2$).

The S_x is independent of the concentration of element x and of all other elements in the sample.

A thin sample is defined [8] as one having a total mass per unit area m, such that

$$m < 0.1(\mu_1 \cosec \theta_1 + \mu_2 \cosec \theta_2)^{-1} \qquad (2)$$

where

μ_1 and μ_2 = average mass absorption coefficients of the whole sample for the incident and characteristic X-rays, respectively, and

θ_1 and θ_2 = glancing angles of incidence and emission, respectively.

The equation for a thin particulate sample can be written in the following form

$$I_x = S_x P_x m_x \qquad (3)$$

where

P_x = measure of the self-absorption in a single particle containing element x [4,7,9], and

S_x and m_x = same as in Eq 1.

Since the rate of attenuation of X-rays increases rapidly as the characteristic X-ray energy decreases, real air particulate deposits fit the thin sample model for medium and high Z elements but tend to deviate for light elements. Both particle size and self-absorption effects in the deposit generally become negligible for determination of elements whose characteristic X-ray energies are above about 6 keV (for example, for K X-rays, iron; for L X-rays, samarium). Absorption effects in the substrate may be significant at higher energies, depending on the filter material and thickness.

Determination of lighter elements can be accomplished using the thin sample model as long as corrections are made for particle size and for deviations from the model [9,10]. These corrections are usually arrived at by a combination of calculation and experimental measurement. For example, particulate standards can be used to find P_x experimentally.

In order to satisfy the specific requirements of X-ray spectrometry, the following criteria for standards were considered: high accuracy in quantitative characterization of the desired amounts of single elements in a wide range of concentrations; feasibility of combinations of several elements in desired concentrations in one standard; homogeneity; uniformity of deposit over at least the measured area of the substrate; reproducibility; similarity of substrates to those of the unknowns; and mechanical and time stability.

Homogeneous Standards

Homogeneous single element standards are needed for the following purposes: energy calibration; optimization, element by element, of spectrometer parameters such as spectral windows, background windows, two theta settings; establishment of calibration curves especially in nonlinear regions (for example, for light elements where normal air particulate samples are no longer thin); storage of a library of standard spectra for use in stripping and fitting programs, especially in computerized energy dispersive X-ray spectrometry; setting-up of correction factors for spectral interferences, for example, zinc K_α–copper K_β, arsenic K_α–lead L_α; and establishment of correction factors for self-absorption in the substrate and the specimen encapsulation material, and for interelement absorption and enhancement effects. Multielement homogeneous standards are needed for quick, convenient recalibration and for monitoring batches of samples in automatic runs. Also, noninterfering sets of elements in one standard are quicker to use than several single element standards for many of the procedures just outlined.

Preparation of Homogeneous Standards

Several methods can be used to obtain homogeneous standards: vacuum evaporation or sputtering; sedimentation or filtration of precipitates from liquids; filtration of powders from air suspension; and deposition and evaporation of solutions. If precipitates or powders are used for preparation of homogeneous standards, they must be of very small particle size, of the order of 0.1 μm, so that no particle size effects occur.

Vacuum evaporation gives high purity deposits, but accurate determination of mass per unit area and uniform thickness over the whole area of the standard is difficult to obtain below 50 μg/cm^2. Also, it is not possible to produce multielement standards by this method, except for a few two-element combinations.

Sedimentation or filtration of fine precipitates or powders is limited in the number of elements and feasible element combinations. Particle size reduction to 0.1 μm is not easy without contaminating the sample. Segregation of components of a multielement precipitate or powder can occur in the course of its deposition. The same limitations apply to the technique of filtration from air suspension. Deposits of less than about 50 μg/cm^2 are also hard to weigh with adequate accuracy.

"Solution" Standards

The technique that meets most of the requirements for homogeneous standards was found to be evaporation of solutions deposited on filters of regular shape. Solutions can be accurately standardized. The original aliquot can be weighed with an accuracy of 0.05 percent. Dilutions to the lowest desired concentration can be made with an accuracy of 0.1 percent. Solutions also have the advantage that many elements can be mixed together easily, accurately, and homogeneously to produce multielement standards. Solution standards can be deposited on any wettable substrate such as filter paper, glass fiber filters, or membrane filters.

Standard stock solutions were prepared by dissolving pure metals in nitric acid, as a rule, or hydrochloric acid when unavoidable. For alkaline earths the metal carbonates were used. For elements occurring in the anionic form ammonium salts were used where possible. These stock solutions were diluted so as to provide the desired mass per unit area of the element in the final standard when a predetermined volume was deposited on the substrate. The deposition of solutions was done with the substrate on a special support, as shown in Fig. 1. The filters were placed on needle points covered with glass capillaries so that the contact area with the filter was negligible, to avoid losses of the deposited solution. For deposition of standardized solutions, a 250-μl syringe (Hamilton) with a Teflon tip plunger, Teflon capillary outlet, and a pushbutton dispenser was used. The syringe was calibrated gravimetrically, and delivered 5-μl aliquots for each push of the button.

The method of preparing standards by evaporation of aqueous solutions on filter paper has been described before [11-14], but poor reproducibility was experienced. In our experiments with evaporation of solutions from filter paper, it was established that the irreproducibility was caused by an effect of migration of ions during evaporation of the solution. In order to minimize these chromatographic effects the following precautions were taken: (a) for multielement standards, all components were added into one solution, and only a single deposition was made per specimen; (b) a "multidrop" technique was developed where the whole area of the filter was rapidly covered with ~5-μl drops in a regular pattern (Fig. 2); (c) the amount of solution was chosen so that the filter was just wetted completely with no excess of solution; and (d) an infrared lamp was used for rapid drying, except in the case of volatile elements. These precautions improved the reproducibility but not to the desired degree. It was concluded that chromatographic effects were eliminated during deposition of the solution but not during the evaporation step. In order to hinder the mobility of ions during evaporation a high molecular weight organic polymer was added.

The uniformity of dried solution standards was checked by cutting ten to twenty equal square or circular areas out of the specimens and measuring

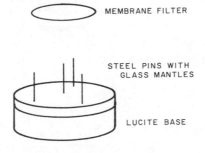

FIG. 1—*Apparatus for deposition of solutions on filters.*

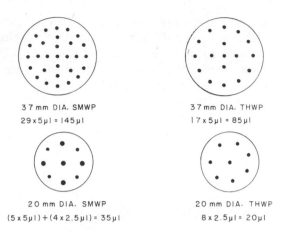

FIG. 2—*Drop patterns used on membrane filters.*

the X-ray intensity of each piece, for each element deposited. Several single element and multielement standards were tested in this way, for all substrate materials and substrate diameters used. Equality of area was checked by weighing each piece. Uniformity of mass per unit area of different substrates was checked in preliminary experiments by weighing blanks. Relative standard deviations of mean weights of both blank and deposited cut-out areas were in the range 1.0 to 1.3 percent. Relative standard deviations of the means of characteristic X-ray counts from sets of cut-out areas ranged from 2 to 4 percent, after allowance for counting statistics (typically 1 percent), weight variations, and positioning errors on the instrument of the small samples (found to be 0.5 to 1 percent). No significant bias was found between areas cut from the center of a standard and areas cut from near the edge.

Reproducibility of replicate standards was determined by measurement of the characteristic X-ray intensities from sets of ten standards prepared one after the other. Standard deviations of the means were typically in the range 1 to 4 percent. Any specimen having an X-ray intensity more than ±5 percent from the mean of its set was rejected. Over 200 such sets have been prepared recently, consisting of 35 single-element standards, each having three to five values of element mass per unit area (listed in Table 1), and six multielement standards (see Table 2) each having three concentration levels.

Particulate Standards

Particulate deposits are not easy to prepare with sufficient elemental range and concentration range to serve as primary calibration standards. However, they are required to provide particle size and particulate loading

TABLE 1—*Loading ranges of single element dried solution standards on Millipore membrane filters.*

Element	Loading, $\mu g/cm^2$	Element	Loading, $\mu g/cm^2$
F	0.34 to 34.0	Cu	0.51 to 50.6
Na	0.10 to 52.0	Zn	0.52 to 52.1
Mg	0.09 to 47.3	As	0.47 to 46.6
Al	0.06 to 60.5	Se	0.65 to 54.1
Si	0.12 to 75.7	Br	0.50 to 22.2
P	0.06 to 52.3	Mo	0.54 to 23.2
S	0.06 to 41.1	Rh	0.54 to 10.8
Cl	0.34 to 27.0	Pd	0.32 to 40.5
K	0.11 to 43.2	Ag	0.47 to 46.5
Ca	0.11 to 35.1	Cd	0.62 to 52.7
Ti	0.09 to 67.0	Sn	0.51 to 50.7
V	0.09 to 44.1	Sb	0.52 to 21.0
Cr	0.10 to 33.6	Ba	0.51 to 50.7
Mn	0.37 to 19.3	W	0.58 to 58.3
Fe	0.46 to 45.5	Pt	0.50 to 62.7
Co	0.49 to 48.9	Au	0.48 to 35.7
Ni	0.56 to 46.4	Pb	0.45 to 44.9
		U	0.51 to 25.6

NOTES—(*a*) Elements up to potassium are on filter Type THWP; all the rest are on SMWP.
(*b*) Filter diameter, 37 mm.

TABLE 2—*Combinations of elements in multielement dried solution standards.*

CSI Serial Number	Elements
640D5-S-MSM	K, Ca, V, Mn, Co, Cu, Cd
651D5-S-MTH	Na, Al, Ti, Cr, Fe, Ni, Zn, Pd
666D5-S-MTH	Ba, Hg, Pb, U
669D5-S-MTH	F, P, S, Cl, K, Br
676D5-S-MSM	Se, Mo, W
685D5-S-MSM	Rh, Sn, Sb, Pt, Au

correction factors for the lighter elements. A number of particulate standards were prepared from the following minerals: kyanite, cryolite, quartz, dolomite, anatase, and pyrite. Only the most perfect single crystals, free from inclusions of rock matrix, were used for the preparation of standards. The selected crystals were first crushed and then ground in an agate mortar to less than 30 μm. Particles were classified by sedimentation in ethanol into three size ranges: 0 to 3, 3 to 10, and 10 to 30 μm. One rock standard was prepared from a Canadian syenite (Standard Reference Rock Sy-2) [15] for use as a multielement particulate standard in an intercomparison study [16]. The standard rock sample was reground to particle size less than 10 μm and deposited on membrane filters (Millipore, Type SMWP), using the method described in the following section.

Deposition of Particulates

Several methods of deposition of particulates are described in the litera-ture: sedimentation [*17*], filtration from a liquid suspension [*18,19*], and filtration from an air suspension [*20,21*].

The preferred method for preparation of particulate standards for X-ray spectrometry was found to be filtration from air suspension. The method was developed as a modification of the technique used in this laboratory for mine dust analysis [*22*]. Figure 3 shows the all-glass device used for deposition of particulates on 37 and 47-mm-diameter filters. Air in the glass jar is sampled through a funnel base (Millipore) with a stainless steel screen filter support. The end of the funnel base is connected to a vacuum pump. Four glass tubes directed at the bottom of the jar provide air inlets used to produce a cloud of the powder to be deposited. The apparatus is operated in the following way. The sample is placed on the bottom of the jar, a filter is placed on the screen surface of the funnel base, the vacuum pump is turned on, air inlets are closed, and the top of the jar is positioned to evacuate the container. After a few seconds, the stopcock connected to the four air inlets is opened rapidly, and the incoming air stirs up a powder cloud which is sampled through the filter base. The baffle above the bottom of the jar prevents particle agglomerates from travelling directly to the filter. A similar deposition method has been described by Giauque et al [*21*].

The filters are weighed on an analytical balance before and after the deposition, to ±5 μg. The amount of material deposited can be roughly controlled through the amount of powder placed in the jar and by the sampling time.

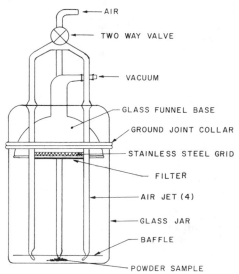

FIG. 3—*Device for deposition of particulates on filters from air suspension.*

All powder deposits were fixed by covering them with a 40 $\mu g/cm^2$ layer of paraffin, as follows: a 0.2 percent weight per volume paraffin in benzene solution is deposited over the powder using the multidrop technique. This is then air dried. Shaking tests showed that particles below 10 μm are fixed well on membrane filters.

Standards for Quality Assessment

Important elements of a quality assurance program in an air pollution analytical network are quality assessment of analytical methods and performance checks of laboratories and individual analysts [23]. The main requirements for standards for these quality assessment measures are: high accuracy of the standardized elements or compounds and closest possible similarity to the real samples. As already pointed up, synthetic standards are the most practical approach toward these requirements. In this laboratory, standard reference samples have been developed for sulfates, nitrates, and trace elements. In contrast to the standards for calibration of X-ray spectrometers, these standard reference samples are not designed for one specific analytical method but are intended for use by all the usual methods for analysis of air particulates collected on glass fiber filters.

As a standard procedure for ambient air [24], particulate samples are collected on 20.3 by 25.4 cm (8 by 10 in.) glass fiber filters from which 20.3 by 1.9 cm (8 by 3/4 in.) strips are cut for chemical analyses.

The standard reference samples for sulfates, nitrates, and trace metals were prepared in the form of such strips containing known amounts of the components. Since these strips are analyzed as they are, without being further divided, the distribution of the components on the strips is not critical.

Solution standards were prepared for sulfates, nitrates, and lead. Combined solution and particulate standards have been developed for sulfates, nitrates, and trace metals.

Solution Standard Reference Strips

Standard reference strips for sulfates and nitrates were prepared by deposition of aliquots of calibrated solutions of potassium sulfate and potassium nitrate. Stock solutions were prepared by dissolving in deionized water weighed aliquots of the reagent grade compounds. The compounds were ground finely in an agate mortar, dried in air at 105°C, and cooled in a dessicator before weighing. They were weighed on an analytical balance with an accuracy better than ±50 μg which for the smallest aliquot corresponded to 0.02 percent error, approximately. The stock solutions were prepared in volumetric flasks of Pyrex brand, Class A. Depositions of 50-μl aliquots were made by using an automatic liquid dispenser. The dispenser was calibrated before deposition of each type of solution by weighing aliquots delivered into a preweighed dish with a cover to prevent evaporation. Ten aliquots were weighed for each calibration. The relative standard deviations of these multiple weighings were in the range 0.1 to 0.2 percent. The densities of the calibrated solutions were measured with a pycnometer which was calibrated with deionized water.

The same procedure was followed for preparation of standard reference strips for lead. Reagent grade lead nitrate, recrystallized and dried in air at 105°C, was used for preparation of calibrated solutions.

In Tables 3 to 5, results are shown of chemical analyses[4] of a batch of standard reference strips for sulfates and nitrates and another batch of strips for lead. Nitrates were determined by the hydrazine reduction and diazotation method [25], sulfates by the Sulfaver[5] turbidimetric method [26], and lead by atomic absorption.

The results for nitrates show good agreement at higher concentrations (except for series 4000), while for the lower concentrations the method is apparently not accurate enough. The data for sulfates show good agreement with the standard values after the blank value is subtracted, except for the three lowest concentrations. The results for lead show excellent agreement for all concentrations.

Particulate Standards for Sulfates, Nitrates, and Trace Metals

The requirement for these standard samples is to incorporate in a particulate matrix sulfates, nitrates, and the following trace metals: arsenic, cadmium, chromium, copper, mercury, manganese, nickel, lead, palladium, platinum, selenium, vanadium, and zinc in concentration ranges similar to national annual averages for air particulates [27]. These requirements can be met by spiking a particulate matrix with appropriate amounts of trace metals.

Preparation of Spiked Particulate Matrix

Pure, fused quartz (General Electric) was reduced to particle sizes below 10 μm by grinding in an agate mortar followed by an air-jet pulverizer. The quartz powder was then washed with nitric and hydrochloric acids and with deionized water until all contamination, mainly, iron, chromium, and nickel abraded from the grinder, was removed. The removal of contaminating metals was checked by energy dispersive X-ray spectrometry. Particle size classification was done by sedimentation from a water suspension. The particle sizes obtained were confirmed by microscopic examination. This

---

[4] The analyses have been performed by the Environmental Protection Agency, Quality Assurance Branch, Environmental Monitoring and Support Laboratory. Permission for publication of the data is gratefully acknowledged.

[5] Trademark of the Hach Chemical Co.

TABLE 3—*Standard and analyzed values for nitrate in standard reference strips.*

| | | Nitrate per Strip, μg | | |
Series	Standard Values	Analyzed Values	Difference After Blank Subtraction	Difference, %
1000	638.3	626.3 ± 20.6	−26.0	−4.1
2000	1636.5	1668.2 ± 29.2	+17.5	+1.1
3000	157.9	173.8 ± 2.8	+1.7	+1.1
4000	962.4	868.8 ± 26.3	−79.4	−8.2
5000	0.0	14.2 ± 2.3	+14.2	...
6000	94.3	124.6 ± 6.7	+16.1	+17.0
7000	1443.0	1383.8 ± 34.4	−73.4	−5.1
8000	1277.7	1247.2 ± 25.3	−44.7	−3.5
9000	299.6	327.6 ± 5.5	+13.8	+4.6

TABLE 4—*Standard and analyzed values of sulfate in standard reference strips.*

| | | Sulfate per Strip, μg | | |
Series	Standard Values	Analyzed Values	Difference After Blank Substration	Difference, %
1000	6382.1	6831.4 ± 89.9	104.0	1.6
2000	1537.4	1894.6 ± 34.3	11.9	0.8
3000	3948.2	4326.0 ± 128.6	32.5	0.8
4000	498.0	936.0 ± 18.6	92.7	18.6
5000	0.0	345.3 ± 25.0	0.0	...
6000	2482.2	2898.5 ± 65.1	71.0	2.9
7000	846.0	1098.0 ± 22.4	−93.3	−11.0
8000	5110.9	5557.6 ± 111.8	101.4	2.0
9000	159.8	469.3 ± 13.2	−35.8	22.0

TABLE 5—*Standard and analyzed values of lead in standard reference strips.*

| | | Lead per Strip, μg | | |
Series	Standard Values	Analyzed Values	Difference	Difference, %
100	1262	1242.4	−19.6	1.6
200	121	121.5	+0.5	0.4
300	1811	1810.1	−0.9	0.05
400	804	821.6	+17.6	2.2
500	0	BDL[a]	...	...
600	350	347.8	−2.2	0.6

[a] BDL = below detection limit.

method was regarded as sufficiently accurate since particle size is not a critical characteristic of this standard reference sample.

The trace metals were divided into two groups, nonvolatile and volatile. The nonvolatile ones (cadmium, chromium, copper, manganese, nickel, palladium, platinum, vanadium, and zinc) were used for spiking in the form of standard solutions of nitrates or chlorides. The standard solutions were prepared by dissolving pure metals in nitric or hydrochloric acid or, in the case of platinum and palladium, in aqua regia. All chemicals were reagent grade or spectral purity.

The matrix was first ignited at 500°C for 2 h and cooled in a desiccator. Two 45-g aliquots were weighed using an analytical balance. Each of the aliquots was placed in a Teflon beaker, and a solution containing the appropriate quantities of the spiking elements was added in small portions. For each of the two aliquots, different amounts of trace metals were used. After each addition, the matrix was mixed thoroughly and dried in an oven. After all the spiking solution was added, the material was dried and ignited in a muffle oven at 500°C for 2 h. At this temperature, all nitric and hydrochloric acids are evaporated, all nitrates are decomposed, and the nitrogen oxides volatilized. Chromium may remain in the form of chloride. The rest of the trace elements remain in the form of oxides. The spiked matrices were homogenized by tumbling in glass jars with several ceramic balls for 24 h, and finally deposited on glass fiber filter strips as described next.

The elements arsenic, selenium,[6] mercury, and lead would volatilize in the course of the treatment just described. Therefore, they were deposited on the glass fiber filter strips from solutions in the same way as the sulfates and nitrates.

The representativity of the trace elements on a single strip was assessed by calculation of the "sampling error," C_ϵ, for a given trace element, using the following approximate formula [28] for the relative standard deviation

$$C_\epsilon = 100 \sqrt{\frac{W_p}{r_1 W_s}} \text{ percent} \tag{4}$$

where

r_1 = weight fraction of the trace element,
W_p = weight of a single particle, and
W_s = weight of the sample.

Assuming that the average particle diameter is 5 μm, the average specific gravity of spiked particulate is 3 g/cm^3, the weight of particulate on a single strip is 45 mg, and the element concentration is 2 μg/strip (the lowest value), a value of 0.75 percent for C_ϵ is obtained.

---

[6] Selenium was eventually omitted because it was found to interfere with subsequent nitrate determinations.

The following tests were performed in order to check the uniformity of distribution of trace elements in the spiked matrix. Five samples of each spiked matrix weighing 2.50000 g each were taken and mixed with an equal amount of cellulose powder (Whatman, chromatography quality). Pellets were pressed and subsequently analyzed using wavelength dispersive X-ray spectrometry. Each sample was measured on both sides, which was equivalent to measuring ten samples, since the samples were "infinitely thick" for the characteristic X-rays of the respective elements. The results of measurements on the eight elements tested are given in Table 6. The sampling errors calculated using Eq 4 were of the order of 0.1 percent.

Deposition Method

The following deposition method was developed. Seven glass fiber filter strips, 1.9 by 20.3 cm (0.75 by 8 in.), are placed in a specially designed holder on top of a high volume sampler. The sampler is placed on top of a cylindrical deposition device (Fig. 4) facing down, and the spiked particulate is placed in a small open container on the bottom of the device, in the center. A particle cloud is stirred up using a compressed air jet fixed in front of the particulate container. The sampler is switched on for a predetermined time (45 s), and the particulates are deposited on the glass fiber filter strips. Each strip is weighed before and after deposition to ±50 μg using an analytical balance. The deposited weight is controlled by the amount of particulate used to make the cloud. The objective is to deposit 45 ± 5 mg on each strip. In production runs, the recovery was found to be in the range 46 to 58 percent, and the weight of deposits ranged from 39 to 50 mg. Single batches of seven strips showed the deviations from their mean weights of 1.1 to 4.7 percent.

TABLE 6—*Results of homogeneity tests of spiked particulate.*

Element and X-Ray	Relative Standard Deviation, %			
	Total $(T)^a$	Statistical $(S)^b$	Instrumental $(I)^c$	Homogeneity $(H)^d$
VK_α	1.29	1.20	0.22	0.42
CrK_α	2.20	2.03	0.22	0.82
MnK_α	1.39	0.77	0.22	1.14
NiK_α	1.19	1.07	0.22	0.47
CuK_α	1.08	0.96	0.22	0.44
ZnK_α	0.87	0.58	0.22	0.61
PtL_α	2.45	2.16	0.22	1.14
PdK_α	5.27	2.18	1.29	4.62

[a] Experimental value for 10 sample sides.
[b] Calculated from counting statistics.
[c] Determined in separate experiment.
[d] Residual, determined as follows

$$H = \sqrt{T^2 - S^2 - I^2}$$

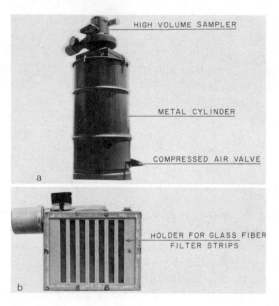

FIG. 4—*Powder deposition device for glass fiber strips:* (a) *general view and* (b) *manifold with mask for seven strips.*

Use of Synthetic Standards in Intercomparison Studies

The dried solution standards have been used in at least three recent intercomparison studies. Some 3000 of the standard reference strips containing sulfates and nitrates, or lead, have been employed with satisfactory results in the Environmental Protection Agency quality assurance programs. Multielement dried solution deposits have been employed in two intercomparison studies designed primarily to test new X-ray spectrometric techniques for trace element analysis of air particulates [16,29]. The synthetic particulate samples have not yet been used in interlaboratory comparisons but are intended for that purpose.

The multielement dried solution deposits used in the preceding two intercomparisons contained 9 and 10 elements, selected (within the constraints of chemical compatibility) to produce characteristic X-ray lines with various types and degrees of spectral interference. In the first study [29], eleven participants used X-ray spectrometry and one, neutron activation. In the second [16], eighteen participants used various X-ray spectrometric techniques, two used atomic absorption, one, emission spectrometry and one, neutron activation. All investigators used calibration and analysis procedures of their own choice. In both studies it was concluded that the multielement dried solution deposits had adequate uniformity, accuracy, and stability for such studies. The estimated uniformity of both sets of standards was 2 to 3 percent (one relative standard deviation of the mean of the monitored characteristic X-ray line intensities). The long-term stability was found to be at least as good as that of the X-ray spectrometer used for monitoring samples sent out and returned, that is, about 1 percent. No significant systematic bias occurred between the amounts of each element deposited and the reported determinations, with the exception of bromine in the first set of samples. Excluding a small proportion of individual results whose large errors could be explained otherwise, the average ratio between amount deposited and amount reported, for 66 element determinations in the first intercomparison, was 0.98 ± 0.09 for deposits on Whatman 41 filters and 1.02 ± 0.10 for deposits on Millipore. In the second intercomparison the best data were obtained by energy dispersive X-ray spectrometry where 120 element determinations (spread between 15 laboratories and 10 elements, aluminum to gold) gave an average ratio of 1.00 ± 0.11.

Acknowledgments

Different parts of this work were performed under the auspices of the U. S. Atomic Energy Commission, now the U. S. Energy Research and Development Administration (Contract AT-(40-1)-4205), and the Environmental Protection Agency (Contracts 68-02-1739 and 68-02-1754). We would also like to acknowledge the untiring efforts of Dr. R. A. Susott (Columbia Scientific Industries) who performed a great deal of supporting experimental work.

References

[1] McNesby, J. R., "Standard Reference Materials for Air Pollution," Special Environmental Report No. 3, WMO No. 368, World Meteorological Organization, Geneva, 1974, pp. 595–603.
[2] Kirchhoff, W., private communication.
[3] Rhodes, J. R., Pradzynski, A. H., Hunter, C. B., Payne, J. S., and Lindgren, J. L., *Environmental Science and Technology*, Vol. 6, No. 10, Oct. 1972, pp. 922–927.
[4] Rhodes, J. R. *American Laboratory*, Vol. 5, No. 7, July 1973, pp. 57–73.
[5] Winslow, E. H. and Liebhafsky, H. A., *Analytical Chemistry*, Vol. 21, 1959, p. 1338.
[6] Hunter, C. B. and Rhodes, J. R., *X-Ray Spectrometry*, Vol. 1, No. 3, July 1972, pp. 107–111.
[7] Rhodes, J. R. and Hunter, C. B., *X-ray Spectrometry*, Vol. 1, No. 3, July 1972, pp. 113–117.
[8] Rhodes, J. R., Pradzynski, A. H., Sieberg, R. D., and Furuta, T. in *Low Energy X- and Gamma-Ray Sources and Applications*, C. A. Ziegler, Ed., Gordon and Breach, London and New York, 1971, p. 317.
[9] Rhodes, J. R., "Recommended Procedures for the Use of Columbia Scientific Industries Thin Standards for X-Ray Fluorescence Spectrometry," Applied Research Division Internal Report No. 206, Columbia Scientific Industries, Austin, Tex., May 1975.
[10] Dzubay, T. G. and Nelson, R. O. in *Advances in X-Ray Analysis*, Vol. 18, W. L. Pickles, C. S. Barrett, J. B. Newkirk, and C. O. Ruud, Eds., Plenum Press, New York, 1975, pp. 619–631.
[11] Pfeiffer, H. G. and Zemany, P. D., *Nature*, Vol. 174, 1954, p. 397.
[12] Felten, E. J., Fankuchen, I., and Steigman, J., *Analytical Chemistry*, Vol. 31, No. 11, Nov. 1959, pp. 1771–1775.

[13] Gunn, E. L., *Analytical Chemistry*, Vol. 33, No. 7, June 1961, pp. 921–926.

[14] Bumsted, H. E., *American Industrial Hygiene Association Journal*, Vol. 25, 1964, p. 392.

[15] Faye, G. H., "Standard Reference Ores and Rocks Available from the Mines Branch as of October 1973," Mines Branch Information Circular 1C 309, Department of Energy, Mines, and Resources, Mines Branch, Ottawa, Canada.

[16] Camp, D. C., Van Lehn, A. L., Rhodes, J. R., and Pradzynski, A. H. in *X-Ray Spectrometry*, Vol. 4, No. 3, July 1975, pp. 123–137.

[17] Verdingh, V., *Nuclear Instruments and Methods*, Vol. 102, 1972, pp. 431–434.

[18] Luke, C. L., *Analytica Chimica Acta*, Vol. 41, 1968, pp. 237–250.

[19] Gilfrich, J. V., Burkhalter, P. G., and Birks, L. S., *Analytical Chemistry*, Vol. 45, No. 12, Oct. 1973, pp. 2002–2009.

[20] Leroux, J., *Staub-Reinhaltung der Luft*, Vol. 29, No. 4, April 1969, pp. 33–36.

[21] Giauque, R. D., Goulding, F. S., Jaklevic, J. M., and Pehl, R. H., *Analytical Chemistry*, Vol. 45, No. 4, April 1973, p. 671.

[22] Rhodes, J. R. and Taylor, M. C., "Rapid Major Element Mine Dust Analyzer," Final Report of U. S. Bureau of Mines Contract H0110985, Bureau of Mines File No. 49-73, Columbia Scientific Industries, 1972.

[23] "Quality Control Practices in Processing Air Pollution Samples," Report APTD-1132, U. S. Environmental Protection Agency, Washington, D. C.

[24] Intersociety Committee, "Methods of Air Sampling and Analysis," No. 501, Tentative Method of Analysis for Suspended Particulate Matter in the Atmosphere: (High-Volume Method), American Public Health Association, Washington, D. C., 1972, pp. 365–372.

[25] Kemphoke, L. et al, *Water Research*, Vol. 1, 1967, p. 205.

[26] *Standard Methods for Examination of Water and Wastewater*, 13th Ed., Method 156C, 1971.

[27] "Air Quality Data for 1968," APTD-0978, U. S. Environmental Protection Agency, Washington, D. C., Aug. 1972, p. 15.

[28] Grant, C. L. and Pelton, P. A. in *Advances in X-Ray Analysis*, Vol. 17, C. L. Grant, C. S. Barrett, J. B. Newkirk, and C. O. Ruud, Eds., Plenum Press, New York, 1974, p. 44.

[29] Camp, D. C., Cooper, J. A., and Rhodes, J. R., *X-ray Spectrometry*, Vol. 3, 1974, pp. 47–50.

D. H. Stedman,[1] G. Kok,[2] R. Delumyea,[3] and H. H. Alvord[1]

Redundant Calibration of Nitric Oxide, Carbon Monoxide, Nitrogen Dioxide, and Ozone Air Pollution Monitors by Chemical and Gravimetric Techniques

REFERENCE: Stedman, G. E., Kok, G., Delumyea, R., and Alvord, H. H., "Redundant Calibration of Nitric Oxide, Carbon Monoxide, Nitrogen Dioxide, and Ozone Air Pollution Monitors by Chemical and Gravimetric Techniques," *Calibration in Air Monitoring, ASTM STP 598,* American Society for Testing and Materials, 1976, pp. 337–344.

ABSTRACT: Calibrated nitric oxide (NO) sources are described using ammonia and nitromethane permeation followed by pyrolysis. A field carbon monoxide calibrator based on nickel carbonyl as the liquid fill is discussed. Two techniques for intercalibrating chemiluminescent NO and ozone (O_3) meters using the photolysis of nitrogen dioxide (NO_2) are demonstrated, together with the feasability of a continuous check on NO, NO_2, and O_3 meters in ambient air, based on a photostationary state measurement.

KEY WORDS: calibration, air pollution, analyzing, chemiluminescence, nitric oxide, carbon monoxide, nitrogen dioxide, ozone, photochemistry

The difficulty of calibrating air pollution monitors at sub-parts-per-million levels is well documented. Thus, we feel that a number of techniques should be applied to one monitor to ensure reliability by redundant calibration. To this end, we have developed gravimetric sources of nitric oxide (NO) and carbon monoxide (CO), and demonstrated several intercalibrations for NO, nitrogen dioxide (NO_2), and ozone (O_3) monitors.

The aim of the gravimetric study was to use permeation tube technology [1–3][4] and quantitative chemical conversion to provide sources of such

---

[1] Assistant professor and research assistant, respectively, Chemistry Department, University of Michigan, Ann Arbor, Mich. 48104.

[2] Assistant professor, Harvey Mudd College, Claremont, Calif. 91711.

[3] Research scientist, Great Lakes Research Division, University of Michigan, Ann Arbor, Mich. 48104.

[4] The italic numbers in brackets refer to the list of references appended to this paper.

species as the permanent gases NO and CO. For NO, two suitable permeands were found which could be converted by pyrolisis to NO. These were ammonia (NH_3) [4] and nitromethane (CH_3NO_2). For CO, no suitable pyrolysable compound has yet been found. Therefore, we investigated the use of nickel carbonyl as the liquid fill for a permeation tube. The equilibrium

$$Ni(CO)_{4(l)} \rightleftharpoons Ni_{(s)} + 4CO_{(g)}$$

is such that, at 30 to 40°C, a pressure of CO of several atmospheres is present. Thus, permeation of CO is expected; stable CO permeation was observed. However, a nonstoichiometric process makes the weight loss less than the observed CO output; thus, this device may not function as an absolute but only as a transfer standard.

Intercalibration of NO, NO_2, and O_3 monitors by the NO + O_3 titration reaction has been demonstrated previously [5]. We demonstrate two alternate approaches to NO/O_3 intercalibration using the photolysis of NO_2. The three fastest reactions in this system are

1. $NO_2 + h\nu \rightarrow NO + O$
2. $O + O_2 + M \rightarrow O_3 + M$
3. $O_3 + NO \rightarrow NO_2 + O_2$

If low concentrations of NO_2 ($\sim$1 ppm) in air are photolyzed, then equal concentrations of NO and O_3 are produced [6,7]. This equality provides a direct NO/O_3 intercalibration. The photolysis of any concentration of NO_2 makes steady-state NO and O_3 concentrations. If the photolysis lamp is turned off, then the stoichiometry of reaction 3 gives equal initial decreases of NO and O_3, again an intercalibration. The photolysis of NO_2 also leads to a method for continuous field testing of NO/NO_2/O_3 monitors via the photostationary state equation

$$k_1[NO_2] = k_3[NO][O_3] \tag{1}$$

where

k_1 = instantaneous rate of solar photolysis of NO_2 and
k_3 = known rate of the reaction NO + $O_3 \rightarrow NO_2 + O_2$.

We have shown recently [8] that the photostationary state, Eq 1, holds under a wide range of conditions, and that measurement of k_1 can be made with available equipment [9]. If Eq 1 is rewritten

$$k_1[NO_2]/k_3[NO][O_3] = 1 \tag{2}$$

then using a k_1 detector and ambient air monitoring data for NO, NO_2, and O_3, continuous calculation of the left hand side should lead to a steady value of 1.0. This test can give extra reliability to NO, NO_2, and O_3 measurements, and deviations will indicate calibration errors in one or more detectors.

Procedure

NO was determined by commercial or home built chemiluminescent NO/O_3 detectors [5]. O_3 was detected with the same detectors using excess NO and with a commercial O_3/ethylene detector. NO_2 was measured with NO as total nitrogen oxides (NO_x) using various chemical converters [10] tested to ensure 100 percent efficiency. CO was determined by methanation gas chromatography [11].

Air flows were measured using calibrated soap film flowmeters. Commercial standard gas cylinders ~50 ppm were used as an original basis for comparison, together with several flow dilution systems based on calibrated syringe pumps for pure gas sources and large flows of air measured with a wet test meter, calibrated using a bell prover.

Weight losses were measured using a single analytical balance.

Photolysis of NO_2 in the laboratory was carried out in a 2-cm inside diameter Pyrex tube, centrally located between four F40 black light (BL) tubes (General Electric). The sampling point was typically 70 cm down the tube, giving 4 s of photolysis of 1-ppm NO_2 (100-ppm NO_2 diluted in air). This system and the k_1 detector are described elsewhere [9]. Permeation tubes were made by tightening Swagelok ferrules over fluorinated ethylene propylene (FEP) Teflon tubing with glass reservoirs. Best results were obtained with nylon back ferrules and brass or aluminum front ferrules.

Results

Permeation Sources for NO

Many organic nitrites decompose readily to NO. We tested several compounds including ethyl and *i*-amyl nitrites; however, they were too unstable to be reliable permeands, apparently due to the instability of the parent compounds to thermal decomposition. All tubes were kept in the dark to minimize photodecomposition.

For NH_3, reliable permeation has already been demonstrated [2]. We observed reliable NH_3 permeation in the 30 to 40°C range. Quantitative 100 percent conversion of NH_3 at parts-per-million levels to NO could be achieved over a platinum gauze packing in a stainless steel tube, at temperatures greater than 800°C. Figure 1 shows this conversion in air at 7-ppm NH_3.

As an alternate, and possibly more easily pyrolysable NO source, CH_3NO_2 was tested. In the range 30 to 40°C, permeation rates were slow and variable. At >100°C, the permeation rate was adequate and independent of humidity. It seems advantageous to work at or near the boiling point of these organic permeands.

We have kept CH_3NO_2 permeation tubes at 100°C with good weight loss rate response for up to 45 days. Typical permeation rates are 3500 to

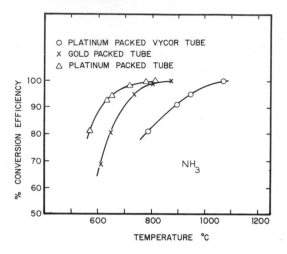

FIG. 1—*Conversion of 7-ppm NH₃ in air to NO as a function of temperature on various substrates.*

7000 ng/min (5 to 10 mg/day) with 0.5 cm of ¼ in. inside diameter by ⅟₁₆-in. wall FEP Teflon tubing. At these permeation rates, our tubes will last a year or more.

The pyrolysis of CH_3NO_2 was studied in detail. Typical conditions are shown in Table 1.

Three pryolysis furnaces were tested for conversion of CH_3NO_2. A plain stainless steel tube reached complete conversion at 600°C, a quartz tube with platinum gauze, at 720°C, and the stainless steel tube with platinum gauze at 550°C. Figure 2 shows the behavior of the stainless steel tube with platinum gauze, which was the best converter.

In studying the pyrolysis of CH_3NO_2 to produce NO, the question as to whether NO_2 was also formed in this process came up. According to Crawforth and Waddington [12], the first step in the pyrolysis of CH_3NO_2 is

$$CH_3NO_2 \overset{\Delta}{\rightarrow} CH_3 + NO_2$$

Since a quantitative conversion to NO was desired, we measured the temperature conversion relationship for NO_2 in our apparatus. The experi-

TABLE 1—*Typical conditions for CH₃NO₂ pyrolysis.*

Air flow	800 ml min⁻¹
CH_3NO_2	1 ppm
Pressure	1 atm
Heated tube ¼ ID 30 cm long	
Residence time in hot zone <0.5 s	

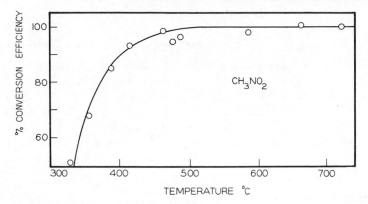

FIG. 2—*Conversion of 5-ppm CH₃NO₂ in air to NO in a stainless steel furnace with platinum gauze catalyst.*

mental conditions were the same as the ones for the CH_3NO_2 pyrolysis except that the NO_2 came from a gas cylinder.

In the stainless steel converter, 100 percent conversion of 2 ppm NO_2 to NO had occurred when the temperature reached 380°C. The results indicate that, in a stainless steel converter, NO_2 formation would not be a problem for our system. Since the converter operates well above 380°C, any NO_2 formed in the first stage of decomposition is converted quantitatively to NO.

The pyrolysis of CH_3NO_2 was also studied using a gas chromatograph (Varian 1520) with a flame ionization detector. Since this detector is sensitive only to carbon compounds, the disappearance of the parent species could be observed as the temperature of the converter tube increased.

The same flow system that was used with the NO detector was also used for this study; however, the flow rate was reduced to 50 cm³/min to concentrate the sample. As a result, sample residence time in the heated converter tube was about 11 s. CH_3NO_2 had disappeared completely by 360°C. No organic products were observed when CH_3NO_2 was pyrolyzed.

Thus, NO production by CH_3NO_2 pyrolysis was expected to be quantitative and interference free. Measured NO formation (calibrated using a number of standard tanks) was plotted versus calculated NO based on weight loss data between 1 and 25 ppm. Data were taken over a 30 day period with no evidence of drift, the observed slope of 1.00 ± 0.03 indicates the success of this method.

NH_3 as a permeant is entirely safe. CH_3NO_2 is listed as a shock sensitive explosive at 100°C; however, in our glass/Teflon systems we have had no problems with our 0.5-ml liquid samples.

Permeation Sources for CO

The use of nickel carbonyl ($Ni(CO)_4$) as a CO source was investigated, together with the question of whether $Ni(CO)_4$ itself permeates.

Several permeation tubes containing $Ni(CO)_4$ were constructed similar to the CH_3NO_2 tubes. Over a period of eight months, their weight loss was linear, yielding 3 to 5 $\mu g/min$ at 44.4°C. Calibration of the CO output revealed, however, that it was a constant factor of 1.95 ± 0.06 larger than the weight loss. This is probably due to the inward permeation of some species, as yet not identified. A tentative mechanism for this process may be

4. $Ni(CO)_4 \rightleftarrows Ni + 4CO$
5. $Ni + \frac{1}{2}O_2 \rightarrow NiO$
6. $NiO + CO_2 \rightarrow NiCO_3$
   $CO \rightarrow$ permeate

where the oxygen and CO_2 are supplied by the air passed over the permeation tube. The foregoing mechanism results in a ratio of permeation-to-weight loss of 1.87.

To determine whether any $Ni(CO)_4$ permeates under the conditions employed, two independent checks were made. The permeation tube was purged with air for 67 h, and the air passed through a solution of $1M$ nitric acid (HNO_3). Under these conditions, any $Ni(CO)_4$ would be converted to divalent nickel. The resulting solution was tested for nickel, using flameless atomic absorption. No nickel was observed at the limit of detection. Another tube was similarly purged, and the purge-air passed through a glass capillary heated to 350°C for 240 h. Since $Ni(CO)_4$ decomposes at $>160°C$, a nickel mirror should form in the capillary. None was observed.

This permeation tube, therefore, provides a source for a constant amount of CO which is reproducible and safe, making it suitable as a field calibration tool. Until the chemistry is better understood, however, it cannot be used for an absolute calibration source due to the lack of stoichiometry.

Intercalibration of NO and O_3

If air containing initially only NO_2 is photolyzed, then by stoichiometry during the first minute of photolysis (at 1 ppm), equal quantities of NO and O_3 are formed [6,7]. The flow system used for k_1 studies [8,9] gave an opportunity to study these products during the first 1 to 15 s of photolysis. The apparatus is shown as Fig. 2 of Ref. 9, and was used with two slight modifications. A potassium dichromate ($K_2Cr_2O_7$) impregnated filter was used at the input to ensure low NO concentrations in the incoming NO_2, and two blackened probes were inserted together into the stream, one for NO, the other for O_3. Well calibrated NO and O_3 detectors gave the same response within their ~1-ppb noise limitations. The residence times from the probes to the NO and O_3 detectors were both <1 s. With NO = O_3 =

0.1 ppm, the largest value we used, the decay of NO and O_3 is $1/NO-1/NO_0 = 25.5/60 = 0.43$ where 25.5 ppm^{-1} min^{-1} is the rate of reaction 3. This shows that a 4 percent decay of NO and O_3 can be expected, but, provided the residence times are equal, the stoichiometry of reaction 3 again ensures the equal response, as observed. Overall the foregoing method uses the stoichiometry of reactions 1 and 2 to produce equal NO and O_3.

The stoichiometry of reaction 3 is the basis of the gas phase titration (GPT) method. Using the apparatus described here, it can also be used as a rapid intercalibration. The system previously used produced 0.1-ppm NO and O_3 each in 0.9-ppm NO_2. If the NO input was not oxidized, some excess NO was always present. Further, if the input NO_2 is increased, then an excess of NO over O_3 can occur readily [6,7,9]. This arbitrary mixture of NO and O_3 is then sampled with a dual probe. First, the sampling is direct as before; then NO and O_3 readings are taken. Next, the lights are turned off, and the differences in NO and O_3 are measured. Again, with well-calibrated instruments, these reductions in NO and O_3 signals are equal. Since the calibrations are performed by GPT, this is not surprising, but it is a simple check with simpler apparatus, since only tank or permeated NO_2 and air are required, together with 110 V power for the lamps, and no flows need be measured.

The final intercalibration technique is based on the photostationary state, Eq 1. The ratio $k_1[NO_2]/k_3[O_3]$ [NO] can be continuously calculated, provided simultaneous data for NO, NO_2, O_3, k_3, and k_1 are available. The first three are available because of the air monitoring application. According to Garvin and Hampson [13], $k_3 = 9 \times 10^{-13}$ exp $(-1200/T)$ $cm^3mol^{-1}s^{-1}$; thus, continuous temperature data can be used to obtain k_3. We have shown that k_1 can be determined using an NO_2 actinometer, and also that k_1 may be adequately determined by an ultraviolet (UV) pyranometer measurement (E) with multiplication by the appropriate calibration factor k_1 $(min^{-1}) = 0.019 E(UV W M^{-2})$. Thus if k_1 is measured by either method, calculation of the photostationary equation can be performed as a continuous check on equipment calibration. The check is most useful during the day, when all parameters are measurable, and the ratio should stay at 1.0. At night, the equation degenerates to the solutions

$$\text{if } [O_3] > 0 \qquad [NO] = 0$$
$$\text{if } [NO] > 0 \qquad [O_3] = 0$$

The validity of these terms is a check on the zeroing of NO and O_3 instruments, provided the monitors are not so close to sources (<30 s downwind) that steady state is not obtained.

The validity of Eq 1 was demonstrated in downtown Detroit [8]. Continuous values of the ratio were derived by hand from strip charts and shown to stay close to 1.0. We are currently extending these measurements to other areas and removing some of the problems associated with the previous study [8]. So far, all data indicate the validity of the equation and its usefulness as a continuous calibration check. Notice that the photostationary state will not prove valid if there is a long residence time between the air sampling and $NO/NO_2/O_3$ detection equipment. Times greater than 2 s can introduce significant concentration errors.

Conclusions

We have demonstrated two techniques for permeation/pyrolysis NO sources. These can be absolute standards. They can also be intercalibrations if an NH_3 or CH_3NO_2 detector should be available. $Ni(CO)_4$ proved to be a stable but nonquantitative CO source with no $Ni(CO)_4$ impurity. This may be a useful transfer standard but is not an absolute calibrator.

Two NO/O_3 intercalibration techniques based on NO_2 photolysis provide simple intercalibrations with portable equipment.

The photostationary state equation has been demonstrated to be a feasible method for a continuous intercalibration check on NO, NO_2, and O_3 monitoring data.

Acknowledgments

For various parts of this study, we acknowledge the efforts of J. O. Jackson, and the support of the Environmental Protection Agency under grant No. R802373.

References

[1] O'Keeffe, A. E. and Ortman, G. C., *Analytical Chemistry*, Vol. 38, 1966, p. 760.

[2] Scaringelli, F. P., O'Keeffe, A. E.,Rosenberg, E., and Bell, J. P., *Analytical Chemistry*, Vol. 42, 1970, p. 871.

[3] Saltzman, B. E., Burg, W. R., and Ramaswamy, G., *Environmental Science and Technology*, Vol. 5, 1971, p. 1121.

[4] Hodgeson, J. A., Bell, J. P., Rehme, K. A., Krost, K. J., and Stevens, R. K., American Institute of Aeronautics and Astronautics Paper, 71-1067, Palo Alto, Calif., 8–10 Nov. 1971.

[5] Stedman, D. H., Daby, E. E., Stuhl, F., and Niki, H., *Journal of the Air Pollution Control Association*, Vol. 22, 1972, p. 260.

[6] Stedman, D. H. and Niki, H., *Environmental Science and Technology*, Vol. 7, 1973, p. 735.

[7] Wu, C. H. and Niki, H., *Environmental Science and Technology*, Vol. 9, No. 46, 1975.

[8] Stedman, D. H. and Jackson, J. O., *International Journal of Chemical Kinetics Symposium*, Vol. 1, 1975, p. 493.

[9] Jackson, J. O., Stedman, D. H., Smith, R. G., Hecker, L. H., and Warner, P. O., *Review of Scientific Instruments*, Vol. 46, 1975, p. 376.

[10] Breitenbach, L. P. and Shelef, M., *Journal of the Air Pollution Control Association*, Vol. 23, 1973, p. 128.

[11] Stevens, R. K., O'Keeffe, A. E., and Ortman, G. C., *Proceedings*, 8th Conference on Air Pollution Control, Purdue University, Oct. 1969.

[12] Crawforth, C. G. and Waddington D. J. *Transactions of the Faraday Society*, Vol. 65, 1969, p. 1334.

[13] Garvin, D. and Hampson, R. F., NBSIR 74-730, National Bureau of Standards, Washington, D. C., 1974.